MODERN PHYSICS

Modern Physics

JOHN C. SLATER

Professor of Physics
Massachusetts Institute of Technology

McGRAW-HILL BOOK COMPANY, INC.

New York   Toronto   London

1955

MODERN PHYSICS

Library of Congress Catalog Card Number 55-7284

II

THE MAPLE PRESS COMPANY, YORK, PA.

PREFACE

Modern physics—the atomic physics of the twentieth century—
forms one of the most fascinating subjects in the whole of science. It
has developed with great speed, helped along by some of the keenest
thinkers of the age. It has taken the structure of the atom, which was
largely a field for speculation in 1900, and has brought it to the point
where it forms a precise, quantitative, mathematical branch of physics.
The way in which these developments have come about is a revealing
chapter in the history of human thought, showing us how great ideas arise.
It is my effort in this volume to trace the development of these ideas.

These developments of the physics of the twentieth century should
interest a broad variety of students. The physicist himself, of course,
and the chemist, whose interest in atomic and molecular structure is
identical with that of the physicist, will see in these topics the whole
foundation of modern work in their fields. Other sciences, too, for
instance biology, are depending more and more on our new knowledge
of the structure of atoms, and the students of all sciences should be
aware of twentieth-century physics.

But in addition to scientists, engineers must take a very lively interest in modern physics. Physics forms the foundation of engineering,
and the older and more conventional branches of engineering are
based on the classical physics of the nineteenth century, or earlier.
It is a characteristic of the present century, however, that new discoveries are being put to use very much faster than ever before. One
has only to contrast the development of the atomic bomb, in the years
leading up to 1945, based on the discovery of nuclear fission in 1939,
with the many decades which elapsed between Faraday's discovery of
electromagnetic induction in 1832, and the practical use of electrical
machinery late in the nineteenth century, to realize this. Some of the
most exciting engineering developments of the present century are
based directly on modern physics: electronics, with which everyone is
now familiar; the application of solid-state physics to electronic problems, in such devices as the transistor; and of course the application of
nuclear or atomic energy to military problems and power development.
These rapid advances are only indications of what will undoubtedly
come in the future.

In all these fields, physicists were the pioneers, because they had followed the developments and were trained to deal with them. If engineers of the future are to be able to keep up with their profession, they too must follow the advances of modern physics. The engineering graduate of today is almost certain, before he finishes his professional career, to be making practical use of discoveries in physics which have not even been made yet. The forward-looking engineer must accustom himself to following the day-to-day progress of physics, keeping his eye constantly open for practical applications. The best way to train himself for this is to follow the exciting developments of physics during the last fifty years, so that he can learn how physicists think, what sort of problems they work on, and can be alert when new discoveries are made. It is no longer true that the physicist is an impractical scientist, working only on useless and theoretical problems. The most unlikely branches of advanced and theoretical physics are proving to have remarkable applications, and a mutual understanding between the engineer and the research physicist is an absolute necessity if practical advances are to continue at their present remarkable rate.

Quite aside from the scientists and engineers, however, modern physics should be of absorbing interest to the student of history, of human thought, and of general culture. In many ways, the most distinguishing feature of the last three or four centuries has been the development of modern science. The human race had gone through millennia of developing culture before a particular combination of circumstances led to the inquiring mind, the experimental method, and the confidence in a rational explanation of the physical world, which started in the time of Galileo and Newton and have continued to the scientific developments of the present day. Here we find a continuing, progressing, intellectual effort, which is finding its culmination before our eyes in the physics of the twentieth century, and which has every indication of advancing in the future from one discovery to another. A study of the confident and vital nature of modern thinking in physics cannot fail to be a refreshing contrast to the pessimistic and uncertain state of thought in many other fields. Modern physics really is a branch of liberal culture, which should be of absorbing interest to the student of the history of thought and civilization. A mark of the narrowness of much current thinking on the part of nonscientists is that they so often treat modern science as a contrast to true culture, rather than realizing that in fact science forms one of its brightest pages.

In writing this book, I have had in mind this whole group of students to whom I wished to appeal. For this reason, I have kept the mathematical level rather low. The only place where I have allowed much mathematics more advanced than elementary calculus to intrude is in the discussion of Schrödinger's equation and its applications to molecules and solids, in Chaps. 9 and 10. I have done it there, because these ideas are hardly comprehensible without some mathematics; but the reader will still be able to get a good deal even if he skips most of the mathematics in those chapters. Even so, there is not enough mathematics to form a proper introduction to the subject; what I have put in is only enough, I hope, to whet the appetite of the student with mathematical inclinations, and to induce him to read further, in more advanced texts.

This volume, in other words, is not a text on mathematical physics, as my other books have been; I have no illusions that the student will have more understanding of mathematical techniques when he finishes reading it than when he started. It is rather a history of the development of ideas, tied together with only enough theory to make it comprehensible. Of course, one cannot escape the fact that the ideas of modern physics are largely mathematical, and that a book on this level cannot completely do justice to them. But if I had written on a mathematical level really adequate for the ideas, I should have defeated my own purpose: for the book would then have grown so big, and so hard to read, that the continuity of the story, which is what I have mainly tried to make clear, would have been lost. There is, I think, no level of mathematical sophistication on which a completely satisfactory brief account of modern physics can be written, and I have tried to make the best compromise I could.

I hope that the book will be useful as a textbook for advanced undergraduate students, both in physics and in other sciences and engineering subjects; more and more such students are realizing their need for studying modern physics. As I have said, for students with less mathematical training, there are some of the mathematical sections which can well be skipped. A student who is not going further with modern physics should be able, I believe, to get more of the spirit of the subject from this sort of development, historical and descriptive, than from a text which puts more emphasis on experiments and their experimental details than on the ideas to which they contributed. I should suppose that a course of this sort would have lectures, preferably with demonstrations, laboratory work, and a good deal of material not contained in this text; but the text would, I hope, tie the general line of development of modern physics together. For the benefit of students in such courses, I have included some problems of a very elementary sort, intended to give facility in the simple sort of calculations possible in some aspects of modern physics rather than leading into the more advanced parts of the subject.

Aside from the student who is not going much further with modern physics, however, I should hope that this book would be useful for more advanced students. The ideas and historical developments which are described here are not elementary, even though they are stated in simple language. A graduate student who has had his training in a number of disconnected courses, without getting a general view of the development of modern physics, could well find this book to be profitable, even though easy, reading. I have even been told by a number of professors that they were fascinated to read of modern physics in the consecutive and historical way in which it is presented here. It could well be that a student who had read the book early in his career would wish to come back to it again, after he had acquired more background.

The student meeting these topics for the first time will, I hope, be inspired to look further into many of the questions which have had to be covered very hurriedly or superficially in these chapters. I have indicated in the Appendix a number of references which may supply good suggestions for additional reading. For the student who is interested in following the mathematical ideas further, I give references to the texts on theoretical physics, written by myself, partly in collaboration with Prof. N. H. Frank, presented in much the same spirit as the present book but going much further into the various branches of theoretical physics. It might well be that some teachers would prefer to present the material of this volume, not in the descriptive way in which it is written, but as part of a more advanced and theoretical course. In that case, a combination of this volume and those on theoretical physics could profitably be used.

Finally I should like to express sincere thanks to a number of professors in various universities, and in particular to my colleague Prof. W. W. Buechner, who have been good enough to read the manuscript and present valuable suggestions.

JOHN C. SLATER

CONTENTS

CHAPTER 1

THE ATOM IN NINETEENTH-CENTURY PHYSICS

1-1. Introduction. The years from 1900 to 1926, when Schrödinger's equation was discovered, saw as striking an example of inductive science as the world has ever witnessed. In 1900, we had only general qualitative ideas of the existence of atoms. By 1926, Schrödinger had set up, in the equation which bears his name, the dynamical basis for the theory of many features of their behavior. By then it had become clear that there were two aspects to the study of atoms, and of matter composed from them. The atoms were found to consist of heavy, concentrated nuclei, positively charged, containing almost all the mass, and surrounded by light negatively charged electrons. Almost all of chemistry, of metallurgy, of the whole field of molecular and solid-state physics, depends on the motion of these electrons; and Schrödinger's equation seems to furnish a complete mathematical basis for the understanding of these problems. Consequently, the progress in those fields since 1926 has been largely deductive; it consists of the application of the known mathematical equations to the vast variety of problems found in the study of matter in its ordinary forms, and the experimental study of these problems.

On the other hand, the atomic nucleus is still far from understood. In Schrödinger's equation, and in Einstein's relativity, we have two building blocks for an eventual theory of nuclear structure, but it is clear that that theory is far from complete. New and confusing experimental facts are being found every day. In this branch of physics, then, the inductive development is continuing, and certainly will go on much longer. We are still seeking the laws; whereas in the physics of atoms, molecules, and solids, we have found the laws, and are exploring the deductions from them.

In this book, we shall study in detail the progress made in the years 1900–1926; we shall treat the developments since 1926 somewhat more briefly, in one chapter on solid-state physics, emphasizing the deductive nature of that development, and in another on nuclear physics, pointing out the problems still unsolved. The period 1900–1926 is one par-

ticularly suited to the historical method of discussion, and that is what
we shall adopt.   The building up of atomic physics was like fitting
together the pieces of a puzzle: as each piece is put in place, it suggests
how the next one should fit in.   It helps us enormously in understanding the whole spirit of the period to look at these steps in order.   This
is not only interesting and helpful; it may well lead the student of
today, whose task it will be to be the productive scholar of tomorrow,
to a better understanding of how to go about inductive science.   We
have pointed out that nuclear physics is far from complete; the workers
in it will have more courage for the future if they realize the difficulties
that faced those who built up an understanding of the physics of the
outer part of the atom.

Twentieth-century physics is essentially atomic physics, the explanation of all the properties of matter in terms of atomic theory.   Though
this is a development of the present century, it has its roots far in the
past.   The Greeks had the idea that matter was made of atoms, though
they had no way of proving it.   The concept did not become precise
until the nineteenth century, when the developments of modern chemistry on the one hand, of the kinetic theory of gases on the other, convinced the scientist of the reality of atoms.   In this chapter we shall
take up some of these nineteenth-century ideas of the atom.   At the
same time, we shall have to consider some of the other features of the
classical physics of the nineteenth century—statistical mechanics in
particular, but some of the other developments of mechanics and electromagnetic theory, as well.   We must realize that, though the development of classical physics is rather far behind us, we cannot disregard
it, for the developments of the future are based on the knowledge of the
past.   In spite of popular impression, new physics does not "over-
throw" old physics; it amplifies it but seldom shows that it was wrong.

1-2. Nineteenth-century Ideas of Atoms.   The great achievement
of the nineteenth century in chemistry was the deduction of the atomic
weights of the elements, and of the chemical formulas for molecules.
Two sorts of experimental evidence entered into these results: the law
of combining proportions and the results of Gay-Lussac and Avogadro
on the weight of a given volume of gas.   As soon as chemistry began
to be quantitative, it was found that a chemical compound contained
the various elements making it up in fixed proportions, and Dalton, the
English chemist, in 1803, suggested that this law was very simply
explained if we assumed that the molecules composing compounds were
made up of atoms of the various elements, in definite proportions.
Soon after, Gay-Lussac's observations on the weight of a given volume
of gas were interpreted by Avogadro as indicating that a given volume

of gas, at a given temperature and pressure, always contains the same number of molecules, no matter what type of gas it is. These simple ideas led gradually to a determination of chemical formulas and atomic and molecular weights, though it is remarkable how long it took to be sure about all of them. We shall not go through the long history of the puzzles which the chemists had to overcome in deciding on the right atomic weights; there were a good many cases where the path was not nearly so easy as the modern student of chemistry might think. But the net result was that by the latter part of the century there was a good understanding of these chemical problems, and it was clear that the whole of chemical theory was tied together by the atomic hypothesis.

During the latter part of the century, the Russian chemist Mendeleev discovered empirically that if the elements were arranged in the order of their atomic weights, their chemical properties showed very interesting periodic behavior. This discovery suggested that the atomic weight was a very significant thing, but the true meaning of its significance was not understood until the development of atomic theory in the present century. One of our important chapters in the present book will deal with the interpretation of the periodic system of the elements.

The branch of science which used atomic ideas in the most literal sense, during the nineteenth century, was the kinetic theory of gases. Maxwell, Boltzmann, and others developed a theory based on the assumption that the molecules of a gas behaved much like small hard spheres, moving around with high velocity, colliding with each other and with the walls of the container. They showed that, starting with this assumption, and applying the ordinary laws of mechanics to the molecules, one could derive the observed laws of gases, including Avogadro's law, and could explain all their properties. One could even get some idea as to molecular dimensions, from some properties of the gas. Our main purpose in this chapter will be to describe these ideas and results of the kinetic theory of gases.

1-3. The Kinetic Theory of Gases. The kinetic theory, in its more elementary forms, is of course familiar to the student. One assumes that the gas consists of atoms or molecules of mass m, moving in all directions with a high velocity. Then the collisions of these molecules with a wall produce the pressure. We can easily give a derivation of the formula for the pressure, or the gas law, somewhat more rigorous than is usually given in elementary texts. Let there be N molecules in the volume V. We must consider the distribution of velocity of these molecules, which can be done most conveniently by considering a so-called momentum space, a three-dimensional space in which the three components of momentum of a molecule, p_x, p_y, p_z, are the three coordinates. Each molecule's momentum can be indicated by placing a point at the suitable place in momentum space, so that we shall have a swarm of points there. We shall later see that the density of these points is determined by the distribution law called the Maxwell-Boltzmann distribution law, or Maxwell's distribution of velocities, indicating that the density is at a maximum at the center of momentum space (for $p = 0$), falling off rapidly from there; but we do not need this for the present purposes. It is enough at the moment to assume that the fraction of all points found in a small volume element $dp_x\,dp_y\,dp_z$ of the momentum space equals $f(p_x,p_y,p_z)\,dp_x\,dp_y\,dp_z$, where the function f is called the distribution function.

Now let us consider the collisions of these molecules with a unit area of wall, which for convenience we may take to be perpendicular to the x axis. We remember that a force equals a time rate of change of momentum. We can then get the pressure, or force per unit area exerted on the wall, by finding the change in momentum per second of all the molecules which strike unit area. We can do this by finding the total momentum carried per second to the wall by all molecules approaching it; and subtracting from this the momentum carried away per second by those leaving it. To do this, let us consider those molecules contained in the element $dp_x\,dp_y\,dp_z$ in momentum space, and

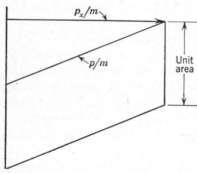

lying in a prism as drawn in Fig. 1-1. Each of these molecules will strike the unit area of the wall in a second, for the normal component of velocity p_x/m represents just the distance along the x axis which they will travel in a second. The number of such molecules is then $(N/V)(p_x/m)f\,dp_x\,dp_y\,dp_z$, equal to the number of all molecules per unit volume, multiplied by the volume of the prism, and by the fraction of all molecules in the desired element of momentum. Each of these molecules will carry an x component of momentum (which alone will contribute to the pressure) of p_x. Thus, the momen-

Fig. 1-1. Diagram to indicate collisions of molecules with a wall. The parallelepiped has a base given by unit area of the wall, slant height given by the velocity vector p/m of the particles. All the molecules contained in the parallelepiped, and only those, will cross the unit area in a second (disregarding collisions).

tum carried per second to unit area of the wall by these molecules is

$(N/V)(p_x^2/m)f\,dp_x\,dp_y\,dp_z$. If p_x is positive, as shown in Fig. 1-1, we are considering molecules approaching the wall; if it is negative, we are considering molecules leaving it after reflection. But in each case our expression represents the amount of momentum delivered to the wall, so that the total pressure is found by summing, or integrating, this expression over all values of the momenta.

Now $f\,dp_x\,dp_y\,dp_z$ represents just the fraction of all molecules in the element $dp_x\,dp_y\,dp_z$. If we multiply it by a function of p (such as p_x^2/m in this case), and sum or integrate over the p's, this means that we are merely taking a weighted mean of the function. The result of our calculation, then, is merely that the pressure equals (N/V) times the average value of p_x^2/m. But we can at once rewrite this in terms of something else. The kinetic energy equals $(p_x^2 + p_y^2 + p_z^2)/2m$. Hence, if we assume that the properties of the gas are the same in all directions, so that the means of p_x^2/m, p_y^2/m, and p_z^2/m are all the same, we find at once that the mean of p_x^2/m is two-thirds of the average kinetic energy per molecule. We have proved, then, that for such a perfect gas P, the pressure, equals $\frac{2}{3}(N/V)$ times the average kinetic energy of a molecule.

In Sec. 1-5, we shall show from the Maxwell-Boltzmann law of distribution of velocities, which can be derived from statistical mechanics, that the average kinetic energy of a molecule is $\frac{3}{2}kT$, where k is a constant, called the Boltzmann constant, and T is the absolute temperature. Hence we find that

$$P = \frac{NkT}{V} \tag{1-1}$$

This is the well-known equation of state of a perfect gas. It is more often expressed, not in terms of the number of molecules in the sample of gas, but in terms of the number of gram-moles, where a gram-mole by definition is a mass of gas equal to the molecular weight. If the sample contains n moles and its molecular weight is M, then its mass is nM. Since the mass of a molecule is m, this means that there are nM/m molecules. If we then replace N by nM/m in Eq. (1-1), we can rewrite that equation in the form $P = n(M/m)kT/V$. But the quantity M/m, the mass of a gram-mole divided by the mass of a molecule, must be a universal constant, for the molecular weight M is of course proportional to the mass of the molecule. This quantity M/m is simply the number of molecules in a gram-mole, called Avogadro's number. If we call it N_0, we have

$$PV = nN_0kT = nRT \tag{1-2}$$

where in Eq. (1-2) we have introduced a new symbol $R = N_0 k$. This quantity R is usually called the gas constant and is given alternatively by the numerical values

$$R = 8.317 \times 10^7 \text{ ergs per degree}$$
$$= 1.987 \text{ cal per degree} \tag{1-3}$$

Equation (1-2) expresses the gas laws, in the familiar form. The fact that PV is constant at constant temperature is Boyle's law; the proportionality with the absolute temperature is Charles' law; and the dependence on the number of moles, including the fact that the volume at a given pressure is dependent only on the number of moles, and not on any further property of the molecules, is a statement of Avogadro's law. The gas constant R of Eq. (1-3) is of course obtained by straightforward large-scale experiment. We shall see later how the number N_0, giving the number of molecules in a gram-mole, is determined. Once it is known, Boltzmann's constant k can obviously be found. We may anticipate by saying that the best modern determinations of N_0 and k are

$$N_0 = 6.025 \times 10^{23} \text{ molecules per gm-mole}$$
$$k = 1.380 \times 10^{-16} \text{ erg per degree} \tag{1-4}$$

The success of this simple derivation of the gas laws furnished, during the latter half of the nineteenth century, one of the most convincing demonstrations of the reality of atoms and molecules, and of the hypothesis that heat really was a form of energy, in this case the kinetic energy of thermal motion of the molecules. Maxwell, Boltzmann, and others derived the gas law, and the laws of distribution of molecular velocities, but carried the problem a good deal further, improving the mathematical rigor, and treating problems of atomic collisions and their relation to the equation of state of imperfect gases, viscosity, and thermal conductivity, with great success, in ways that have been gradually improved since, but not fundamentally altered. This work led to the concept of the mean free path: the average distance which a molecule travels through a gas before it has a collision. This mean free path obviously depends on the size of the molecules: the smaller the molecules, the longer the mean free path. Thus an estimate of molecular dimensions could be made from study of these phenomena, anticipating the much more accurate determinations of molecular sizes by the methods of the present century.

1-4. The Maxwell-Boltzmann Distribution Law. One very important part of the work of Maxwell and Boltzmann consisted in the derivation of the law of distribution of velocities of the molecules in a gas.

Boltzmann's derivation was particularly interesting and fundamental. He started by considering a gas whose molecules had some arbitrary distribution of velocity, which would not in general correspond to a steady state. He then considered the collisions of the gas molecules and asked how these collisions would change the distribution function as time went on. He was able to show in an elegant way that the distribution function would always tend toward one particular final result, which would then persist indefinitely. He naturally considered that this distribution represented the steady state, the condition of thermal equilibrium. Maxwell had also derived the same law, but by less fundamental methods, and it is called the Maxwell-Boltzmann distribution law. It tells us not only the distribution of velocities of molecules but also the distribution of energy between any other modes of motion of the molecule; for instance, the distribution of rotational energy, in case the molecules can rotate.

The Maxwell-Boltzmann distribution law is stated in terms of the phase space, a concept which we shall now describe. To determine the configuration of a molecule completely, we need to specify a number of variables, which we call its coordinates. For instance, we could choose the x, y, and z coordinates of each of the atoms, so that there would be three times as many coordinates as there were atoms. The number of such coordinates is called the number of degrees of freedom which the molecule possesses. Associated with each of these coordinates, there is a component of velocity, or of momentum; in this case, the x, y, and z components of momentum of each atom.

The phase space is then a many-dimensional space in which all the coordinates, and all the momenta, are plotted as separate variables. Thus, if there are n coordinates and n momenta in the problem, the phase space will have $2n$ variables. It need not distress the reader to think of this many-dimensional space; we shall use it only in a mathematical way, and in the examples which we shall give, we shall often be dealing with only a single coordinate and its momentum, so that we can use a two-dimensional phase space. In case we need notation for the coordinates and momenta, we shall denote the coordinates by the symbols $q_1 \cdots q_n$, and the corresponding momenta by $p_1 \cdots p_n$. Thus, in the case of the molecule composed of several atoms, the coordinates q_1, q_2, q_3 would be the x, y, z coordinates of the first atom, q_4, q_5, q_6 would be the coordinates of the second, and so on.

The problem of statistical mechanics is then to determine the probability of finding molecules with specified values of coordinates and momenta. More particularly, what is the probability of finding a molecule with its coordinate q_1 in a range dq_1, q_2 in dq_2, and so on, and its momentum p_1 in dp_1, etc? To describe this probability mathematically, we introduce a distribution function $f(q_1 \cdots p_n)$, such that $f(q_1 \cdots p_n) dq_1 \cdots dp_n$ gives the probability of finding a molecule in the range $dq_1 dq_2 \cdots dp_n$. We have seen an example of such a distribution function in Sec. 1-3, where we assumed that the fraction of molecules in an element $dp_x dp_y dp_z$ was $f(p_x,p_y,p_z) dp_x dp_y dp_z$. In that case, we did not have to consider the distribution in coordinates, because we assumed that the properties of the gas were independent of coordinates, so that the distribution function depended only on the momenta. The case of Sec. 1-3 was dealing with only the momentum of the molecule as a whole, not considering the individual atoms of which it was composed. One feature of the distribution function f is that its integral over all values of the coordinates and momenta $q_1 \cdots p_n$ must be unity provided we interpret f as giving the probability that one particular molecule will be found in the region $dq_1 \cdots dp_n$; for this particular molecule must be found somewhere. If there are N independent molecules in the problem, the average number of molecules found in $dq_1 \cdots dp_n$ will then be $Nf(q_1 \cdots p_n) dq_1 \cdots dp_n$.

Once we have the distribution function, we can find the average value of any physical quantity depending on the coordinates and momenta of a molecule. If we have a function $F(q_1 \cdots p_n)$ whose average we desire (for instance, the kinetic energy of the molecule), it is given by

$$(F)_{av} = \int F(q_1 \cdots p_n) f(q_1 \cdots p_n) \, dq_1 \cdots dp_n \qquad (1\text{-}5)$$

This is merely a weighted mean, such as we dealt with in Sec. 1-3, the function F which we are averaging being weighted by the probability f of finding the molecule lying in the appropriate element of volume in the phase space.

We can now state the Maxwell-Boltzmann distribution law. This law states that the function f is given by

$$f(q_1 \cdots p_n) = \frac{\exp\left[-E(q_1 \cdots p_n)/kT\right]}{\int \exp\left[-E(q_1 \cdots p_n)/kT\right] dq_1 \cdots dp_n} \qquad (1\text{-}6)$$

Here $E(q_1 \cdots p_n)$ is the energy of the molecule, expressed as a function of the coordinates and momenta. For example, for a monatomic gas, this energy is a sum of the potential energy of the molecule in the field of any external force field, such as the earth's gravitational field, which we could write as $V(q_1,q_2,q_3)$, and the kinetic energy $\frac{1}{2}mv^2$, which can be expressed in terms of the momenta in the form $(p_1^2 + p_2^2 + p_3^2)/2m$. The integral in the denominator of Eq. (1-6), which is to be extended over all values of the q's and p's, ensures that the integral of the distribution function f over all q's and p's should equal unity, as we have seen that it must.

We have described the Maxwell-Boltzmann distribution law in rather restricted terms, as if the coordinates $q_1 \cdots q_n$ had to be the rectangular coordinates of the atoms in the molecule. Actually, however, it is far more general. In advanced mechanics one learns that one can introduce what are called generalized coordinates. In a case like this, with n coordinates, one can introduce any n independent functions of these as new coordinates, the generalized coordinates. One then has rules for introducing the generalized momenta associated with these generalized coordinates. For example, if one of the coordinates is an angle, as for instance the angle through which a rigid body has rotated, the associated momentum proves to be an appropriate component of the angular momentum. The Maxwell-Boltzmann distribution law proves to hold in terms of these generalized coordinates, as well as in terms of the original rectangular coordinates.

1-5. The Equipartition of Energy and Specific Heats. Let us give a few examples of the applications of the Maxwell-Boltzmann distribution law. First we take the problem of the distribution of velocities of the molecules of a monatomic gas. Here the energy E is merely the kinetic energy $(p_x^2 + p_y^2 + p_z^2)/2m$. From Eq. (1-6) we see that the probability of finding the momenta of a molecule in the range $dp_x\, dp_y\, dp_z$ is proportional to exp $(-p^2/2mkT)$, which equals exp $(-mv^2/2kT)$, where v is the magnitude of the velocity. From this, we can find the probability that the magnitude of the velocity be found in the range between v and $v + dv$; it is this function which is usually described as the Maxwellian distribution of velocities.

In our momentum space, all those points corresponding to the same magnitude of velocity will lie on a sphere, whose radius is p, or mv, if p and mv are the magnitudes of the momentum. The volume of momentum space for which the velocity is between v and $v + dv$ will be the thin spherical shell between the spheres of radii mv and $m(v + dv)$. The volume of this shell will be $4\pi m^3 v^2\, dv$. Thus the probability of finding the velocity between v and $v + dv$ will be proportional to the volume of this shell times the Boltzmann factor exp $(-mv^2/2kT)$. Hence we have

$$\text{Prob. of finding molecule in } dv = \text{constant } v^2 \exp\left(-\frac{mv^2}{2kT}\right) dv \quad (1\text{-}7)$$

In Eq. (1-7) we have the Maxwellian distribution of velocities; the value of the constant can be easily found, from the condition that the integral or sum of the probability, over all values of v, must be unity.

Next, let us find the average kinetic energy of the molecules of the monatomic gas we have just been considering. To find this, we must substitute the kinetic energy $(p_x^2 + p_y^2 + p_z^2)/2m$ for the function F, in Eq. (1-5), and perform the average indicated. Let us first average merely the first term, $p_x^2/2m$; each of the other terms will give the same answer. On account of the fact that the exponential exp $[-(p_x^2 + p_y^2 + p_z^2)/2mkT]$ factors into the factors exp $(-p_x^2/2mkT)$, exp $(-p_y^2/2mkT)$, and exp $(-p_z^2/2mkT)$, we can factor the integrals appearing in the numerator and denominator and cancel the terms in p_y and p_z, which are common to numerator and denominator. We are left then, with

$$\left(\frac{p_x^2}{2m}\right)_{\text{av}} = \frac{\int_{-\infty}^{\infty} (p_x^2/2m) \exp (-p_x^2/2mkT)\ dp_x}{\int_{-\infty}^{\infty} \exp (-p_x^2/2mkT)\ dp_x} = \frac{1}{2}\ kT \quad (1\text{-}8)$$

We see, in other words, that each of the components of momentum contributes $\frac{1}{2}kT$ to the average of the kinetic energy, so that the whole average kinetic energy is $\frac{3}{2}kT$, the result which we used in Sec. 1-3 in calculating the gas law. Furthermore, the derivative of this quantity with respect to temperature, $\frac{3}{2}k$, represents the heat capacity of the gas per molecule, a result which agrees accurately with the observed specific heat of monatomic gases.

As another example, let us find the average energy of a linear oscillator. By a linear oscillator, one means a particle which is held to a position of equilibrium by a linear restoring force, or a force proportional to the displacement. This is an important problem, because the atoms of a solid, held in position by forces obeying Hooke's law, can be approximated as linear oscillators. If the displacement of the particle from the position of equilibrium is x, the force acting on it, by hypothesis, is $-kx$, where k is a constant. Then its potential energy is $\frac{1}{2}kx^2$, so that its energy, as a function of the coordinate x and the momentum p, is $\frac{1}{2}kx^2 + p^2/2m$. In finding the average of this quantity, the Maxwell distribution function exp $(-E/kT)$ again factors, since the energy is the sum of a function of x and a function of p. We can separately find the averages of $\frac{1}{2}kx^2$ and $p^2/2m$, and we find, by analogy with Eq. (1-8), that each of these equals $\frac{1}{2}kT$. Hence we conclude that the average energy of a linear oscillator is kT, of which half is potential energy, half kinetic.

An application of this result, as we have suggested, is found in the theory of solids. If we have a monatomic crystal, containing N atoms, each of these will be capable of vibration in each of the three coordinate directions. We can handle the x, y, and z motions separately, and shall find an average energy of kT for each of these, or of $3kT$ per atom. Dulong and Petit, in the early part of the nineteenth century, found experimentally that the heat capacity of a monatomic solid was very approximately $3k$ per atom. This verification of the experimental law represented one of the strong pieces of evidence in favor of the correctness of the Maxwell-Boltzmann distribution law.

From the examples which we have just discussed, we see that the fact that the distribution function exp $(-E/kT)$ has an exponential form has an important consequence: if the energy E is a sum of terms, one depending on each coordinate or momentum, then the exponential function is a product of terms, and we can handle each of these terms separately in taking the average. Furthermore, we see that any coordinate or momentum which appears in the energy as a square will contribute just the same amount, $\frac{1}{2}kT$, to the average energy. This very important result of the Maxwell-Boltzmann distribution law, and of classical statistical mechanics, is called the law of equipartition of energy. As we shall see shortly, it is not by any means always verified experimentally, and this fact, which was a puzzle to nineteenth-century physics, was one of the facts which led to the postulation of the quantum theory in the twentieth century.

We shall describe qualitatively several further examples of the application of the Maxwell-Boltzmann distribution law, or the law of equipartition of energy. One of these examples deals with a more accurate treatment of the theory of solids. The atoms of a solid are not really bound to fixed positions of space by forces proportional to the displacement; they are rather bound to each other. They form what is called a coupled system, all the atoms being coupled together. In such a case, more advanced methods of mechanics than we shall use in this text show that one can introduce what are called normal coordinates and normal modes of vibration. Each one of these normal coordinates consists of a linear combination of the coordinates of all the atoms of the system. If there are N atoms, each with three coordinates, there will be $3N$ coordinates in all, and each of the normal coordinates is a linear combination of all $3N$. Furthermore, there are just $3N$ of these normal coordinates.

Then it can be shown that any one of these normal coordinates is capable of vibrating independently of the others, with a definite frequency of vibration. If only one of these normal coordinates is vibrating, we call this a normal mode of vibration; and we find the interesting fact that this mode of vibration consists essentially of a standing wave of sound, of very short wavelength, the wavelength often being com-

parable with the interatomic distance.   A more general type of motion
is a superposition of all these normal modes of vibration, each with its
independent amplitude and phase, and each vibrating with a different
frequency.

One can express the energy of the system, not in terms of the original
coordinates and momenta, but in terms of these normal coordinates
and the momenta related to them.   We still find, however, that the
potential and kinetic energies are given by a sum of squares of normal
coordinates and their related momenta.   Hence we still find the same
equipartition energy of $3kT$ per atom, and the law of Dulong and Petit
is still expected to hold, even when we consider the interatomic forces
in this more accurate way. We shall find this concept of normal coordinates of use in Chap. 3, where we shall take up Debye's theory of
specific heat, which is based on it.

Another example of the Maxwell-Boltzmann distribution law, and
the equipartition of energy, is found in the distribution of velocities of
diatomic and polyatomic gases.   In treating the dynamics of a molecule of such a gas, it can be proved that one can use as three coordinates
the coordinates of the center of mass, and as the remaining coordinates
the coordinates of all particles relative to the center of mass.   Furthermore, by more advanced methods of mechanics, it proves to be the case
that the momenta associated with the coordinates of the center of mass
are simply the momenta of the molecule as a whole, and that they
appear in the expression for the total energy of the molecule only in the
form $p^2/2m$, where m is the mass of the molecule as a whole.   Hence as
far as the distribution of velocity of the molecule as a whole is concerned, the Maxwell-Boltzmann distribution law shows that it is
exactly as it would be for a monatomic gas whose molecules had mass
m.   This is the justification of the derivation of the gas law which we
gave in Sec. 1-3, when applied to polyatomic gases.

A diatomic or polyatomic molecule, however, has other energy
besides the kinetic energy of its translational motion.   It can be
rotating or vibrating.   For instance, a diatomic molecule has six
degrees of freedom, three for each atom.   We can describe these in
terms of the three coordinates of the center of mass of the molecule, two
additional coordinates in the form of angles (like latitude and longi-
tude) required to locate the orientation of the axis of the molecule in
space, and one coordinate measuring the distance between the two
atoms.   We may well assume that there is an elastic force between the
two atoms, so that they have a definite equilibrium distance which they
assume in the position of minimum energy, with a potential energy of
interaction which increases as the square of the deviation of the dis-

tance from the equilibrium value.   Aside from this term in the potential energy, there are six terms in the kinetic energy: three relating to the momentum of the center of mass, two relating to the rotation, and one relating to the vibrational motion in which the interatomic distance changes.   We should expect, then, that the heat capacity would include terms $\frac{3}{2}k$ per molecule from translational motion, k from the rotational motion, and k from the potential and kinetic energy associated with the vibrational motion.   This is not the observed result, however.   One finds experimentally a heat capacity of $\frac{5}{2}k$ per molecule, as if the vibration were not contributing; in some cases there is a gradually increasing quantity added to this, as if the vibrational specific heat were gradually building up from a value of zero at low temperatures to perhaps the value k at high temperatures.   But we definitely do not find equipartition.

Similarly, even in the case of the solid, the situation is not so simple as equipartition would lead us to expect.   It is true that the heat capacity of elementary solids at room temperature approximates well to the value of $3k$ per atom suggested by equipartition; but it decreases as the temperature decreases.   We know the experimental values better now than in the nineteenth century; we know that, as a matter of fact, in all cases where we have vibrational degrees of freedom, the specific heat associated with these degrees of freedom goes down to zero as the temperature approaches the absolute zero.   In other words, we have a definite contradiction to the law of equipartition.   And yet we have seen how simple and straightforward is the derivation of this law.   This contradiction was plain in the late nineteenth century, though not as plain as it is now with our more complete experimental information; and it is one of the indications, of which many were coming up during those years, that all was not well with classical statistical mechanics, or in fact with classical physics in general.   There is no simple way of getting around the law of equipartition of energy; only the quantum theory leads to a substitute which is in agreement with experiment. And it was in statistical problems that the necessity for a modification of classical physics first became obvious.

1-6. Black-body Radiation.   We have just seen that the equipartition of energy did not work very well in the theory of specific heat. An even more striking case in which it failed was in the theory of black-body radiation.   This was a celebrated problem, for it resulted in the paradox which first led to the discovery of the quantum theory.   We shall now go on to describe this paradox, though in terms of nineteenth-century physics we cannot give its answer.

Everyone knows that, as a furnace is heated up, the light that emerges from it at first is red, then gets more white, and increases greatly in intensity. There was a good deal of study of this radiation during the latter half of the nineteenth century. It was a particularly interesting problem, because studies by Kirchhoff and others, using general thermodynamical methods, had shown that this radiation had a very fundamental importance, and that it was a function of the temperature only, not of the material of the walls of the furnace, or of anything else. Experimental study of the spectral distribution of the intensity of this black-body radiation, as it is called, as a function of temperature, yielded curves like those shown in Fig. 1-2. Study of

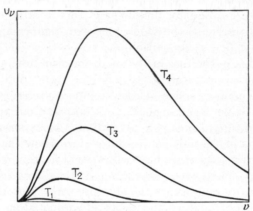

FIG. 1-2. Energy density u_ν from Planck's distribution law, as a function of the frequency ν, for four temperatures in the ratio $1:2:3:4$.

these curves resulted in two important laws. One was the law of Stefan and Boltzmann: the total intensity, integrated over all wavelengths, is proportional to the fourth power of the absolute temperature, explaining why the intensity goes up so very rapidly with temperature. The distribution curve, measuring the intensity as a function of wavelength, then has an area proportional to the fourth power of the temperature. Furthermore, this curve showed a maximum which moved toward higher frequencies at higher temperatures, in accordance with another experimental law, Wien's displacement law, which stated that the frequency at which this maximum occurred was proportional to the absolute temperature.

These were both interesting generalizations; and they both proved to be capable of theoretical proof, on the basis of electromagnetic theory. The arguments ran something like this. Suppose we start with black-body radiation, such as is found in a furnace at a given temperature, and enclose it in a cavity with perfectly reflecting walls, such as electromagnetic theory shows is provided by a cavity with perfect conductors for the walls. Then let us change the volume of this cavity, as by having it in the form of a cylinder with a piston and by pushing in the piston. A combination of electromagnetic theory and thermodynamics allows us to predict how the distribution will change. In the first place, radiation exerts a pressure, called the pressure of light, which can be calculated by electromagnetic theory. Thus, as the piston is pushed in, the piston does work, and increases the energy of the radiation. Furthermore, the moving piston, as it is pushed in, acts like a moving mirror, which on account of the Doppler effect reflects each incident beam of light with a higher frequency. Thus, the radiation, as it is compressed, increases both its total amount and its frequency. It was possible to show that it was also increasing its temperature, and to correlate the change in total intensity and wavelength distribution with the change of temperature, leading to a rigorous theoretical proof of the laws of Stefan and Boltzmann and of Wien.

All this seemed very gratifying, and made it look as if we could really explain black-body radiation by a suitable combination of electromagnetic theory and thermodynamics; but nobody was able to derive the complete equation of the curve of distribution as a function of frequency. Many tried it and failed; and the only derivation which seemed completely rigorous was that of Rayleigh and Jeans, leading to the law known by their name, which not only was not right but failed in a laughable way: it predicted an infinite amount of radiation at any temperature, with an intensity rising continually as the frequency increased, rather than going to a maximum and then coming down again. Yet as time went on, all physicists gradually agreed that this ridiculous result was the rigorous result of classical physics. It is no wonder that it led to a total revision of our ideas of physics; and it was such an important result that we shall sketch the derivation here, so that we can understand later how the quantum theory overcame the difficulties.

The first step in the derivation is to realize that the electromagnetic field inside a cavity with perfectly reflecting walls can be treated as a superposition of standing electromagnetic waves. In these days, when we are familiar with microwaves, this is a natural hypothesis, though in the nineteenth century when the calculations were being carried out, it must have seemed somewhat abstract. Anyway, such waves can be set up, with wavelengths satisfying conditions much like those of the vibrating string, though modified for a three-dimensional problem. That is, we start with a case where a half wavelength equals the dimension of the cavity (this would give us a vibration in the microwave range), then when two half waves equal this dimension, three half waves, and so on and so on, until we get to the optical wavelengths. But there is nothing to stop us. We can have waves of any wavelength, no matter how small, or of any frequency, no matter how large. It is not a hard matter to calculate the number of such vibrational waves whose frequencies lie in an interval between ν and $\nu + d\nu$. When we do this, we find that the number is

$$N(\nu)\, d\nu = \frac{8\pi \nu^2\, d\nu}{c^3} \tag{1-9}$$

per unit volume, where c is the velocity of light. The dependence on ν shows how the number of modes increases with increasing frequency.

The next step in the derivation is to realize that one can introduce normal coordinates in this problem, and that each of these modes of oscillation is connected with a single normal coordinate. This process goes very much like that of introducing normal coordinates in the problem of the vibrating elastic solid, which we have sketched in the preceding section. It can be shown that one can formulate the problem of the electromagnetic oscillations in a manner analogous to a mechanical problem, so that the whole thing can be handled like a problem in vibrations. Furthermore, the vibration of each mode is like a single particle held by a linear restoring force.

After this, we carry through a treatment of the problem by statistical mechanics. This shows, as we should suspect, that equipartition of energy holds, and that the mean energy of each of the standing waves, or modes of vibration, should be kT, at temperature T. Hence we are led to the result that the energy per unit volume in the black-body radiation, in the frequency range $d\nu$, should be

$$u_\nu\, d\nu = \frac{8\pi \nu^2 kT\, d\nu}{c^3} \tag{1-10}$$

This is the Rayleigh-Jeans law. We see how ridiculous it is. If we try to integrate it from zero to infinite frequency, we are integrating ν^2, which of course gives no finite answer; and the function u_ν keeps on increasing with frequency without limit.

In spite of the absurd nature of this result, there are features of it which are correct. Experimentally, we have stated that the curve for u_ν has a maximum. It proves to be the case that the experimental curve agrees well with the Rayleigh-Jeans law on the low-frequency side of the maximum; the failure comes on the high-frequency side. Clearly there is some sense to the derivation. But also clearly something is very wrong. Those modes of oscillation of higher frequency obviously do not really have the equipartition energy kT, but instead an enormously lower energy, falling to zero as the frequency goes up. It is such a modification which is given by the quantum theory; it appears that there is nothing wrong with the distribution of frequencies given by Eq. (1-9), but that the equipartition law is what is failing. We shall study this failure further in Chap. 3, and there we shall see that the same modifications required to bring the law of black-body radiation into agreement with experiment also clear up the puzzles which we had noted in the theory of specific heat.

1-7. Indications of the Future. In the preceding sections, we have outlined the views of the nineteenth century regarding atoms. The chemists hardly made use of any of their properties except their existence. The physicists, developing the kinetic theory, treated them as small round balls. To many physicists, this sort of treatment seemed entirely adequate, and the thought of any structure inside an atom seemed repugnant. In fact, when the electron was first discovered, some scientists refused to admit its existence, simply because the atom by its definition was indivisible, and therefore any particle which formed a part of it was impossible. This type of smugness was rather common in that period. Mechanics, sound, heat and statistical mechanics, electromagnetism, and optics, all were well formulated, and their results were verified in many sorts of ways (if we were willing to overlook such things as the difficulties with equipartition). Practical applications, in the way of mechanical and electrical engineering, showed the usefulness of the concepts. Some workers felt that physics was mostly finished, except for more and more accurate measurements of the various physical constants.

But such smugness was premature. Practically every branch of physics was shown in the twentieth century to need fundamental revision; not, as we have emphasized before, that the results were essentially wrong, but that they were limited. The limitations were shown particularly when one got to phenomena on an atomic scale. There were well-known indications that atoms were more complicated than one liked to think. Atomic spectra, for instance, showed bewildering complexity. Sharp lines in the spectrum could be measured with extreme accuracy. In the simpler spectra, like those of hydrogen and the alkali metals, the spectroscopists Balmer and Rydberg had been able to fit the frequencies with very accurate empirical laws. But no one in 1900 had any idea why the atoms had the sort of spectra they did, though a few physicists had tried, without success, to explain them in terms of classical models. It is really only in the present century that the structure of the atom has been studied successfully and has come to be recognized as one of the great subjects of study of the physicist.

A number of observations during the nineteenth century had indicated that atoms had some sort of internal structure, of an electrical nature. One type of information came from Faraday's experiments on electrolysis. Faraday found that, when electric current passed through an ionic solution, material was deposited on the electrodes. But furthermore, he observed that the amount deposited was always proportional to the amount of charge transferred by the current. It was as if each ion that had passed through the electrolytic tank had carried just so much charge. If there had only been a good measurement of the mass of an atom in those days, Faraday from his experiments could have said just how big this charge was. Crude estimates of atomic masses were available, and hence crude guesses as to this charge were possible. We know now that the charge, for a monovalent ion, is just one electronic charge; and in the way indicated, there were rough estimates of this quantity by the end of the nineteenth century. The name electron, for this unit of charge, was invented by the Englishman Stoney, in the 1880's.

Before the end of the century, the electron had been discovered as an isolated particle. Crookes, J. J. Thomson, and many others had been making experiments on electrical discharges in gases. They found very good evidence that charged particles, carrying both positive and negative charges, existed in these discharges. They deflected those particles in electric and magnetic fields, just about at the close of the century, and from their dynamics made estimates of the ratio of their charge to mass. From this information it was found that some of the negatively charged particles had a mass small compared to an atomic mass; it was assumed that these particles were the electrons themselves. The positively charged particles, however, called ions, proved to have masses of atomic size.

There was evidence that atoms contained not only electrons but building blocks of other types as well. One could not fail to observe, as Prout had noticed fairly early in the century, that the atomic weights of many of the elements proved to be surprisingly close to whole integers; and Prout had suggested that they were made out of fundamental particles, perhaps hydrogen atoms, all alike. This hypothesis of course came up against the obvious obstacle that some of the atomic weights were very far from integers, and it remained for the discovery of isotopes in the present century to remove this difficulty, and show that Prout's hypothesis really had foundation.

Finally, during the last years of the century, two new discoveries greatly excited the physicists. Röntgen, in 1895, discovered the X rays, or roentgen rays. These rays, capable of passing through matter, were completely different from anything observed before. Their discovery was followed almost immediately, however, by Becquerel's discovery of radioactivity, from the observation that uranium emitted rays which, like the X rays, could pass through matter and in fact could blacken a photographic plate even if it were wrapped up in an opaque covering. It was discovered that in radioactive disintegrations several types of particles were shot off, and experiments were under way at the end of the century to find what they were. Some of these proved to be negatively charged and light in mass; Thomson was able to show that they were identical with the electrons which had been observed in other ways. Others proved to be positively charged and much heavier; and the first experiments were being made on them, before 1900. Clearly, there were things in atoms which the nineteenth century had hardly suspected.

A variety of new experiments, then, were all crowding together just before 1900. And these combined with the puzzles of the apparent breakdown of the law of equipartition of energy, to convince the physicists of 1900 that all was not so simple with classical physics as had been supposed. The year 1900 can conveniently be taken as a turning point, marking a real division between classical physics and modern atomic physics; but there were plenty of indications in 1900 that great new things were in the air. The rest of our story will deal with these new things.

PROBLEMS

1-1. One liter of H_2 and one liter of Cl_2, at pressure of 1 atm, temperature of 273°K, combine to form HCl. How many liters will the resulting HCl occupy, at the same pressure and temperature? Answer the same question for 2 liters of H_2, and 1 liter of O_2, combining to give H_2O. How much would the samples of gas weigh, in each case?

1-2. The specific heat of He is about 0.75 cal/g; that of N_2 is about 0.18 cal/g. How closely do these agree with expectations?

1-3. The specific heat of Pb is approximately 0.03 cal/g, at room temperature. That of diamond at room temperature is about 0.10 cal/g. How closely do they satisfy Dulong and Petit's law?

1-4. Assume that we have a gas in a constant gravitational field, like the atmosphere of the earth. The Maxwell-Boltzmann distribution law states that the density of a gas at constant temperature goes as exp $(-mgh/kT)$, where m is the mass of the molecule, g the acceleration of gravity, h the height. Find how much the density of nitrogen gas at 300°K should decrease in the earth's gravitational field, when the altitude increases by 1 km; 10 km.

1-5. The formula of Prob. 1-4, called the barometer formula, can be derived by elementary methods, without use of the Maxwell-Boltzmann distribution law. Carry through such a derivation, using the following hints: Consider a volume of atmosphere of unit cross section, and bounded by horizontal planes at height h, $h + dh$. Consider the variation of the pressure P with height. The pressure acting on the lower face of the column must be greater than that acting on the upper face, by just enough to hold the column up against gravity. Assuming the gas law, find the derivative of the pressure with respect to dh, and integrate the resulting expression to show how P, and hence the density, varies with height.

1-6. The density of NaCl is 2.165. Its crystal structure consists of a cubic lattice, successive lattice sites being occupied by Na^+ and Cl^- ions, respectively. Using Avogadro's number, find the spacing between nearest neighbor ions (that is, the side of an elementary cube).

1-7. In a gas at 1 atm pressure, 273°K, find the average volume per atom

1-8. A monatomic gas is confined in a box within which the potential energy of a molecule is zero, while at the boundaries of the box the potential energy suddenly jumps to the higher value W. The molecules of the gas satisfy the Maxwell-Boltzmann distribution law. Find the number of molecules escaping per second across unit area of the surface, showing that this number is proportional to $T^{1/2}$ exp $(-W/kT)$.

1-9. Find the root-mean-square velocity of a hydrogen molecule at temperature 300°K.

1-10. The velocity of sound in a monatomic gas is equal to $(\frac{5}{3}p/\rho)^{1/2}$, where p is the pressure, ρ the density. Find the ratio of the root-mean-square velocity of the molecule to the velocity of sound.

CHAPTER 2

THE ELECTRON THEORY AND RELATIVITY

2-1. Introduction. We have already stated that the existence of the electron, and its general properties, were known in 1900. The emission of electrons thermionically from a hot filament had been discovered years before by Edison. Electrons were found in gas discharges. It was found that the beta particles emitted in some radioactive disintegrations were electrons, of rather high velocity. And preliminary measurements were available of their charge and mass. The simplest measurements were those of the ratio of the charge e to the mass m. J. J. Thomson had deflected a beam of electrons by electric and magnetic fields, in an experiment which allowed him to make a measurement of e/m; this experiment was the forerunner of later ones by Aston and others, leading to the mass spectrograph, in which similar measurements of e/m for positive ions allowed a determination of atomic masses.

Rough estimates were also available of the electronic charge, or e. Some of these had been made from positive nuclei; for it was realized at once that, since atoms are electrically neutral, the charges on positive ions must be multiples of the electronic charge in magnitude. In radioactive disintegrations, charged particles are thrown off by nuclei. The number of such disintegrations could be estimated by observing nuclear processes by scintillation methods. By allowing the particles to impinge on a luminescent screen, each nuclear disintegration became visible, and could be seen with a microscope. The total amount of charge released in such disintegrations could be measured by electrical methods. From these two pieces of information, the charge involved in a single disintegration could be found. Measurements of this type were not accurate, however; and it was not until the development of Millikan's oil-drop method in 1911, refining a method used earlier by Townsend in a cruder form, that we had really good measurements of the electronic charge. Though this experiment came after the electron theory was well worked out, there was no fundamental reason why it could not have been carried out earlier, and we can well consider it along with other parts of the electron theory.   Obviously, once e and e/m were both known, the electronic mass was known.   Similarly, from the measurements by the mass spectrograph, which gave values of e/m for ions, a knowledge of e led to atomic masses.   The fact that the mass of an electron was only $1/1,837$ of the mass of a hydrogen atom was verified.   Furthermore, once we knew the mass of an atom, it was possible to find Avogadro's number N_0, which we have already mentioned, the number of atoms or molecules in a gram-molecular weight.

These fundamental experiments, which we shall discuss in this chapter, gave physicists a feeling that they really understood the electron. At this point, a number of workers in the early 1900's, particularly H. A. Lorentz, the great Dutch theoretical physicist, began to try very systematically to build up a theory of matter as composed of electrons. The classical electromagnetism of Maxwell treated electric charge as being a quantity distributed through space; but the new experimental knowledge showed that it must be concentrated in discrete atomlike particles.   Lorentz tried to amplify the Maxwellian theory to take account of this.   He investigated the laws of motion of such electrons; and by straightforward methods of electromagnetic theory, he was led to the study of the relation between the laws of motion of electrons in fixed and in moving coordinate systems, which resulted in what we call the Lorentz transformation, including the change of mass of particles with velocity, which we now think of as consequences of the principle of relativity.

Einstein followed immediately afterward, in 1905, with his first paper on relativity, in which he showed independently that these same results could be obtained, in a very straightforward way, from a single postulate: that the velocity of light would be found to be the same, whether measured in a fixed or a moving coordinate system.   Einstein, like Lorentz, had been led to his investigations by the Michelson-Morley experiment, in which these experimenters had tried to measure the change of velocity of light with the velocity of the observer, and had found no such change; we shall discuss this experiment in more detail later.   Einstein's results were of fundamental importance; but the very close relation of them to the Lorentz transformation shows that they were not completely revolutionary, but rather represented a necessary consequence of classical electromagnetic theory.

Lorentz tried to go further and deduce the complete structure of the electron from electromagnetic theory; but he found that this was impossible, and it has proved impossible ever since.   If one tried to build up a finite electron out of infinitesimal elements of charge, in a perfectly classical way, it is obvious that these elements would repel each other, and the structure would blow up. No way of avoiding this appears in classical theory, and Lorentz had to assume that there were additional nonelectrical forces preventing the explosion. Here he was touching on points that still are not entirely clear. The theory of the structure of the electron, like the theory of the structure of the nucleus, is among those problems which still await a final answer. Nevertheless, Lorentz showed that there are some important consequences that can be drawn from electron theory, and which do not depend on these difficult problems of the structure of the electron. In particular, he was able to prove very rigorously that the accelerating electron must radiate energy. This radiation is no different in principle from the radiation of radio waves from the motion of the electrons in the antenna. But it proved to be a very important concept, and for a long time a puzzling one, in connection with building up a theory of atomic structure. For most such theories led to the assumption that the electrons involved in the structure of the atom were in rapid and accelerated motion. Why, then, did they not radiate all their energy away? This was a puzzle which was only solved by the quantum theory.

Lorentz tried not only to discuss the theory of the individual electron but also to ask how matter, consisting of atoms and molecules and solids, was constructed out of electrons. We know how much of the fundamentals of such a theory he lacked; for he did not have the nuclear atom or the quantum theory to work with. It is remarkable, nevertheless, how far he could get. He and Drude, a German worker of the same period interested in optics, tried to explain electrical conductivity, the dielectric constant of solids, and numerous more complicated phenomena, including the recently discovered Zeeman effect, the slight effect of a magnetic field on the frequency of spectrum lines, on the basis of electron theory, and they got surprisingly far with it. We shall take up some of these theories in the present chapter; they will help us a good deal in studying the same phenomena later. It almost seemed, in some ways, as if Lorentz were on the right track in his electron theory, and in some ways he certainly was.

But the problems were nevertheless in existence which such a theory could not solve. We already have noted the Rayleigh-Jeans law of black-body radiation, and the specific heat of solids. Another similar paradox shown up in the Lorentz-Drude theory related to the specific heat of electrons in a metal. But much broader than this was the whole question as to how atoms were constructed. Why did they have the sharp spectrum lines that were observed? How were they related to radioactivity and X rays? J. J. Thomson made an unsuccessful attempt to set up an electronic model of atomic structure to explain

these things; its very failure showed that new conceptions were necessary to understand these problems.   The new conceptions were not
long in coming; in fact, the first steps were made in the year 1901, when
Planck first proposed the quantum theory.   But these matters will be
put off for later chapters.   In the present chapter, we shall examine
how surprisingly far Lorentz, along with Einstein, and Drude, were
able to go in their electron theory, without use of the quantum theory
or the nuclear atom.

2-2. The Determination of Electronic Charge and Mass.   We have
already given a pretty good idea, in the introductory section, of the
experiments which went into the determinations of the charge and mass
of the electron.   In the first place, we note that any experiment on the
deviation of a beam of electrons by electric and magnetic fields will
measure e/m, and not the charge and mass separately.   The reason is

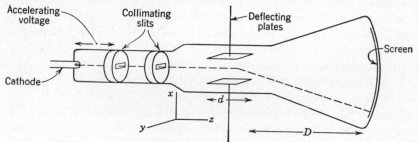

FIG. 2-1. Schematic arrangement of Thomson's e/m experiment.   Magnetic field
is along y direction, perpendicular to the plane of the paper.

simple.   The electric or magnetic force is proportional to e, as well
as to the electric or magnetic field.   This, by Newton's second law,
must equal m times the acceleration.   Thus e appears as a factor
on one side of the equation, m on the other, and we can immediately
divide through and see that only the ratio e/m is concerned in the final
answer.   The deviation of such a beam will of course also depend on
the velocity of the particles; a fast particle will not be deviated as much
by an external force as a slow one.   Hence somehow two experiments
are necessary in any deflection experiment, one to measure the velocity,
and the other to get e/m.   Many schemes have been devised for doing
this; but the original experiment of J. J. Thomson, the most famous
one historically, illustrates their principles as well as any other.

Thomson's apparatus is shown schematically in Fig. 2-1.   He took a
beam of electrons which he had accelerated by application of a voltage
in a vacuum tube, and had collimated by passing them through two
slits, the first one being in the anode.   Let us assume that they are

traveling with a velocity v_z along the z axis.   Then he allowed this beam to pass through a short region of length d, in which it was acted on simultaneously by a transverse electric field E, say along the x direction, and by a transverse magnetic field B, in the y direction.   He adjusted these two fields so that the beam was not deflected, and from the relative magnitudes of the electric and magnetic fields he could find the velocity of the electrons.

To see this, we note that the transverse electric force is eE, if e is the charge on the electron.   The transverse magnetic force, on a moving charge e, moving with a velocity v in a magnetic field B, is equal in magnitude to $evB \sin \theta$, where θ is the angle between v and B, if we use mks units, or is $(e/c)vH \sin \theta$, if we use Gaussian units; that is, electromagnetic units for the magnetic field H, electrostatic units for the charge e, where c is the velocity of light.   In our case, where v is along z, B along y, we have $\sin \theta = 1$, so that the force is equal in magnitude to ev_zB.   By the rule giving the direction of the magnetic force, it is along the direction of $-x$.   If now the beam is not deflected, the electric and magnetic forces must be equal and opposite.   That is, we must have E equal to v_zB or v_zH/c, depending on units; from which

$$v_z = \frac{E}{B} \text{ or } \frac{E}{H} c \qquad (2\text{-}1)$$

depending on units.   In this way Thomson carried out the first of his experiments, determining the velocity of the electrons.   He found this velocity to be an appreciable fraction of the velocity of light.   He realized that the velocity could also have been found from a knowledge of the accelerating voltage acting on the electron between cathode and anode, but his measurements were not accurate enough to make this comparison.

For Thomson's second experiment, he turned off the electric field and allowed the beam to be deflected by the magnetic field, measuring the deflection.   While traversing the region d, the transverse force acting on the electron was ev_zB (we shall use mks units from now on), and the transverse acceleration was $(e/m)v_zB$, in the x direction, if we assume that the particle is only slightly deflected.   The electron will emerge from the accelerating region with a transverse velocity v_x, which is the transverse acceleration times d/v_z, the time of transit.   Thus we have v_x equal to $(e/m) \, dB$.   Then the beam is allowed to travel for a considerable distance D in a field-free space.   On account of the transverse component of velocity, the beam will be deflected from its original path, and can be detected in its deflected position by falling on a fluorescent screen.   The electron takes a time D/v_z to reach the fluorescent screen, and in this time there is a transverse displacement along the x direction equal to the velocity v_x times this time. That is, the displacement x of the beam, from its undeflected position, produced by the magnetic field alone, is

$$x = \frac{e}{m} \frac{dDB}{v_z} \tag{2-2}$$

By measuring this deflection, and knowing v_z from the previous experiment, Thomson was able to determine the ratio e/m.

In other experiments, and more particularly in experiments dealing by similar methods with positive ions, Thomson arranged the electric and magnetic fields to be parallel to each other, so that the displacements would be at right angles to each other. In this case he applied the fields simultaneously, using a beam with particles of a variety of velocities. Particles of a particular velocity will be displaced along one direction, say x, by the magnetic field, the deflection being as given in Eq. (2-2). They will also be displaced in the direction at right angles y by the electric field, which is now along y. Since the electric force is E/Bv_z times the magnetic force, the electric deflection must equal the magnetic deflection multiplied by this factor, or we must have

$$y = \frac{e}{m} \frac{dDE}{v_z^2} \tag{2-3}$$

Particles of a given velocity will then fall at a particular point of the fluorescent screen, or of a photographic plate, which is often used to detect them. Thus, from Eqs. (2-2) and (2-3), we can eliminate v_z, and find the equation of the curve on the photographic plate on which the particles will fall. We find

$$y = \left(\frac{m}{e} \frac{1}{dD} \frac{E}{B^2} \right) x^2 \tag{2-4}$$

or the equation of a parabola, whose coefficient can be used to find e/m, since the other quantities involved, the dimensions and field strengths, can be experimentally measured.

Many other experiments involving electron dynamics can be used to find e/m. We have already stated that the mass spectrograph is a device using similar principles, but used to determine e/m, and hence m, for positive ions; and it has been produced in many different forms, all leading to consistent results. Thomson himself used the parabola method for this purpose, obtaining results similar to that shown in Fig. 2-2. F. W. Aston, the English physicist, was the first after Thomson to take up this type of work. He started using Thomson's parabola method but later changed the geometrical arrangements so as to bring all particles of a given e/m to a focus at a single position, independent of their velocities; the name mass spectrograph is given to any such instrument. Many forms of mass spectrographs have since been devised. There are also many other completely different devices which could now be used for determining e/m. For instance, all particle accelerators, such as cyclotrons, synchrotrons, and cosmotrons or bevatrons, which depend on simultaneous use of magnetic fields and accelerations and timing, could in principle be used to check the values of e/m, though often we must use relativistic rather than classical mechanics in computing the trajectories. Such devices are discussed later in Chap. 11.

We see, then, that determinations of e/m can be made; they were moderately accurate in the days of Thomson, and have been made more and more accurate since then. As for the electronic charge e, we have already stated that none of the determinations of the early 1900's were nearly so good as Millikan's experiment performed some years later. The method of Millikan's experiment is very well known. He produced a very small spray of exceedingly fine oil drops, so fine that they settle very slowly under the effect of gravity. They are hindered

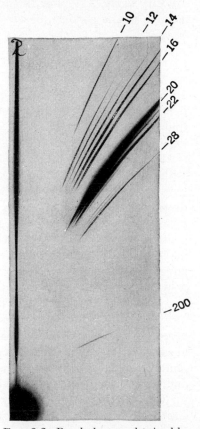

FIG. 2-2. Parabolas, as obtained by the Thomson method. The numbers indicate atomic weights per unit charge (in electronic charges). 10 is Ne doubly charged; 12 is C; 13 is CH; 14 is CH_2 and N; 15 is CH_3; 16 is CH_4 and O; 20 and 22 are Ne; 28 is N_2; 200 is Hg. (*Courtesy of K. T. Bainbridge and O. Oldenberg.*)

from falling by the viscous drag of the air. This exerts a force proportional to their velocity, and of course opposite to the velocity; we may write it as $-Av$, where A is a constant, which depends in a known way on the diameter of the particle, and the viscosity of the air, equaling in fact $6\pi\eta a$, where η is the coefficient of viscosity, a the radius.   Under the action of gravity, we have mg, the gravitational force, balancing $-Av$, the frictional force, so that the magnitude of the resultant velocity is mg/A.   Now the mass m is the density of the oil, times the volume of the particle, or is $\tfrac{4}{3}\pi a^3\rho$, where ρ is the density.   Thus we have

$$v = \frac{2}{9}\frac{a^2\rho g}{\eta} \tag{2-5}$$

In other words, by measuring the velocity of fall, and knowing the density of the oil drop and the coefficient of viscosity of the air, we can find the radius of the droplet, which is needed in the next part of the experiment.

Millikan measured the velocity of fall of his oil drop by observing it with a microscope.   Then he imposed a vertical electric field E, between two electrodes, one above and one below the region where the drops were falling.   Ordinarily the drop would have picked up a small charge, say of n electronic charges, where n is an integer, from frictional contact with the air.   Then there would be a vertical force neE, in addition to the gravitational force mg, which would hence produce an added velocity, upward or downward depending on the sign of the field, given by neE/A, where the constant A was already determined by measuring the free fall of the oil drop, as we just described.   He measured this added velocity and found the quantity ne.   Then he observed the very interesting, though expected, fact that this quantity always had one of a set of discrete values, always equal to an integral multiple of a fundamental quantity.   Obviously this quantity was e, and he was observing drops with different integral numbers of electrons for their charge.   In this way, he determined the magnitude of the electronic charge.   The most recent and accurate determinations of this quantity, and of the mass of the electron, give

$$\begin{aligned} e &= 4.80 \times 10^{-10} \text{ esu} \\ &= 1.60 \times 10^{-19} \text{ coulomb} \\ m &= 9.11 \times 10^{-28} \text{ g} \\ &= 9.11 \times 10^{-31} \text{ kg} \end{aligned} \tag{2-6}$$

We have already stated that a combination of Millikan's determination of e and the determination of e/m for atoms by the mass spectrograph made possible the absolute determination of atomic masses, and hence of Avogadro's number, the number of atoms in a gram-mole. Later, another entirely independent measurement of this quantity became possible, in the following way: We shall find in Chap. 6 that the methods of X-ray diffraction allow an absolute determination of the spacing of atoms in a crystal, and hence an absolute measurement of the number of atoms in a cubic centimeter of a crystal. Since we can also measure the density, this gives us the number of atoms in a unit mass, leading again to Avogadro's number. It is a comforting demonstration of the soundness of our results that these two entirely independent measurements agree within their very small experimental errors.

One final point regarding the electron and positive ion is almost too trivial to mention: the question as to how we know the electron is negatively charged, the ions positively. This comes immediately from the deflection experiments, where particles of opposite charge are oppositely deflected. Thomson and Aston could verify the sign of the charges from the most elementary observation of their deflections. It is to be noted that in our derivations, when we have spoken of e for the electron, we have assumed that e is to be taken as a negative number; if we had wished to use it for the absolute value of the electronic charge, as is often done, we should have changed the sign of the electric or magnetic force in each case.

2-3. Electron Dynamics and Relativity. Lorentz, in his study of electron dynamics, wished to investigate the propagation of light in moving media, for there had been interesting experimental studies of this problem. He was using models of solids consisting of electrons held to positions of equilibrium by elastic forces, which we shall come to presently. Naturally he was led to the following question: if this whole set of atoms and electrons were set in motion, how would the forces change, and what effect would this have on vibration frequencies, and such questions? It is obvious to anyone with a little knowledge of electrodynamics that there will be changes in the forces. Since the time of Maxwell, it had been known that a charge in motion, producing therefore a time rate of change of the electric field at a given point of space, results in a magnetic field. Furthermore, this magnetic field exerts forces on other charges in motion. In other words, if we take two electrons or other charges, which would exert only electric forces on each other if they were both at rest, and merely give both of them the same velocity, so that they are still at rest with respect to each other, there will be a new, magnetic force acting between them.

Similarly, two magnetic poles which are both moving, but are at rest with respect to each other, will exert an electric force on each other. This is partly obvious: we know that a magnetic pole in motion corresponds to a time rate of change of magnetic field, and thus, by Faraday's induction law, to an induced emf and an electric field. The other part of the explanation is a law, which Lorentz had to work out, showing that a magnetic pole in motion in the presence of an electric field has a force exerted on it, much as an electric charge in motion in a magnetic field has a force on it, in each case proportional to the velocity of the particle as well as the field.

Lorentz investigated carefully these forces exerted in a moving system; and set up transformation equations, so that one could express the laws of motion in moving coordinates in terms of the law in fixed coordinates, and vice versa.   As far as the electric and magnetic fields were concerned, this was simple, and followed from the elementary considerations that we have mentioned.   The effect of the transformation on the mechanical quantities, however, the momentum, kinetic energy, and so on, was a good deal more complicated.   Lorentz tried, as a predecessor, Abraham, had already tried, to investigate the detailed dynamics of a moving electron, by setting up a specific model of this electron, in the form of a charged sphere, with certain nonelectrical forces introduced to keep it from blowing up on account of the mutual repulsion of the charges of which it was composed.   He computed the force exerted by each element of charge on each other, not only when the electron was in uniform motion, but also even when it was accelerated.   And the results which he obtained were extremely interesting.

In the first place, he had to consider the nature of the stresses that held the electron together.   Abraham had assumed that these were always such as to maintain the electron in a spherical shape, irrespective of its velocity.   Lorentz, however, found that this assumption led to contradictions, and concluded that the only reasonable postulate for the force was one which required that the electron should shrink along the direction of motion, if it were going at high velocity.   This was the Lorentz contraction.   If a dimension of the electron along the direction of motion is a when it is at rest, Lorentz found that it had to shrink to a length $a(1 - v^2/c^2)^{1/2}$ when it was traveling with a velocity v, c being the velocity of light.   He even found that if one had any system of atoms held together by electromagnetic forces, and set it into motion with the velocity v, the forces would be modified in such a way that the whole system would shrink in this same ratio; the dimensions transverse to the motion are not affected by the motion.

This Lorentz contraction was not, as a matter of fact, a new idea in physics.   It had been suggested some years previously by FitzGerald, an Irish physicist, to explain the remarkable Michelson-Morley experiment, performed in 1887, which we have already mentioned, and it is often called the FitzGerald-Lorentz contraction for this reason. Michelson and Morley were working in the period when it was the fashion to think of light as a wave motion in a material medium, the ether. It was only natural to assume that this ether was fixed in space, providing an absolute frame of reference with respect to which ordinary bodies move. An absorbing question was that of finding how fast the earth moved with respect to the ether. Certainly it cannot always be at rest with respect to it; its motion in its orbit will make it move with different speeds at different times of year, and furthermore, there is good astronomical evidence that the whole solar system is moving rather rapidly with respect to the galaxy as a whole. Michelson and Morley devised an experiment which would detect the velocity of the earth with respect to the ether.

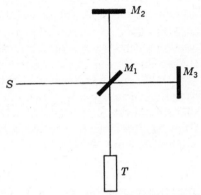

To do this, they arranged an interferometer as shown in Fig. 2-3. A beam of light from a source S falls on a mirror M_1, which is partially silvered, so that part of the beam is reflected to mirror M_2, part to M_3. The beams returned from these mirrors are again partly reflected by mirror M_1, into the telescope T, where they are observed. They set up interference fringes in the telescope, and by observing these fringes one can determine the difference in path between the two beams; that is, the difference in the number of wavelengths in the path $M_1M_2M_1$ and the path $M_1M_3M_1$. If now the apparatus is

FIG. 2-3. Schematic arrangement of the Michelson-Morley experiment. Light from source S is partially reflected by half-silvered mirror M_1 to mirror M_2, half transmitted to mirror M_3. The reflected beam from M_2 passes through M_1, that from M_3 is partly reflected by M_1, combining in the telescope T, in which interference fringes are observed. The whole apparatus is horizontal, and is arranged to rotate in a horizontal plane about a vertical axis through M_1.

moving with respect to the ether, say in the direction M_1M_3, one can show that it will take light slightly longer to traverse the path $M_1M_3M_1$ than the path $M_1M_2M_1$, resulting in a greater number of waves in the path first mentioned, and a consequent displacement of the observed fringes. If, on the other hand, the motion with respect to the ether were along the direction M_1M_2, the situation would be reversed, and the fringes displaced in the opposite direction.

To compare these cases, Michelson and Morley floated their apparatus in a tank of mercury, so that it could rotate slowly, and they expected to find a displacement of the fringes as it rotated from one position to another position 90° from the first. They found no displacement of anything like the expected order of magnitude, which seemed to show that the apparatus was not moving with respect to the ether. To obviate the possibility that they had happened to strike a time of year when the earth was really at rest with respect to the ether, they repeated the experiment months later and still got the same answer. This provided a fundamental puzzle and seemed to contradict the whole idea of an ether.

FitzGerald, however, showed that there was a simple hypothesis which could explain the experiment, without upsetting the general idea of the ether. He assumed that, since the forces holding the atoms of a solid together were electrical, these forces might well be affected by motion of the body as a whole through the ether. In particular, he found that if it was assumed that the body as a whole contracted in the direction of motion, in a ratio $(1 - v^2/c^2)^{\frac{1}{2}}$, this would be just enough to explain the experiment. The light would now not take a longer time to traverse the path $M_1 M_3 M_1$, if that was the direction of motion through the ether, for the path would be shortened just enough to compensate the effect of the motion, and no displacement of the fringes would be observed. What Lorentz did later, then, was to investigate in detail the laws of force acting between the atoms of the solid and to show that they were such as to bring about this contraction automatically, without further hypothesis.

With his assumptions about the stresses holding the material bodies together, Lorentz was then able to investigate the internal structure of the electron and the forces which it exerted on itself, so to speak, when it was in motion. That is, he computed the force exerted by each element of volume on each other element, and added these to get the total force exerted on the electron. The leading term turned out to be a negative constant times the acceleration. This led to an interesting hypothesis: perhaps this constant could be identified with the mass. In other words, suppose we had an electron accelerated in an external field E, so that there was an electric force eE acting on it. Lorentz then showed that there was this additional force $-ma$, if m is a constant, on account of action of the electron on itself. It was then a very attractive hypothesis to assume that the true equation of motion of this electron was the simple statement that the total force acting on it was zero; in other words, that its equation of motion was $eE - ma = 0$, which of course is just Newton's second law. This electromagnetic derivation of mass and inertia was very attractive; but it has not been borne out by later study. It appears now for many reasons that a naïve picture of the electron as being a sphere of charge, the different elements exerting forces on each other, is too simple. In many ways it is much more like a point charge, and it is not justified to break it up into separate volume elements of charge, but our understanding of its structure is still not complete enough to allow us to be dogmatic about such things.

Lorentz's study of the electron dynamics made it possible, however, to draw some extremely interesting conclusions, which have proved to be correct. The mass which he found, by the argument outlined above, proved not to be a constant but to depend on the velocity of the particle. His law of motion could be stated most simply, as a matter of fact, not in terms of the acceleration, but by using Newton's second law, that the force equaled the time rate of change of the momentum. And it could be given by the simple statement that the momentum of a particle whose mass at low velocities (the so-called rest mass) was m_0 was equal to

$$\text{Momentum} = \frac{m_0 v}{(1 - v^2/c^2)^{1/2}} \qquad (2\text{-}7)$$

at the velocity v. If we have this value of the momentum, and subject the particle to a transverse force, then one can show that the force equals one mass, called the transverse mass m_t, times the transverse acceleration; while if it is subjected to a longitudinal force, along the direction of motion, the force equals another mass, called the longitudinal mass m_l, times the longitudinal acceleration. These two masses are given by

$$m_t = \frac{m_0}{(1 - v^2/c^2)^{1/2}} \qquad m_l = \frac{m_0}{(1 - v^2/c^2)^{3/2}} \qquad (2\text{-}8)$$

These results proved to be right, for reasons that we shall soon see, even though the general concept of electromagnetic mass has not been justified by further work.

These laws of motion were obviously things capable of experimental proof, and verification was soon given, by experimenters named Bucherer and Kaufmann, who were working with deflection experiments like those of J. J. Thomson. It is clear that in the derivation of the parabola law of Eq. (2-4) we should be using the transverse mass; and since this is a function of velocity, we should not really have a parabola but should have deviations at the high-velocity end. If one puts numbers into the formula, one finds that the deviations would not be detectable until the energy of the electrons corresponded to a good many kilovolts, and Thomson had not used high enough energies to observe these effects. Bucherer and Kaufmann, however, used beta particles from radioactive disintegrations, which were known to be electrons moving very fast, and their results agreed definitely with Lorentz's formulas. They did not agree with alternative formulas which had been derived by Abraham on the basis of his theory of the rigid electron; thus the results indirectly verified the Lorentz contraction of the electron, which formed the difference between the two theories.

We shall see shortly that the reason why these formulas are right, even though they are based on incorrect hypotheses, is that they are required by the theory of relativity, and while Lorentz's derivation did not really describe the electron, it was in accordance with the theory of relativity, of which it formed in fact the predecessor. Thus the change of mass with velocity, described in Eq. (2-8), is a relativistic effect, and as such it has been verified since the time of Bucherer and Kaufmann in countless ways. In particular, as we have mentioned earlier, most of the high-energy accelerators, both for electrons and positively charged particles, operate in the range where the relativistic equations must be used, and the success of their design shows that the relativistic equations of motion must be correct. These results of relativity, embodied in Eq. (2-8), stand on just as solid engineering foundation as any of the laws of physics.

It was immediately after Lorentz's derivation of these results, in 1905, that Einstein published his first paper on the theory of relativity. As we have stated earlier, he started from a completely different postulate from Lorentz, and in fact he was not then aware of Lorentz's results. He was not working on detailed mechanisms of interelectronic forces. Rather, he started from one postulate, the experimentally verified constancy of the velocity of light for observers moving with different velocities. If we start with the naïvest hypotheses, we should suppose that moving observers would find different velocities for light, just as moving observers would find different velocities of sound. It is now commonplace knowledge, for instance, that an airplane can move with the velocity of sound, and if it does so, an observer in the plane finds that sound does not travel away from his plane at all, in the forward direction. Its velocity is reduced to zero, and this is the origin of the peculiar dynamics of this region of velocities. Airplanes were not known in 1905, but the nature of sound was, and these results of aerodynamics were well understood then. How can this be consistent with an observed constancy of the velocity of light?

Einstein explained this by supposing that very profound changes occurred in actual physical objects as they approached the velocity of light. He found that his one postulate led uniquely to many predictions. For one thing, any real object would shrink in the direction of motion, exactly according to the Lorentz contraction, so that it would become infinitesimally short as its velocity approached c. For another thing, the rate of clocks would change, the clock slowing down as the velocity approached c, coming to a standstill in the limit. Other consequences came in, all of which were incorporated in the laws giving the motion in moving coordinates, in terms of those in fixed coordinates. These laws incorporated the Lorentz transformation and showed that all the results Lorentz had worked out were correct. Einstein, however, postulated that his law of the constancy of the velocity of light was an absolute law, to which every other law must conform; so that the fact that Lorentz had derived the same transformation as Einstein only showed that he had worked through his electromagnetic laws properly, and they were consistent with relativity, not necessarily that his electromagnetic model of the electron was correct. According to Einstein, every mass, no matter how constituted, would have to show the dynamics described by the transverse and longitudinal masses of Eq. (2-8). This is why we stated that the experimental verification of those equations did not prove that Lorentz's model of the electron was right.

One of the results of Einstein's theory, which has proved to be extremely important, has been his formula for the energy of a moving body, which is

$$\text{Energy} = \frac{m_0 c^2}{\sqrt{1 - v^2/c^2}} \tag{2-9}$$

This is derived straightforwardly by applying the work-energy theorem to the system of dynamics using the longitudinal and transverse masses of Eq. (2-8). If we expand this energy as a power series in v^2/c^2, we find at once that it equals

$$\text{Energy} = m_0 c^2 + \tfrac{1}{2} m_0 v^2 + \cdots \tag{2-10}$$

where the further terms represent relativistic corrections. The term $\tfrac{1}{2} m_0 v^2$ is of course the familiar kinetic energy; but the term $m_0 c^2$ represents an additive constant, which is the origin of the well-known relation between mass and energy, which has proved to be so important in subsequent work.

This relation can be seen by writing Eq. (2-9) in the form

$$\text{Energy} = m c^2 \tag{2-11}$$

where the mass m is the transverse mass defined in Eq. (2-8). This equation of course is equivalent to Eq. (2-10), but it has additional implications.   The additive constant m_0c^2 in Eq. (2-10) could have been dismissed as far as the work-energy theorem is concerned; one can always add a constant to the energy, without making any difference in the dynamics of particles.   Einstein assumed, however, that this quantity was more fundamental.   He assumed, in fact, that there was a possibility of converting mass into energy, and vice versa, and that if there was any change in the energy of a particle, there is a compensating change in its mass, as given by Eq. (2-11).   He verified this postulate by working out the theory of a body which radiates a certain amount of energy in the form of electromagnetic radiation, or light.   He found that, in order that his equations behave properly according to relativity, the mass of the body would have to decrease in the process, by just the amount computed by Eq. (2-11).   In other words, instead of having two separate conservation laws, the conservation of mass and the conservation of energy, as we had been familiar with from older mechanics, Einstein combined the two into a single conservation law, with Eq. (2-11) serving as the relation between them.   This was a little like the earlier generalization in the theory of heat, in which heat and energy were found to be interchangeable, and a mechanical equivalent of heat was measured experimentally.   Equation (2-11), in a sense, gives the mechanical equivalent of mass.

An experimental verification of this consequence of the theory of relativity could not be given at once.   The best way to do it would be to find the mass of objects containing different amounts of kinetic or potential energy and see whether this added energy really made a change of mass, equal to the change of energy divided by c^2.   We shall see later, when we come to the theory of nuclear structure, that it is there that one can get definite experimental checks for these very important predictions of the theory of relativity.   One can find the masses of atoms, before and after nuclear transformations in which their energies are changed by known amounts; and one finds that there is an experimental change of mass, just enough to be described as the mass of the energy, as determined by Einstein's relation.   Thus, in nuclear physics, Einstein's results have shown themselves to be fundamental to the study of nuclear energy.   It is interesting to note that Einstein suggested the possibility of such applications in the paper in 1905 in which he first proposed the equivalence of mass and energy.

We have now discussed Lorentz's study of the change of mass with velocity, and Einstein's demonstration that these changes could be predicted from very fundamental postulates.   It remains to discuss the next higher terms which Lorentz found in his derivation.   We have stated that he considered a spherical model of an electron moving with a high velocity and found the force exerted by this electron on itself. If the velocity is uniform, there are no more terms than we have described. But if it is accelerated, a further term appears, and this one, remarkably enough, proves to be independent of the hypothesis made about the shape and size of the electron. This is a term, opposing the motion, and proportional to the time rate of change of the acceleration. This term, on account of the fact that it is independent of the particular model used, is certainly correct in a sense; still higher terms, on the contrary, depend again on the details of the electronic model, and cannot necessarily be assumed to be correct.

This acceleration term of Lorentz's can be derived in an alternative way, not depending on the details of the electron at all; and this alternative derivation throws a great deal of light on its meaning. Directly from Maxwell's equations, one can show that surrounding an oscillating charge there is a spherical electromagnetic field, radiating out into space, and carrying energy with it. This radiation field was first examined exhaustively by Hertz, in connection with his study of Hertzian or radio waves in the 1880's, and its reality is experimentally verified by all our modern study of radio propagation. As we have said, this field really carries energy; hence, by conservation of energy, the oscillating charge must be losing energy. This requires a retarding force, similar to friction, opposing the motion. And when we examine the force found by Lorentz, proportional to the time rate of change of acceleration, it is just what is needed to describe this retarding force, and lead to conservation of energy. We can be very sure, then, that as long as electromagnetic theory is correct, there must be such a term in the equation of motion of the electron.

We have already mentioned the paradox which this leads to, when we study the structure of an atom. For many of the models of atomic structure which were to be proposed in the next few years involved electrons rotating in orbits of some sort. These electrons, then, would have to radiate. If the effect of this on their motion is examined carefully, it proves to be impossible to set up any model of the atom which can persist; the atom will radiate more and more energy, until finally a catastrophe of some sort occurs. This difficulty is one of those which led Bohr to his quantum theory of the atom, and it leads us to the conviction that the classical electromagnetic theory of Maxwell cannot be right for atomic processes. This was not clear to Lorentz, however. For as we shall see in the next section, Lorentz was thinking in terms of the only model of the atom in which this difficulty does not occur.

2-4. Lorentz and Drude's Electron Theory of Solids. One of the interesting branches of optics in the latter half of the nineteenth cen-

tury was the study of anomalous dispersion.   It was known that the
index of refraction of many solids, regarded as a function of the frequency of the light, rose with increasing frequency; this is merely the
effect which makes prisms useful in spectroscopic equipment.   But at
certain regions of the spectrum, in which absorption is observed, the
index of refraction is found to increase very rapidly and very greatly as
this absorption frequency is approached, then to drop precipitously as
we pass through the absorption band, to start rising again with increasing frequency beyond the band.   It was well understood by the physicists of that period that such an effect would be produced if there were
within the material some sort of linear oscillators which could be set
into oscillation by the light and which had their natural frequencies of
oscillation at the absorption bands.   In the earlier theory of optics,
before the electromagnetic theory had been accepted, it was supposed
that these oscillators were merely mechanical particles held by something equivalent to springs to their positions of equilibrium, which
were then acted on by the mechanical vibrations of which light was
supposed to consist.   Once the electromagnetic theory was accepted,
it seemed natural to replace these oscillators by electrically charged
particles, which could be acted on by the electric field in the light wave.

Such assumptions were made by Drude, and Lorentz followed along
the same path.   The arguments are familiar, and simple enough so
that we can give them here.   Suppose we have a particle of charge e,
mass m, held to a position of equilibrium by a force proportional to the
displacement.   If the displacement is x, the force is a negative constant times x; our mathematics will come out rather neatly if we call
this constant $-m\omega_0^2$ (for then we shall find out that ω_0 turns out to be
the angular frequency of free oscillation of the particle).   We also have
to assume, in order to give a description of absorption, that there is a
frictionlike term, proportional to the velocity and opposite to it; here
again we can make the mathematics neat by calling this constant $-mg$.
If now, in addition, there is an electric field E acting on the particle
(which will be taken to be the electric field in the light wave), the
equation of motion is

$$m\,\frac{d^2x}{dt^2} = -m\omega_0^2 x - mg\,\frac{dx}{dt} + eE$$

$$\text{or} \qquad \frac{d^2x}{dt^2} + g\,\frac{dx}{dt} + \omega_0^2 x = \frac{eE}{m}$$

(2-12)

Now in a problem in optics, the electric field will be a sinusoidal
function of the time, say with an angular frequency ω.   It is convenient in this problem to use the complex exponential method of

handling sinusoidal problems; that is, to write E as being equal to $E_0 e^{i\omega t}$, where E_0 is a constant, and where we are to assume that the real field is the real part of this exponential, or $E_0 \cos \omega t$. We assume that the reader is familiar with this complex exponential notation; if he is not, it can be looked up in texts on calculus or on the theory of alternating current. We now assume in the same way that x is to be given as the real part of the complex exponential $x_0 e^{i\omega t}$. We note that differentiating this function with respect to time merely multiplies by $i\omega$. Then, when we substitute in Eq. (2-12), we find that the exponential will cancel out, leaving only the equation

$$x_0(-\omega^2 + i\omega g + \omega_0^2) = \frac{e}{m} E_0$$

or

$$x_0 = \frac{e}{m} E_0 \frac{1}{-\omega^2 + i\omega g + \omega_0^2}$$

(2-13)

We must now inquire regarding the relation of this result to the theory of dispersion. In elementary electromagnetic theory it is shown that a charge e, displaced through a distance x, forms a dipole of dipole moment ex. If there are N such dipoles per unit volume, there is said to be a polarization Nex. This polarization, divided by the electric field, is said to be the polarizability. Then it is shown that the dielectric constant equals 1 plus a constant times the polarizability, this constant being 4π in the cgs or Gaussian set of units, $1/\epsilon_0$ in the mks units, where $\epsilon_0 = 8.85 \times 10^{-12}$ farad/m.

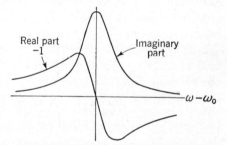

Fig. 2-4. Anomalous dispersion, showing index of refraction and absorption coefficient, real and imaginary parts of the quantity $n - ik$, as function of frequency.

Furthermore, one finds that the index of refraction n and the absorption coefficient k are related by the equation that $(n - ik)^2$ equals the dielectric constant.

If we use these results, we then find at once that

$$(n - ik)^2 = 1 + \frac{1}{\epsilon_0} N \frac{e^2}{m} \frac{1}{-\omega^2 + i\omega g + \omega_0^2}$$

(2-14)

This formula is given for the mks units; to get the equivalent formula in Gaussian units, we replace $1/\epsilon_0$ by 4π. It is now a simple matter of solving for real and imaginary quantities to find n and k, and when we do so, we find curves of the sort in Fig. 2-4. It is clear that these demonstrate the qualitative behavior which we have already shown as describing the experimental results. Theories of this sort, in fact, can give formulas in good agreement with experiment, though there are some further refinements required to get really good results.

Clearly, then, this model of linear oscillators has some sort of relation to the actual facts. Such a model seemed, in the time of Drude and Lorentz, to fit in rather well with a model of the atom which J. J. Thomson was proposing, on the basis of what was then known. We must remember that the nuclear atom was not yet discovered. Thomson assumed that the positive charge of the atom consisted of a large uniformly charged sphere, which the electron could penetrate, and that the electron oscillated inside it.

In elementary electrostatics, it is proved that under these circumstances the force acting on a charge displaced from the center acts toward the center, and is proportional to the displacement. Thus, let the charge be at a distance r from the center, and let the volume density of charge in the uniformly charged sphere be ρ. One can show that the electric field in such a spherical charge distribution is determined by Coulomb's law by imagining the charge within the sphere of radius r to be concentrated at the origin and by disregarding the charge outside this sphere, whose electrostatic effect cancels. In other words, the field at distance r is determined by the charge $\frac{4}{3}\pi r^3 \rho$ contained within the sphere. The field of this charge, determined by Coulomb's law, is proportional to the charge, divided by the square of the distance. In other words, it is proportional to $\frac{4}{3}\dfrac{\pi r^3 \rho}{r^2} = \frac{4}{3}\pi r \rho$, proportional to r, the displacement, as we have stated.

The Thomson atom, then, led to a linear restoring force acting on the electron in the atom, and hence the dynamics of the electrons would be just what Drude and Lorentz had assumed (if in addition to the restoring force we assumed a resistance). Such a model even gets around the difficulty of the energy loss by radiation; for we assume that in an unexcited state the electron is at rest at the center of the atom and is not in motion. When it oscillates, we can see immediately from Eq. (2-12) that, if there is no external field E, it will oscillate with a damped simple harmonic motion of angular frequency ω_0, and a damping depending on g. Such a motion will lead to radiation, and its energy will gradually be dissipated. In fact, we can even choose g to represent just the frictional force equivalent to the resistive term resulting from the radiation. We may assume, then, that an atom excited, either by the absorption of radiation or by being struck with another particle, will have an oscillating electron in it which will radiate energy with frequency ω_0, the same as the frequency at which it absorbs and has its anomalous dispersion. This is in agreement with experiment: the anomalous dispersion and absorption actually do come at the positions of frequencies at which the atom can also emit radiation. The excited atom will then radiate until it has lost its energy, when the electron will come to rest at the center of the atom.

All this, then, makes a self-consistent theory, and Drude and Lorentz could propose it with a clear conscience. Even in the days of Thomson, Drude, and Lorentz, however, there could be one serious question as to the correctness of the theory. We have got a perfectly reasonable explanation for the existence of a single resonant frequency per atom; but the experimental spectroscopists knew at that time that every atom has a very large number of spectrum lines, different frequencies at which it could emit radiation and could show anomalous dispersion and absorption. It would obviously be impossible to incorporate this complication into the Thomson atom; and this difficulty worried the experts in optics a great deal, so that it was not at all obvious, even in the time of Lorentz, that his theory was right.

There were other very attractive features to the theory of Drude and Lorentz, however, aside from the theory of dispersion. One of these, which had a great deal of influence, was Lorentz's theory of the Zeeman effect. Zeeman, the Dutch spectroscopist, had observed shortly before that, if a luminous gas is placed in a magnetic field, the spectrum lines, which otherwise were sharp, become split into several lines. This was one of the first experimental proofs of the relation between atoms and their radiation, on the one hand, and electromagnetic fields on the other. Now Lorentz was able to give a very simple explanation of at least the simpler features of the Zeeman effect. He studied the motion of an electron in a magnetic field, and in a linear restoring force, such as one would find in a Thomson atom; and he found, by quite elementary methods, that each spectrum line would be split into three, the separations depending on e/m, and being proportional to the magnetic field. Furthermore, he found interesting polarization relations for these various components, some being circularly polarized, others linearly polarized. The remarkable thing was that, in some of the simpler cases studied by Zeeman, the splitting had been precisely of this sort, even agreeing quantitatively with Lorentz's theories. Other cases were more complicated, with splitting into more components. Nevertheless this was the first case in which a measurement of an atomic spectrum had been able to yield the same value of e/m that was being found in the deflection experiments; it definitely seemed to prove that electronic vibrations in the atom were at the bottom of spectroscopy.

Still another success of the theory of Drude and Lorentz came in their explanation of metallic conductivity. They assumed that in a metal there were free electrons, that is, electrons which were not held to any positions of equilibrium, but were free to move, subject only to resistive forces. The equation of motion would then be like that of Eq. (2-12), but with the term in ω_0 omitted. When we study the solutions of such a differential equation when an electric field is suddenly applied, we find that the velocity of the electron starts from zero, rapidly builds up in an exponential fashion to a terminal velocity, which thereafter remains constant. This terminal velocity can be found at once from Eq. (2-12), by setting not only ω_0 but also the acceleration d^2x/dt^2 equal to zero; it is $dx/dt = eE/mg$, proportional to the electric field E. Now if we have N electrons of charge e per unit volume, each moving with a velocity v, it is easily shown that this corresponds to a volume density of current equal to Nev. If this current density is called J, we then have

$$J = \frac{Ne^2}{mg} E = \sigma E \tag{2-15}$$

stating that the current density is proportional to the electric field, or Ohm's law.

This theory, then, led to a simple interpretation of Ohm's law; but it went further, for it was possible to get information about the optical properties of metals at high frequencies. Hagen and Rubens had been making experiments on the optics of thin metallic films in the infrared. From Eq. (2-14), if we set ω_0 equal to zero, we can find the behavior of n and k given by this model, and we note that the frequency appears in the denominator of Eq. (2-14), so that n and k both approach infinity at low frequencies, or in the infrared. Hagen and Rubens had found results much like those predicted by this equation, and in fact had been able to find the expected relations between these optical properties and the conductivity found under direct-current conditions; for it is obvious that by using Eq. (2-15), we can rewrite the constants in Eq. (2-14) in terms of σ. Thus here too the theory of Drude and Lorentz seemed to have a good deal of validity.

With all these successes, still of course we know now that the fundamental basis of this theory was not right. It is an interesting fact that such an extremely able man as Lorentz, even though he worked on the basis of hypotheses that we now know were incorrect, yet was able to derive so many valid results. He was a man of very great intuition, working before many of the essential facts were available. We have seen that he anticipated Einstein on the relativistic laws, even though his model of the electron has not proved to be correct. The theory of dispersion derived on the basis of the Thomson atom proved later, when the same problem could be investigated on the basis of wave mechanics, to lead to precisely the correct mathematical formulation of the index of refraction, even though we must now derive the equations, not from simple Newtonian equations of motion as in Eq. (2-12), but from some of the more complicated methods of quantum electrodynamics. And his theory of metals, which he really carried much further than we have indicated, also proves to lie at the foundation of the modern theory of metals and semiconductors, even though we know that electrons in metals are by no means free.

Only one consequence of this theory of metals proves to be definitely wrong. Lorentz's theory led to the prediction that the electrons in a metal acted like a gas of free electrons. Such a gas should have a specific heat of $\frac{3}{2}k$ per electron, as we saw in the last chapter. And yet the specific heat of metals as found experimentally includes no such term. This points to another of those difficulties with equipartition, of which we have already seen several, which can be removed only by the quantum theory. In spite of all these qualifications, however, Lorentz's electron theory stands as a remarkable achievement, considering the period when it was worked out.

PROBLEMS

Note: An electron is said to have an energy of 1 kev if it has been accelerated through a potential difference of 1,000 volts; of 1 Mev if it has been accelerated through 1,000,000 volts. Thus its energy is eV, where e is the electronic charge, V the voltage. If e is given in coulombs (1.60×10^{-19} coulomb), V in volts, the energy comes out in joules.

2-1. An electron beam accelerated to an energy of 1 kev passes through a region 1 cm long in which it is subjected to a transverse electric field of 100 volts/cm. After emerging from this region, it traverses a field-free distance of 50 cm and strikes a screen. How far does the electric field deflect the beam from its undeflected position?

2-2. An electron beam accelerated to an energy of 1 kev passes through a region 1 cm long in which it is subjected to a transverse magnetic field of 1 gauss. After emerging from this region, it traverses a field-free distance of 50 cm and strikes a screen. How far does the magnetic field deflect the beam from its undeflected position?

2-3. Derive Eq. (2-8), for the longitudinal and transverse masses, from Eq. (2-7), for the relativistic momentum, using Newton's second law, that the force equals the time rate of change of the momentum.

2-4. What is the rest energy of an electron, in million electron-volts? Of a proton?

2-5. An electron has an energy of 1 kev. How fast is it moving? Do you need to use relativistic methods to calculate the velocity in this case? Answer the same question for 100 kev; 1 Mev.

2-6. A particle moves in a constant magnetic field, transverse to the field. Show that it moves in a circle, and that the product of the magnetic field and the radius of curvature of the circle is proportional to the momentum of the particle, even in the relativistic case.

2-7. An ion of boron, mass 10, with a single positive charge, accelerated to an energy of 1 Mev, moves in a transverse magnetic field of 10,000 gauss. Find the radius of curvature of its circular path.

2-8. An electron moves with nonrelativistic velocity in a transverse magnetic field of 10,000 gauss. Show that the frequency of rotation in the orbit is independent of the velocity of the particle (so long as it is nonrelativistic). Find the rotation frequency.

2-9. A Thomson atom is constructed by distributing a positive charge of magnitude e (the electronic charge) uniformly through a sphere whose radius is 10^{-8} cm, and allowing an electron to vibrate inside this sphere. Find the frequency of oscillation and the wavelength of the resulting electromagnetic radiation.

2-10. A solid is constructed out of Thomson atoms as described in Prob. 2-9, forming a simple cubic lattice with the atoms at the lattice points, and touching each other. Find the dielectric constant and index of refraction of this hypothetical solid. Neglect damping forces.

CHAPTER 3

BEGINNING OF THE QUANTUM THEORY

3-1. Introduction. Max Planck was a German theoretical physicist specializing in thermodynamics and statistical mechanics, who was worried more than anyone else by the discrepancies between the observed law of black-body radiation and the Rayleigh-Jeans law. An attempt at a solution of the problem had been made by Wien, another German physicist, who devised a law, called Wien's law, which seemed to agree pretty well with experiment, except in the region of low frequencies. In that limit, the Rayleigh-Jeans law proved to be experimentally correct, and Wien's law did not have the same form. Furthermore, the more Wien's derivation was studied, the more it became obvious that it was not sound; the formula which Wien developed was apparently just a lucky accident, which worked pretty well. Planck started his consideration by finding, empirically, an interpolation formula between Wien's law and the Rayleigh-Jeans law, which proved to agree so remarkably with experiment that one immediately suspected that it represented the real law of black-body radiation. This supposition has since proved to be justified, and Planck's interpolation formula turned into Planck's law, which we now believe to be exactly true. He then tried to explain how this law, which started out to be an empirical one, worked so well.

Planck approached the theory of black-body radiation, not as Rayleigh and Jeans had done, by considering the oscillations of the electromagnetic field in a vacuum, but rather by considering the emission and absorption of radiation by linear oscillators, much like the Thomson atom and the oscillators of Lorentz and Drude. He found that, by treating everything according to classical methods, he could obtain the Rayleigh-Jeans law by this method too. In the derivation, instead of replacing the average energy of a mode of electromagnetic oscillation by its equipartition value kT, as we did in Chap. 1, he had to replace the energy of one of his oscillators by this value; but the final result was the same as with Rayleigh and Jeans.

By the use of a great deal of insight, he guessed at the way the law

could be modified to agree with experiment.   His guess proved to be
the quantum hypothesis which has revolutionized physics since his
day: the hypothesis, in this particular case, that the energy of a linear
oscillator could not take on any arbitrary value but had to be an
integral multiple of the amount $h\nu$, where h was a constant which he
had to introduce, now called Planck's constant, and ν was the frequency
of the oscillator.   By making this assumption and still using the
classical statistics resulting from the Maxwell-Boltzmann distribution
law, he found at once that equipartition no longer held, except at high
temperatures; and the deviation from equipartition was just such as to
lead to a law of black-body radiation in agreement with experiment
In fact, the law which he obtained proved to form precisely the interpolation formula between Wien's law at high frequencies, and the
Rayleigh-Jeans law at low frequencies, which he had already found
empirically.

Planck's quantum hypothesis (the "quantum" of energy being the
amount $h\nu$ concerned in the energy of the oscillator) changed completely the ordinary ideas of mechanics.   Certainly there is nothing in
classical mechanics to suggest that some values of energy should be
allowed, others should not.   This one great discovery really exhausted
Planck's powers.   He lived a good many years after his first proposal
of the quantum theory, in 1901, but spent the rest of his life trying to
understand the quantum hypothesis along the lines of a partial compromise with classical mechanics, attempts which did not prove to be
successful.   •

The greater genius of Einstein was required to make the next
decisive step in the development of quantum theory.   He saw that the
quantum hypothesis could be of just as much importance in other
branches of physics as in the study of black-body radiation, and that
the proper thing to do next was not to try to understand the hypothesis
in classical terms, but was rather to take it and see some of its further
consequences.   In particular, we have already pointed out one place
where the law of equipartition broke down: the theory of specific heat.
Einstein realized that this breakdown was just like that met in the
theory of black-body radiation, and he set up a theory of specific heat,
on the basis of the quantum hypothesis, which has laid the basis for all
further work in that field.

There was another recently discovered phenomenon, however, in
which the quantum hypothesis was even more obviously needed: the
photoelectric effect.   It had been known for some time that light,
falling on a metallic surface, caused electrons to be ejected from the
surface.   There was nothing very remarkable about this, at first sight;

it was known that electrons could be ejected thermionically, if the temperature were high enough. Obviously, the light falling on the surface carried energy, this energy could be absorbed by the electrons, and they could thus acquire energy just as they could from thermal agitation and so be able to escape the potential barrier which would keep slow electrons from leaving the metal.

It was only when the laws of photoelectric emission began to be examined quantitatively that its truly remarkable behavior was discovered. The German physicist Lenard made some of the first studies of these laws; later Millikan made the results more quantitative. Lenard found that, when the intensity of the impinging light was changed, without changing its spectral distribution, the energy of the ejected electrons did not change, but only their number. We know now that this continues, as the light gets weaker and weaker, until the rate of emission can be so small that only a few electrons per second are ejected. Each of these few, however, has a large energy, which can well be several electron-volts. Millikan established just what this energy was, by studying photoelectric emission in case the impinging light was monochromatic. He found that the energy of the electrons was distributed through a range of energies, up to a maximum limit, which equaled $h\nu - e\phi$, where h was the same Planck constant which we have mentioned earlier, ν was the frequency of the light, e was the magnitude of the electronic charge, and ϕ the work-function, which was known from the work of Richardson on thermionic emission, and which represented the difference in electrical potential between the interior of the metal and empty space outside.

These results looked exactly as if each electron liberated inside the metal by the action of the light was initially given an energy $h\nu$, of which it then lost an amount $e\phi$ in getting through the surface, and a further arbitrary amount in its collisions with the atoms on the way out, so that the ejected electrons would have an energy anywhere from $h\nu - e\phi$ on down, the maximum representing the case where no energy was lost on collision. But this result seemed almost inconceivable, when one looked at the case of light of weak intensity, in which electrons were ejected only occasionally. One could compute the energy in the light wave falling on the sample, and compare it with the energy of the ejected electrons. On the average, things came out all right; the impinging energy was greater than the energy of the electrons. But it seemed as if, in the case of weak light, almost all the light falling on the whole sample for an appreciable fraction of a second would have to be concentrated in one single electron, to give it the required energy. How could this possibly happen?

It was to explain this fact, known qualitatively from the work of Lenard, though Millikan had not yet performed his more accurate experiments, that Einstein made the bold hypothesis which really put the quantum theory on its feet. He assumed that the energy in the radiation field really existed in discrete particles, quanta (now called photons), each of amount $h\nu$, and that it was not continuously distributed through the field at all, as classical electrodynamics would suggest. In that case, the photoelectric results no longer seemed queer. In a weak light, there were very few photons per second; but when one of these photons struck the sample, it could convey all its energy to a single electron with which it collided, and the electron would then behave just as Lenard and Millikan had found that it did. A change in the intensity of light would mean merely a change in the number of photons per second, and hence in the number of ejected electrons. But so long as the frequency stayed the same, each photon would still have the same energy.

This hypothesis went far beyond what Planck was willing to accept. Planck had tried to assume that the energy of the radiation field varied continuously, and that only the energies of the oscillators emitting and absorbing it changed discontinuously. This seemed inconsistent to almost everyone except Planck; if the oscillators changed their energy discontinuously, certainly the radiation field should do the same. Nevertheless Einstein's proposal that the energy in a radiation field really existed as particles proved a very difficult one for physicists to accept. Of course, the difficulty was that it seemed to contradict the wave nature of light, and yet interference and diffraction provided indisputable proof of the correctness of the wave theory. We shall later come to the type of compromise which finally satisfied people as an explanation of this paradox: essentially a coexistence of the two types of theories, the energy being carried in photons, but with a wave field to guide them. It was only with the wave mechanics in 1926, when it appeared that the same sort of duality occurred in mechanics too, that physicists felt satisfied with this state of things.

This only shows how much ahead of his time Einstein was. The year 1905 was a great one for Einstein. In the volumes of the *Annalen der Physik* for that year, there appeared three striking papers from this physicist who up to then had been unknown: one introducing the theory of special relativity; one proposing the theory of light quanta, or photons, which we have just described, with its application to the photoelectric effect; and a third, less important one, dealing with Brownian motions. Only two years later, in 1907, there was another extremely important paper explaining the application of the quantum theory to the specific heat of solids. Einstein is popularly known only for his theory of relativity; but these contributions to the quantum theory, which he made at about the same time, even if made alone, would still have entitled him to a leading place in physics. For, as we have said, he was years before his time. It was not until that other great genius of twentieth-century theoretical physics, Niels Bohr, came along in 1913, that the quantum theory made another decisive step forward.

The three developments, Planck's explanation of the black-body radiation law, Einstein's hypothesis of light quanta and his explanation of the law of photoelectric emission, and his work on specific heat, really launched the quantum theory, and we shall discuss them in this chapter. Of the three, the black-body radiation and the specific heat are closely related and involve the same mathematics; they are the problems with which we shall principally concern ourselves. The photoelectric problem is so essentially simple that there is really little more to say about it than we have said already. It was one of those exceedingly simple, but exceedingly profound, suggestions which change the whole direction of science. Nevertheless, it found a new interest in its applications to X rays, and we shall discuss this result and the light which it throws on the nature of X rays.

3-2. Planck's Radiation Law. In the present section, we should like to take the reader through the sort of line of thought which led to the quantum theory. Yet we do not wish to follow Planck's rather devious argument, which actually was hidden behind complicated formalism of thermodynamics and statistical mechanics. We have already said that Planck refused to accept Einstein's later proposal that the energy in the electromagnetic field existed only in quanta, or photons; he tried to preserve a purely classical theory of the field. A much more comprehensible point of view was put forward by Debye in 1910. Debye tried to proceed along the same lines as Rayleigh and Jeans, but to ask how the introduction of the quantum theory into the radiation field could lead to the Planck law. This led him to a derivation which is very straightforward, and which we can reproduce easily. Let us try to suggest a line of reasoning which we might have followed, if we had proceeded along Debye's lines before the time of Planck. We might well have started, as Planck actually did, by inventing the correct law as an interpolation formula between the Wien and the Rayleigh-Jeans law, and then by looking for a theory to explain it.

We remember that the Rayleigh-Jeans radiation law, quoted in Eq. (1-10) stated that u_ν, the energy per unit volume and per unit frequency range in the radiation field, equaled $8\pi\nu^2 kT/c^3$. On the other

hand, Wien's law, which as we have mentioned worked well in the limit
of high frequencies, was

$$u_\nu = \frac{8\pi h\nu^3}{c^3} \exp \frac{-h\nu}{kT} \qquad (3\text{-}1)$$

where h was an empirical constant. This obviously avoids the difficulty present in the Rayleigh-Jeans law: as the frequency goes infinite,
the exponential makes u_ν go to zero, instead of to infinity, as with the
Rayleigh-Jeans law. We have stated that empirically Wien's law
works well at high frequencies, as the Rayleigh-Jeans law does at low
frequencies. Now it does not take very much insight to see that a
good interpolation formula is

$$u_\nu = \frac{8\pi h\nu^3}{c^3} \frac{1}{\exp\,(h\nu/kT) - 1} \qquad (3\text{-}2)$$

At high frequencies, the exponential will be large compared to unity,
we can disregard the term -1 in the denominator, and Eq. (3-2)
reduces to Eq. (3-1). On the other hand, at low frequencies, we can
expand the exponential in power series, $1 + h\nu/kT + \cdots$, and
Eq. (3-2) reduces to the Rayleigh-Jeans law. Equation (3-2) represents Planck's law; and we have stated that, by this simple interpolation, Planck is said to have guessed at the exactly correct law of black-
body radiation. The experimental results were already good enough
to verify this law with high precision.

Now let us ask how we might have proceeded, if this discovery had
been made, but if no theoretical explanation of Eq. (3-2) had been
given. Two things went into the derivation of the Rayleigh-Jeans
law: the distribution of modes of oscillation in the radiation field, given
in Eq. (1-9), and the law of equipartition of energy. We have already
seen that other problems, in particular the specific heat of solids, threw
doubt on the correctness of equipartition. Let us assume, then, that
that is what is wrong with classical physics. We can obviously work
backward from Eq. (3-2), assuming its correctness, to see what must be
the substitute for the equipartition law. Comparing Eq. (3-2) with
Eq. (1-9), it is evident that the average energy of an oscillator, at
temperature T, must be

$$\text{Energy} = \frac{h\nu}{\exp\,(h\nu/kT) - 1} \qquad (3\text{-}3)$$

At high temperatures, where $h\nu/kT$ is small, we can expand the exponential in power series, as we have just described, and get just the
classical value kT. But at temperatures such that kT is small compared to $h\nu$, the exponential becomes very large, and the energy very

small.   In fact, if we plot the energy, as given in Eq. (3-3), as a function of $kT/h\nu$, we find the curve given in Fig. 3-1.   It rises very slowly with temperature at low temperatures, in contrast to the linear rise of the equipartition value kT.   At high temperatures, it approaches a straight line parallel to the line kT, but if we carry the expansion of the exponential one term further than we have done, we find that it actually approaches the line $kT - \frac{1}{2}h\nu$, so that it never quite attains the equipartition value.

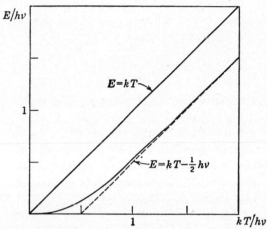

Fig. 3-1. Average energy of an oscillator, according to the quantum theory, Eq. (3-3).   Straight line with 45° slope passing through the origin represents energy kT according to equipartition.   Dotted line with equation $E = kT - \frac{1}{2}h\nu$ represents asymptotic behavior at high temperature, according to quantum theory.

Here, then, we have what seems to be indicated empirically as the correct substitute for the incorrect law of equipartition of energy. The reason why the Rayleigh-Jeans law goes wrong at high frequencies is that the oscillators are down on the lower part of the curve of Fig. 3-1, where their energies are very much less than the equipartition values. It is just this fact that keeps bodies from glowing in the dark at room temperature.   For the visible frequencies, and room temperature, the exponential in the denominator of Eq. (3-3) is so exceedingly large that there is, for all practical purposes, no energy at all in the radiation field.   If we now accept Eq. (3-3) as being correct, we next ask what must be modified in the ordinary derivation of the law of equipartition, to arrive at it.   Two things go into the derivation of equipartition: the Maxwell-Boltzmann distribution law, or the statistical part of the theory, and the formula for the energy of a linear oscillator.   Let us try out the hypothesis that it is the formula for the energy that is wrong. It was obviously revolutionary at the time of Planck to change this, for it implied that classical mechanics was wrong; but there seemed nothing else to do.

What sort of change in the energy formula could possibly have the desired effect? We remember the statistical result of the Maxwell-Boltzmann distribution law: if we set up a phase space for a linear oscillator, with just two coordinates, q and p, the generalized coordinate and momentum describing the oscillator, then the density of points in the phase space, at temperature T, is proportional to $\exp(-E/kT)$, where E is the energy. For a linear oscillator consisting of a particle of mass m, angular frequency ω_0, this energy is

$$E = \frac{p^2}{2m} + \frac{m\omega_0^2}{2} q^2 \tag{3-4}$$

Of course, our actual problem is electromagnetic, so that the p and q must be chosen as generalized coordinates describing the electromagnetic field; but this does not change the general situation.

We note that Eq. (3-4) states that E equals zero at the origin of the phase space and increases as we go out from the origin. It is interesting to ask on what curves in phase space the energy is constant. From Eq. (3-4) we see that these curves are ellipses. We remember that the equation of an ellipse, of semiaxes a and b, is $x^2/a^2 + y^2/b^2 = 1$. Equation (3-4) can be put in this form, if we divide by E; the semiaxes along the p and q directions, respectively, are $(2mE)^{1/2}$ and $(2E/m\omega_0^2)^{1/2}$. In the phase space, then, the density will be constant on one of these ellipses, but will decrease as we go out from one ellipse to a larger one; the density is always a maximum at the origin. At very low temperatures, the representative points in the phase space will be almost all concentrated very close to the origin, so that the average energy will be almost exactly zero. It will fall off very rapidly, on account of the exponential $\exp(-E/kT)$, which falls extremely rapidly with E, if T is small enough. At high temperatures, however, it will fall off much more slowly. Thus there will be many more points falling far out in the phase space, and the average energy will increase. We know that it increases proportionally to the temperature.

We can, as a matter of fact, derive the law of equipartition very simply, by considering our elliptical lines of constant energy in the phase space; and it helps us in our further derivation if we see how this is done. In so doing, we are following the general argument of Planck. We can convert our integrations in phase space, from integrations over p and q, to integrations with respect to the energy E. Let us take as an element of volume the ring between two ellipses corresponding to energies E and $E + dE$. Our density function $\exp(-E/kT)$ will be constant throughout this element of volume, so that it is very convenient to make the calculation in this way. The area of an ellipse corresponding to the energy E can be found from the ordinary formula for the area of an ellipse of semiaxes a and b, which is πab. Inserting our values of these semiaxes, we find in the present case that this area is $2\pi E/\omega_0$, or E/ν, where $\nu = \omega_0/2\pi$ is the frequency of the oscillator. Thus the area of the ring between energies E and $E + dE$ is dE/ν.

We now know that the average energy of the oscillator is the average of E, averaged over the Maxwell-Boltzmann distribution. That is, it is

$$
\begin{aligned}
\text{Energy} &= \frac{\int E \exp(-E/kT)\, dp\, dq}{\int \exp(-E/kT)\, dp\, dq} \\
&= \frac{\int_0^\infty E \exp(-E/kT)\, dE/\nu}{\int_0^\infty \exp(-E/kT)\, dE/\nu}
\end{aligned}
\tag{3-5}
$$

where we have introduced our new element of volume. But this can be rewritten

$$
\text{Energy} = \frac{(kT)^2 \int_0^\infty x e^{-x}\, dx}{(kT) \int_0^\infty e^{-x}\, dx} = kT
\tag{3-6}
$$

since each integral equals unity. This, then, verifies the law of equipartition in a very straightforward way.

Now let us ask, how would the situation have to be changed if the energy were not to vary nearly so rapidly with temperature at low temperature as equipartition would demand? To do this, the points of the distribution must continue to lie almost all at zero energy, even at a quite finite temperature. In other words, the factor $\exp(-E/kT)$ must be practically zero at all those points of the phase space for which E is different from zero. But this is impossible unless all those points for which E is different from zero have quite a large value of E; then it follows at once. We conclude straightforwardly, then, that the phase space must be divided into two parts: a finite region in which the energy is zero, and then a remaining region in which the energy is much greater than zero, with no regions at all in which the energy has an intermediate value. The formulas tell us unequivocally that the energy cannot be the continuous function of position in phase space which classical mechanics demands.

Once we see this fundamental fact, it is not hard to guess at a reason-

able assumption for the energy.   We must combine the situation we
have just described, with some sort of distribution which will lead to
equipartition at high temperature.   That is, looked at in a broad way,
the energy must have the classical value; but in the inner part of the
phase space, it must be zero for a finite region, and then suddenly jump.
What more natural than to assume that the energy really behaves sort
of like a flight of steps, starting at zero for a while, then taking on
another finite value, then another larger one, and so on, in such a way
that the average value of this energy approximates the classical value?
This, as a matter of fact, is essentially what Planck did.

We have seen that the area of phase space inside an ellipse corresponding to energy E equals E/ν, proportional to the energy E.
Planck's hypothesis, and we can see that it was a very plausible one,
was that the actual, nonclassical energy of an oscillator was to be zero
out to a finite ellipse, which might have an area h (which soon turns
out to be the same Planck constant which we have met before).   The
energy of the classical oscillator at the boundary of this ellipse would
be $h\nu$; let us then assume that our nonclassical energy equals $h\nu$ in the
ring, of area h, between this ellipse and a next larger one enclosing an
area twice as large as the first.   The classical energy at the boundary
of this second ring would be $2h\nu$; let us then assume that the nonclassical energy has this value through another ring of area h, and so on.
Clearly our nonclassical energy will approximate the classical one,
though it will everywhere lie below it.   In fact, from very simple
geometry, we can see that its average will lie below the classical amount
by just $\frac{1}{2}\,h\nu$, which we have already seen is the proper thing, for our
empirical energy given by Eq. (3-3) lies below the classical amount by
just this amount at high temperatures.   Our assumption, then, is
bound to behave right at very low temperatures, and to approach the
right value at high temperature.   Let us try it out, and see whether it
works in between.

It is a simple calculation to do this.   Over each ring of area h, the
integrands of both numerator and denominator of Eq. (3-5) will now
be a constant, for E is a constant over such a ring.   Thus the integration over such a ring is trivial, and the integrations in Eq. (3-5) reduce
to summations.   We can cancel common factors from numerator and
denominator, and Eq. (3-5) reduces to

$$\text{Energy} = \frac{\begin{aligned}h\nu \exp\,(-h\nu/kT) + 2h\nu \exp\,(-2h\nu/kT)\\ + 3h\nu \exp\,(-3h\nu/kT) + \cdots\end{aligned}}{\begin{aligned}1 + \exp\,(-h\nu/kT) + \exp\,(-2h\nu/kT)\\ + \exp\,(-3h\nu/kT) + \cdots\end{aligned}} \quad (3\text{-}7)$$

It we write x for exp $(-h\nu/kT)$, the denominator is just

$$1 + x + x^2 + \cdots = \frac{1}{(1 - x)}$$

The derivative of this series with respect to x is $1 + 2x + 3x^2 + \cdots$, which is equal to the numerator, divided by $xh\nu$. Thus the numerator of Eq. (3-7) equals $xh\nu/(1 - x)^2$. The whole expression of Eq. (3-7), then, equals $xh\nu/(1 - x)$. But when we remember the meaning of x, this is just the expression of Eq. (3-3) which we were looking for.

In other words, we have guessed correctly at the answer, and we have followed a general line which Planck might have used in doing so. Actually, as we have stated, he used a good deal more devious and abstruse method, but the principle is the same. We have gone through this argument in detail, to illustrate the sort of thinking that usually goes into the great intuitive flights of physics. It is not belittling them to compare them slightly to the well-known procedure of a college undergraduate in a course in which he uses a text with an answer book. There must be hints, many of them; and it helps enormously to know the answer ahead of time. We shall find in the other really inspired guesses which have gone into the present development of quantum theory, Bohr's theory of the hydrogen atom, de Broglie's suggestion of electron waves, and Schrödinger's equation, that they had hints too. It has taken some of the cleverest thinkers of the age to work out this theory, even with all the hints they had available. Complete theories do not spring full-grown into existence, in spite of the fact that many textbooks give the impression that they do. But neither do they occur to conventional or timid thinkers. All the hints in the world will do no good to one who is afraid to use them.

Planck did not go much further than we have indicated. We have already said that Einstein followed the line of argument through to its logical conclusion, assuming that the electromagnetic field really could only have certain definite energies corresponding to having so many photons of energy. There is one very significant feature of the argument we have given, however, which was in the background for a number of years, but which later took a position of much importance. This is the way in which the phase space was divided up into regions of area h, each associated with a given energy. This was the forerunner of Bohr's theory, of Sommerfeld's quantum condition, of quantum statistics, and of the principle of uncertainty in quantum mechanics. It appeared in Planck's earliest thoughts, much in the way we have presented it; but it took the genius of Bohr to use this hint in the further flight of intuition which led to his atomic model in 1913.

3-3. The Specific Heat of Solids.   We have mentioned Einstein's brilliant suggestion regarding the photoelectric effect.   In contrast to this, his suggestions regarding the specific heat of solids, valuable though they were, were very straightforward following Planck's work. The insight they demanded was principally in the way of realizing that the same type of argument used by Planck for explaining black-body radiation might well represent a very general extension of mechanics, and that very likely any linear oscillator, no matter of what sort, should obey the same law which Planck had assumed, that its energy could only take on the discrete values of an integral multiple of $h\nu$. Once we assume this, Eq. (3-3) will hold for the average energy of any oscillator in place of the law of equipartition, and it follows at once that the classical predictions regarding specific heat will be wrong.   If a molecule or a solid has many oscillators in it, each will have an energy as a function of temperature of the form shown in Fig. 3-1.   The contribution of this oscillator to the heat capacity will be given by the derivative of this curve.   Thus at high temperatures it will give the classical value, but at low temperatures it will fall way below it, reducing to zero at the absolute zero.   The curve falls from its classical value to a low value in the neighborhood of the temperature where $h\nu = kT$.

Einstein, in his 1907 paper, merely assumed that a crystal containing N atoms, and therefore $3N$ degrees of freedom, could be replaced by a set of oscillators all having the same frequency.   In other words, the Einstein specific heat curve, which he derived, has just the form of the derivative of Eq. (3-3), or the slope of the curve of Fig. 3-1, reducing to the classical Dulong-Petit value at high temperature.   Naturally this is an oversimplified picture, and while the general nature of this curve is correct, it is not quantitatively accurate.

A much better theory was worked out in 1912 by Debye.   He started with a more realistic model of a solid.   To understand this, let us remember our arguments regarding the vibrating solid, in Chap. 1. One can discuss the normal modes for a three-dimensional set of particles held together by springs, which approaches very closely to a model of a crystal composed of atoms held by some sort of elastic forces. Here, since each of the atoms has three degrees of freedom, there will be $3N$ normal modes, if there are N atoms.   These will consist of standing waves, and the wavelengths of the shortest of these waves will be of the order of magnitude of twice the distance between atoms. These standing waves are of the nature of sound waves; it is an interesting feature of this theory that the thermal vibrations of a solid can really be decomposed into the superposition of a great many sound waves. These mostly have wavelengths very short compared with ordinary sound waves, however, and frequencies so far above the audible range that, in fact, most of them are found in the infrared region of the spectrum, frequencies of the order of 10^{13} cycles/second.

Each of these normal modes will act like a single linear oscillator, as we saw in Chap. 1, and if its energy is treated according to the quantum theory, it will have an average energy given by Eq. (3-3). To find the total internal energy of a crystal, we have only to find the frequencies of the $3N$ normal modes and to add terms like that of Eq. (3-3) together for each of these frequencies. Debye used a simplified way of doing this, which has proved to be very useful, even though it is only an approximation. In the region of fairly low frequencies, we can find a formula for the number of sound vibrations between frequencies ν and $\nu + d\nu$ which is very much like the corresponding formula for optical vibrations given in Eq. (1-9). The only difference is that we have to handle the transverse and longitudinal vibrations separately. One can have transverse vibrations of a solid, propagating with a velocity v_t, and longitudinal vibrations propagating with a velocity v_l; both of these velocities can be easily deduced from the elastic constants of the solid. There are two modes of transverse vibration, corresponding to two directions of vibration, for each frequency, and one mode of longitudinal vibration. Then the formula which we find in place of Eq. (1-9) is

$$N(\nu)\, d\nu = 4\pi\nu^2 \left(\frac{2}{v_t^3} + \frac{1}{v_l^3} \right) d\nu \qquad (3\text{-}8)$$

Debye simply assumed that Eq. (3-8) represented the number of modes in the range $d\nu$, provided ν was less than a limit, determined so that the total number of modes, found by integrating $N(\nu)$ from zero frequency up to this limit, equaled the correct number $3N$. Further work has shown that this distribution is not very accurate, at the higher frequencies, but that nevertheless the specific heat derived from it is not seriously in error.

Debye, then, assumed that the total energy of his crystal, the internal energy whose derivative with respect to temperature gives the specific heat, was to be found by multiplying the number of oscillators $N(\nu)$ given by Eq. (3-8), by the energy of an oscillator given by Eq. (3-3), and integrating over all frequencies from zero up to this limit. The resulting Debye specific heat curve is shown in Fig. 3-2. It falls to zero at zero frequency, as we have seen that the Einstein curve must, and rises to the classical Dulong-Petit value of $3R$, or approximately 6 cal/mole degree, at high temperatures. It works surprisingly well for monatomic crystals; we shall mention shortly the extensions which have to be made for polyatomic crystals.

At low temperatures, the Debye curve proves to be proportional to T^3, a law which agrees with experiment. This limiting case can be easily proved. For if T is small, the exponential exp $(h\nu/kT)$ will be very large for even a moderately large value of ν, resulting in a very small value of the energy of Eq. (3-3). It can well be that the energy has fallen practically to zero by the upper limiting frequency to which we must extend our integration; we shall therefore make no appreciable error, in this limit, in integrating to infinity. We see, then, from

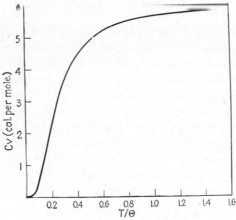

FIG. 3-2. Specific heat of a solid as a function of the temperature, according to Debye's theory. The quantity Θ is the Debye temperature, equal to $h\nu_{max}/k$, where ν_{max} is the limiting frequency mentioned in the text.

Eqs. (3-3) and (3-8), that the internal energy is going to be given by an integral proportional to

$$\int_0^\infty \frac{\nu^3 \, d\nu}{\exp (h\nu/kT) - 1} \tag{3-9}$$

If we let $h\nu/kT = x$, this can be transformed at once into a constant times $T^4 \int_0^\infty x^3 [\exp (x) - 1]^{-1} \, dx$, which is proportional to T^4. This proportionality of the energy to T^4 is, in fact, mathematically equivalent to the Stefan-Boltzmann law which we have at all temperatures with black-body radiation; but in the specific-heat case it holds only at low temperatures. If the energy is proportional to T^4, it is obvious that its derivative with respect to T, which is the specific heat, will be proportional to T^3.

The Debye curve of Fig. 3-2 has a universal form; only the horizontal scale is modified in going from one substance to another. This scale is ordinarily expressed in terms of a so-called Debye temperature Θ; in Fig. 3-2 we have plotted the specific heat as a function of T/Θ. This Debye temperature is defined as follows: We first compute the high-frequency limit of the spectrum, the frequency ν up to which we must integrate $N(\nu)$, from Eq. (3-8), in order to get the correct number $3N$ of normal modes. Then the Debye temperature is that temperature for which $kT = h\nu$, if ν is the limiting frequency just mentioned. It is easy to show that the Debye temperature will be high for a substance with a high velocity of sound, and vice versa. Thus, for example, diamond, which has a very high velocity of sound on account of its high elastic constants and the small mass of its atoms, has a very high Debye temperature, so that its specific heat is appreciably below the Dulong-Petit value at room temperature; whereas the values of the Debye temperatures for most solids come below room temperatures, so that the room-temperature values of the specific heat have nearly the classical values, though they fall a great deal by the time we get to liquid-air temperatures.

We mentioned in Chap. 1 that the specific heats, not only of solids but of gases, did not behave according to the equipartition theory. For a diatomic molecule, for instance, we said that there did not appear to be much contribution to the specific heat from the vibration of the molecule. This vibration acts like an oscillator, whose energy should be given by Eq. (3-3). The vibrational frequencies can be determined from band spectra, by methods which we shall describe later, and if we set up characteristic temperatures for them, by the equation $h\nu = kT$, we find that these characteristic temperatures are ordinarily well above room temperature. Hence Eq. (3-3), or Fig. 3-1, would suggest that such vibrations should not be appreciably excited at room temperature, in accordance with experiment. Furthermore, if we know the vibrational frequencies, we should be able to add terms like that of Eq. (3-3) for the effect of vibration on the internal energy, or the derivatives of such curves to the specific heat, to take account of the vibrational contribution to the specific heat. Such terms are called Einstein terms in the specific heat, since they represent the whole specific heat according to Einstein's simplified theory; and it is actually found that these Einstein terms give a very good account of the molecular specific heat. The same thing holds for more complicated molecules, where there are a number of vibrational degrees of freedom, which can be handled by normal coordinates, and each of which has its own vibrational frequency, so that we need a sum of a number of Einstein terms to express the specific heat properly.

In a polyatomic crystal, the whole theory of the vibrations is quite complicated. The theory shows, however, that the vibrational spectrum falls into two parts: the so-called acoustical branch, consisting of oscillations going down to zero frequency, and arranged with a frequency distribution more or less like that of Eq. (3-8); and various optical branches, bands of frequencies which lie in the infrared part of the spectrum. One then gets a rather good approximation to the specific heat by using a Debye term for the acoustical branch and various Einstein terms for the optical branches. By analysis of this sort, the experimenters in the field of specific heat are able to get good agreement with their experimental results. There is every reason to think that if we analyze the vibrations of a molecule or crystal properly into its normal modes, and give each one an energy according to Eq. (3-3), we get a good account of its internal energy. The only exception to this statement comes when the oscillations are of such large amplitude that the restoring forces are no longer nearly linear, so that the oscillator becomes appreciably different from a linear oscillator. Then more complicated analysis becomes necessary, but this does not affect the general correctness of the theory of specific heat which we have outlined, and which furnishes a very fine verification of the basic ideas of the quantum theory.

3-4. The Photoelectric Effect and X Rays. We have already said about all there is to say in an elementary way about the ordinary photoelectric effect; the further study of the subject is concerned with the details of the energy losses of the electrons, and such problems as that. However, we have mentioned that very interesting results are obtained by considering the photoelectric effect produced by X rays.

For a number of years after the X rays were discovered by Röntgen in 1895, their nature was rather a puzzle. It did not take long, however, to conclude that they were most likely radiations of just the same nature as light, but with much shorter wavelength. This hypothesis was later completely confirmed by the diffraction experiments which we shall mention in Chap. 6, and by much additional evidence. One of the early arguments favoring this view, however, came from the fact that they produce a photoelectric effect, just as ordinary light does. Having much shorter wavelengths, however, or much greater frequency, the photon has a great deal more energy than with ordinary light. It is convenient to measure the energy of a photon in electron-volts, the amount of energy given up by an electron in falling through a difference of potential of a volt; since the charge on the electron is 1.60×10^{-19} coulomb, this energy is 1.60×10^{-19} joule. In terms of this unit, we can easily find the relation between the frequency or wavelength of a photon and the energy in electron-volts.   Thus, if V is the energy in electron-volts, we have $eV = h\nu$, where e is the electronic charge just given, $h = 6.625 \times 10^{-27}$ erg-sec $= 6.625 \times 10^{-34}$ joule-sec, and ν is the frequency, equal to c/λ, where c is the velocity of light, which is 3.00×10^{10} cm/sec.   We then have

$$V = \frac{hc}{e} = \frac{6.625 \times 10^{-34} \times 3.00 \times 10^{10}}{1.60 \times 10^{-19}} \frac{1}{\lambda}$$

$$= \frac{1.24 \times 10^{-4}}{\lambda} \qquad\qquad (3\text{-}10)$$

where λ is expressed in centimeters, or

$$V = \frac{12,400}{\lambda}$$

where λ is expressed in angstroms (1 A $= 10^{-8}$ cm).   Equation (3-10) is a very convenient one for relating wavelengths and electron-volts. It tells us that a photon of, say, 6,000 A, in the visible region, will give an energy of only 2 ev to an electron in a metal, so that the electron will not be ejected photoelectrically unless the work function is less than 2 volts, which is not the case for most metals.   In the ultraviolet the energy gets rapidly greater.   In the X-ray region, on the contrary, where we now know the wavelengths are of the order of a few tenths of an angstrom, the energy can be tens or hundreds of thousands of volts.

It is clear, then, that X rays can liberate very energetic electrons from a metal, and that in comparison with this energy the work function is almost entirely negligible, so that the photoelectron will have almost the whole energy of the photon.   There is a very interesting inverse relationship which comes in in the production of X rays, and which furnished another of the convincing early demonstrations of the quantum theory.   X rays are produced when fast electrons strike a target.   Now that we can measure their spectra, we know that the emitted X rays are of two sorts: There is a line spectrum, characteristic of the atoms in the target, whose study we shall examine extensively in a later chapter, since they are extremely interesting in the study of atomic structure.   But also there is a continuous spectrum, which has the property that all frequencies are observed in it, up to a sharp upper limit.   And this upper limit is related to the energy of the electron producing the X rays by the simple relation $eV = h\nu$.

This continuous spectrum is explained qualitatively in a very simple way.   The photoelectric effect is one in which a photon is absorbed by a solid, and its energy goes into an electron, ejecting it from the metal.

Any such process, however, must have an inverse process. Hence, in this particular case, it must be possible for an electron to strike the solid and lose its energy, and for this energy to reappear as a photon of radiation. This, in very simplified language, is what is supposed to be going on in the emission of the continuous X-ray spectrum; and it is quite obvious that the photon cannot carry more energy than was acquired from the impinging electron, so that the frequency limit is at once explained.

In the field of X rays, we can have a photon ejecting a photoelectron, this photoelectron can strike another target and produce a new photon or produce new X rays, this photon in turn can eject another photo-electron, and so on. In such processes as this, it became very clear, in the period we are discussing, that there was a great deal of reality in Einstein's idea that the energy in a light wave really was concentrated in discrete photons. And, as we shall see later, such an idea of electrons losing their energy and radiating it in the form of a photon, whose frequency was given by the relation that $h\nu$ equaled the loss of energy by the electron, proved to be one of the bases of Bohr's theory of the hydrogen atom, and of atoms in general. Planck had spoken only of linear oscillators gaining and losing energy in quanta; but here we have an electron striking an X-ray target, being brought suddenly to rest there, and turning over its energy to a photon. Certainly the reality of photons, and of the way in which they constitute the energy in a radiation field, can hardly be doubted when one knows of such facts.

PROBLEMS

3-1. Show that the maximum energy density u_ν in black-body radiation, as given by Eq. (3-2), as a function of frequency, comes when $h\nu/kT$ equals a fixed numerical value. Hence show that the frequency associated with the maximum density is proportional to the temperature. This is called Wien's displacement law.

3-2. Show that, in a radiation field obeying Planck's law, those oscillators whose frequency is high compared to that for which u_ν is a maximum have an average energy which is small compared to $h\nu$, while those whose frequency is low compared to this value have an energy large compared to $h\nu$.

3-3. Compute u_ν from Planck's radiation law, for a temperature of 500°K, as a function of ν; for a temperature of 2000°K. Plot curves of u_ν versus ν for each case. Show that at the lower temperature there is no appreciable visible radiation, while in the second case there is a large amount of visible radiation.

3-4. From Eq. (3-3), for the average energy E of a linear oscillator in quantum theory, find the heat capacity of an oscillator dE/dT. Compute a table of values of dE/dT as a function of T, and plot a curve of heat capacity as a function of temperature.

3-5. The Debye temperature of copper is found to be about 320°K. Find the specific heat at 273°K, in calories per gram per degree, according to the Debye theory, using Fig. 3-2. Compare with the observed specific heat of 0.0910 at this temperature. (The atomic weight of copper is 63.57.)

3-6. The low-temperature limit of Debye's specific-heat formula can be shown to be $C = (12\frac{2}{5})\pi^4 Nk(T/\Theta)^3$, where C is the heat capacity of N atoms. Using the value $\Theta = 320°$K for copper, find its specific heat, in calories per gram per degree, at 15°K; at 1°K.

3-7. Find the number of electron-volts corresponding to wavelength of 7,000 A; 2,000 A; 0.1 A.

3-8. Photoelectrons are ejected from a target by X rays of wavelength 0.15 A. It is desired to bend the paths of these photoelectrons into a circle of radius 25 cm, by a magnetic field. Find the strength of the magnetic field required.

3-9. Radiation of wavelength 5,000 A, and of intensity 2×10^{-3} watt/sq cm, falls on a photosensitive surface. Assuming that every absorbed photon results in the ejection of a photoelectron, find how many photoelectrons are produced per square centimeter per second.

3-10. Find the energy in electron-volts of a particle whose energy equals the value kT for $T = 273°$K.

CHAPTER 4

THE NUCLEAR ATOM

4-1 Introduction. Radioactivity furnished the clues which led to the discovery that the positive charge in an atom was localized in a very small nucleus, rather than being spread through the whole volume of the atom, as Thomson had supposed. Becquerel, in 1896, had discovered that compounds of uranium emitted radiations similar in some ways to the X rays found by Röntgen a year before, in that they could be photographed by a photographic plate through a sheet of black paper. By 1900 the Curies, Crookes, Rutherford, and Soddy were all working actively on the problem, and soon the chemical separation of radium from uranium by the Curies, and other similar experiments, had shown that a number of elements were radioactive. The first experiments were directed toward finding the nature of the emitted radiations. Rutherford showed that these were of three sorts, which he called alpha, beta, and gamma radiation. Later work showed that alpha and beta radiation consisted of streams of fast particles, while gamma radiation showed all the characteristics of electromagnetic radiation, like light or X rays.

It did not take long to establish the exact nature of these three types of radiation. Rutherford examined the alpha and beta particles by deflection experiments, similar to those of Thomson which we have described in Chap. 2. It was immediately obvious that alpha particles were positively charged, and that their e/m indicated that their mass was in the neighborhood of atomic masses. By comparison with e/m experiments on other positive ions, it appeared that one possibility was that the alpha particles were helium ions, with a charge equal to twice the electronic charge. Of course, the same e/m would be found for a particle half as heavy as the helium atom, with the electronic charge, but the hypothesis that alpha particles were really helium ions was soon completely verified in a number of ways, including finally the decisive fact that a sufficiently large accumulation of alpha particles stopped in a limited volume showed the ordinary properties of gaseous helium. The beta particles were shown very early to be electrons of high velocity, and the gamma rays proved, as had been suspected at first, to be simply X rays of considerably shorter wavelengths.

The next question which arose was, how did these radiations come to be emitted from the radioactive atoms? This question was closely connected with another one, which at first seemed very puzzling: when a sample of radioactive material was examined, its properties often changed with time, in complicated ways, as if its composition were not staying constant. Rutherford and Soddy, in 1903, proposed an explanation which has proved to be correct, and which tied together all the known facts about radioactivity. This explanation suggested that radioactive atoms could spontaneously explode, transforming themselves into other atoms, and that this explosion went on all the time, so that in a given time interval a certain fraction of the atoms would always blow up, quite independent of outside influences. If we have a number of atoms of which a fixed fraction is destroyed per second, this means that the number existing at any time will fall off exponentially with the time (provided there are no new atoms being produced), and the length of time required for the number to be reduced to half its original value is called the half-life. Rutherford and Soddy found elements with all sorts of half-lives, from short ones of a few minutes to long ones of thousands or millions of years.

The theory of Rutherford and Soddy went much further than this simple hypothesis of explosion, for they also were able to find out what were the products of one of the explosions. If an atom when it explodes transforms itself into another, then the number of atoms of this other type will gradually increase with time, unless an equilibrium is established by a subsequent explosion of the new type of atoms. By an elaborate series of tests, Rutherford and Soddy were able to show which atoms were transformed radioactively into which others, with the half-lives of each type. They were able to set up simultaneous differential equations for the numbers of the atoms of the various types as functions of time, to solve these equations, and to show that they gave a complete explanation of the complicated effects which they had observed as to the time dependence of radioactivity. The case they made out for the transformation hypothesis was so convincing that it has never been questioned.

They found extremely interesting correlations between the chemical properties of the various radioactive elements which they discovered and the types of radiations which they emitted. They found that, when an atom emitted an alpha particle, the resulting atomic species showed chemical properties which would place it two units before the parent atom in the periodic table of elements; while if it emitted a beta particle, its chemical properties would indicate that it should be one unit beyond the parent atom. This suggested immediately an extremely important generalization, which is in a way the foundation of our whole present understanding of the periodic system of the elements: it suggested that the number of an atom in the periodic table of the elements, starting with hydrogen 1, helium 2, lithium 3, and so on, which we now call the atomic number, represented in some way the number of units of positive charge in the atom. For if this were the case, the emission of an alpha particle, which should have two units of positive charge, should decrease the atomic number by two, while the emission of a beta particle, with one unit of negative charge, should increase the atomic number by unity. Many sorts of subsequent evidence have verified the correctness of this hypothesis. A corollary of the hypothesis is obvious: since an atom as a whole is uncharged, a neutral atom must contain a number of electrons equal numerically to its atomic number.

One of the early verifications of this hypothesis came from the so-called Thomson scattering formula for X rays. Thomson, assuming that X rays were simply electromagnetic rays of short wavelength, investigated the law of scattering by matter containing electrons. His formula showed that the scattering should simply be proportional to the number of electrons per unit volume. It was later shown that X-ray scattering is really much more complicated than this, on account of the crystal diffraction which we shall take up in Chap. 6; but there are important cases where Thomson's scattering formula holds, and it was shown experimentally by Barkla and others that the scattering was approximately in agreement with the hypothesis that the number of scattering electrons per atom was equal to the atomic number.

Rutherford and Soddy could draw definite conclusions regarding atomic masses, or atomic weights. The helium atom, or alpha particle, has four units of atomic weight. Hence it is clear that if an atom emits an alpha particle, the new atom resulting from it must have an atomic weight which is less by four units. The electron, or beta particle, on the other hand, has practically no mass compared with the mass of an atom, so that if an atom emits a beta particle, its atomic weight should not change. There were a number of cases where these hypotheses could be verified. In particular, the radioactive series of elements terminated in lead as a final product, and the atomic weight of this lead could be determined from certain minerals whose lead content apparently resulted as an end product of radioactive disintegration; its atomic weight had the predicted value, as found from the uranium or thorium which was the original element from which the lead was descended. Furthermore, the atomic weight of this lead was different from that of ordinary lead, a fact which seemed very remarkable to the chemists of that time, but which became clear soon afterward with the discovery of isotopes. Thus radium disintegrates into lead of atomic weight 206, thorium into lead of atomic weight 208, while ordinary lead has an atomic weight of about 207.

This line of argument suggested that one element could be produced from another by adding helium atoms. Obviously the atomic number must be an integer; but this would suggest that the atomic weight also should be an integer. This hypothesis had been made by Prout, in the early nineteenth century; he supposed that all elements were made from hydrogen. Rutherford and Soddy could modify this to the assumption that elements were made largely from helium atoms. Since the atomic number of a helium atom is 2, and its atomic weight is 4, this would suggest that to a first approximation the atomic weight of all elements should be twice the atomic number; and to a first approximation this is true, though with the heavier elements the atomic weight is considerably larger than this quantity. To account for atomic weights which were integers not divisible by four, one would have to assume, in this simple view, that there were also some hydrogen atoms, and perhaps some electrons, involved in the nuclear structure. We know now that the true situation is more complicated than this, but the fundamental result of these arguments remains true, that we should expect all atomic weights, as well as atomic numbers, to be integers, as Prout had supposed.

The obvious experimental objection to Prout's hypothesis, of course, had been the existence of chemical elements, like chlorine with its atomic weight of 35.46, whose atomic weights were not integrals. The number of elements with integral atomic weights was far too large to be explained by chance but how could one explain these nonintegral values? A solution was immediately suggested by Rutherford and Soddy's explanation of radioactive disintegration. They found in a number of cases that there were several elements of the same atomic number, but of different atomic weight, arising in various stages of radioactive disintegrations; the case of lead, which we have already mentioned, was an obvious one. Their hypothesis indicated that the chemical properties of the element depended only on the atomic number. Hence these elements should be chemically identical, and, in fact, as far as chemical tests showed, they were. It was very natural to assume that the same thing might be going on among the nonradioactive elements: that many of our ordinary elements might be mixtures of a number of different nuclear species, all with the same atomic number, but with different atomic weights. The elements whose atomic weights were known to be integral would be assumed to consist of only one such nuclear species, whereas those, like chlorine, which obviously had fractional atomic weights would have to be mixtures.

This hypothesis was soon verified, in a brilliant way, by the work of Aston with his mass spectrograph, following up the pioneer work of Thomson with his parabola method. Thomson and Aston examined ordinary elements, neon being one of the very early ones worked on, found the values of e/m for the ions, and hence found the masses of the atoms. And they found in fact that in many cases the elements as they existed in nature did consist of mixtures of atoms of different atomic weights, and that these atomic weights were integers, as accurately as they could tell. Aston invented the name isotopes, to represent different atoms with the same atomic number, and hence chemical behavior, but different atomic weight.

Continuation of this work of Aston into the 1920's and later has disclosed the isotopic constitution of all the elements, and has shown that the chemical atomic weights are nothing but a suitably weighted mean of the atomic weights of the various isotopes. The fact that the chemical atomic weight is found to be the same in almost all natural samples of a given element shows that the matter composing the earth must have once been well mixed, presumably while the earth was still molten, so that all chlorine, for instance, is made up from the original mixture having definite ratios of its various isotopes. The only observed cases where natural atomic weights vary are in those elements which have been produced by radioactive disintegration since the earth solidified. It is these few cases which form the basis of the radio-active method of dating the ages of rocks and other substances: for from the known half-lives of the radioactive elements in these substances, one can work backward and find how long it is since the substances in question were molten, or otherwise were in equilibrium with the rest of the material of the earth. We shall come back later to the results of the mass spectrograph in its interpretation of the nature of isotopes.

We have now sketched the main outlines of the arguments that went into the elucidation of the relations between atomic number, atomic weight, and chemical properties. The next great step was that taken by Rutherford in 1911, when his experiments on the scattering of alpha particles by matter led to the hypothesis of the nuclear atom. We shall go on now to these results, returning later in Chap. 11 to more discussion of the general nature of nuclei, and of their relation to the properties of the elements. As a first step, we shall consider some of the experimental methods of detecting individual atoms and ions which were worked out in the early 1900's, for these experimental methods were really what led to the understanding of the nuclear atom.

4-2. Scintillations, Counters, and Cloud Chambers. Three experimental methods which were made available very early in the history of radioactivity made the existence of atoms so obvious that no one could deny their reality. First, Crookes observed that certain fluorescent screens were made luminous when radioactive elements were placed near them. He examined the screens under a microscope, and found that instead of being continuously bright, they showed sudden sharp flashes of light. It seemed practically obvious that each of these flashes was produced by the impact of a fast particle, such as, for instance, an alpha particle. The counting of these scintillations was one of the earliest, and most powerful, methods of detecting individual atomic events. We shall be talking shortly about Rutherford's experiments on the deflection of alpha particles by collisions with atoms; the deflections were observed by letting the particles fall on a fluorescent screen, and counting the scintillations, finding how many were observed per unit area per second in different directions from the target. A spinthariscope—a combination of a bit of radioactive material, a luminous substance, and a lens to observe the results —forms one of the simplest devices for seeing the existence of single atoms. One can get the same effect by examining the luminous dial of a watch with a microscope, for the luminous material consists merely of the radioactive substance and the fluorescent material. Such spinthariscopes can be made exceedingly simple; they have even been distributed as advertising devices, with the statement that they allowed one to see individual atomic explosions. Remarkably enough, the advertising claim was true.

It is worthwhile mentioning here that recent electronic devices have made possible an extension of the scintillation method, which has turned it into a very valuable detection scheme. The difficulty with the original method was that the flashes were very faint, it was a severe strain on the eyesight to count them, and the response of the eye was so slow that very long times of observation were required to get good statistics. Now, however, it is possible to let the emitted light fall on a photomultiplier tube and be detected electrically. The light falls on a photoelectrically sensitive surface, where it ejects electrons by ordinary photoelectric emission. The photomultiplier is then a device which accelerates these ejected electrons by means of a difference of potential, and allows them to fall on a second surface. There they eject secondary electrons, which under certain circumstances can come off in larger numbers than the number of incident electrons. These secondary electrons are accelerated by still another potential difference, they fall on another surface, and so on, the surfaces being arranged somewhat as in Fig. 4-1. The final result is a large enough electrical pulse so that it can be amplified by ordinary electronic means, and finally can be used to operate a mechanical counter or other device. In other words, such a combination of scintillations and photomultiplier tube can give an automatic mechanical count of all the atomic projectiles produced in the sensitive volume of the fluorescent material.

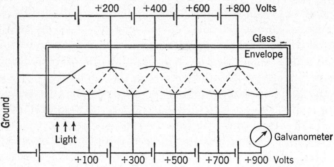

FIG. 4-1. Schematic diagram of photomultiplier. (*Courtesy of O. Oldenberg.*)

The second detection method worked out in the early days was the counter. Rutherford observed that a discharge tube containing gas, with a voltage between the electrodes, could under certain circumstances be very unstable: if a discharge could be started by any method, it developed almost explosively. Furthermore, he found that such explosive discharges could be started if there were radioactive materials in the neighborhood, suggesting that it was the passage of charged particles from the radioactive disintegrations which produced the discharges. Geiger and Mueller developed this idea further, into the Geiger-Mueller counter, which has had very important consequences in the study both of nuclear disintegrations and of cosmic rays.

We shall not go into the details of the construction, for they involve a good many properties of a gas discharge. The essential features are simple, however. Under the unstable conditions present in the counter, a single ionizing particle traversing the counter will knock electrons out of the gaseous molecules and out of the walls of the tube as it travels through. These electrons will be accelerated by the electric field present in the tube, and they, after acceleration, will also be able to ionize further atoms. A sort of avalanche of electrons results, and a pulse of charge flows through the tube. The particular feature of the Geiger-Mueller counter which makes it so useful is that its circuit is so designed that it automatically shuts itself off after this avalanche of charge flows, so that it is ready after a very short time interval to break down again if another particle passes through it. The electrical pulse can of course be amplified in external circuits, and can be used to work a mechanical counter, such as we have already described in the case of the photomultiplier tube and scintillation counter.

A third detection device, much more spectacular than either of these, was the cloud chamber, invented by C. T. R. Wilson. Wilson worked with an enclosure containing air saturated with water vapor. We are familiar with the fact that warm air can hold more water vapor than cold air can, and also that a rapid expansion of a gas cools it. Wilson tried the effect of rapidly expanding the container of saturated air, by making his enclosure in the form of a cylinder with a piston, and suddenly withdrawing the piston. When he did this, of course the air became supersaturated, and a fog tended to form, just as happens in the atmosphere when the temperature suddenly is lowered on a day with very high humidity. It is one of the characteristics of supersaturated air that the fog droplets tend to form only on foreign particles in the air. These can be dust particles, but Wilson suspected that they could also be ions. In particular, an alpha or beta particle passing through the air ionizes many of the atoms in its path (it is this ionization which makes the Geiger-Mueller counter work), and Wilson suspected that these ions would form centers for the condensation of water vapor.

When he tried the experiment, he found that this was the case. The cloud chamber, after its rapid expansion, showed condensation of vapor along well-defined paths, which he interpreted as being the trails left by ionizing particles which had traversed it just before the expansion, so that the ions left along the path had not had time to recombine to form neutral atoms again, or to diffuse out of the path. This technique has been continually improved, until one can see beautiful tracks of all sorts of ionizing particles. Such a cloud-chamber photograph is shown in Fig. 4-2. After seeing such tracks, there can be no remaining doubt but that the radioactive source really is emitting particles. Furthermore, careful study of the amount of ionization along the path has made it possible to get a great deal of information about the nature of the ionizing particles. In modern cloud-chamber technique, a strong magnetic field is often imposed, so that the paths of the particles are curved. From a measurement of this curvature and a study of the density of ionization, it is possible to find the sign of the charge and to deduce quite accurately the mass and velocity of the particle, if the magnitude of its charge is assumed known (a small multiple of the electronic charge).

4-3. Rutherford's Scattering Experiment. We now see the sort of experimental tools which were available to Rutherford and the other workers who were investigating the nature of radioactive disintegration. A particularly interesting observation was made in the study of the scattering of alpha particles passing through matter, by the scintillation method. Most of these particles showed slight deflec-

(a)   (b)

Fig. 4-2. Alpha-particle tracks in a cloud chamber, showing collisions with atomic nuclei. (a) With helium. (b) With oxygen. (*Courtesy of P. M. S. Blackett, Proceedings of the Royal Society, and O. Oldenberg.*)

tions from a straight path. Rutherford interpreted this as coming from the deflections of the alpha particles by the electrons of the atoms they were passing through. It was assumed that the electrons were distributed through the atoms. A particle as fast as an alpha particle would naturally be able to plough right through the atoms. In so doing, it would pass near to many electrons, and be acted on by their electric fields. In a collision of a heavy particle like an alpha particle and a light one like an electron, it is a simple problem in mechanics to find what will happen. The heavy particle will be very slightly deflected, whereas the electron can receive a very strong kick, which may well be enough to eject it from the atom to which it is attached. This ejection is another way of describing the ionization of the gas atoms, to which we referred in the last section. At the same time, however, we cannot forget the slight deflection of the alpha particle.

One electron, of course, may deflect the alpha particle in one direction, while another one may deflect it the other way; for since the alpha particle ploughs through the atoms, it is as likely to find an electron on one side as on another. If it were not for chance fluctuations, the deflections in different directions would cancel, and the alpha particle would not be deflected at all; it would gradually lose energy, for it has supplied the energy necessary to ionize the atoms, but it would continue to travel in a straight line. However, by statistical chance, there are likely to be somewhat more collisions tending to push the alpha particle in one direction than in another, so that on the average the alpha particles will be slightly deflected, though in a random direction. This probable deflection was calculated, from the assumption that each atom contained a number of electrons equal numerically to its atomic number, and the predicted deflections proved to agree in order of magnitude with those which were observed.

Thus the paths of the alpha particles seemed to be explained, except for one peculiar feature: occasional particles showed deflections through very large angles, and calculation of the dynamics of a collision between an alpha particle and an electron showed that such a deflection could not result from such a collision, under any circumstances; the electron is simply too light to be able to deflect a heavy particle that much, no matter how close the collision is. This mathematical analysis, carried out by C. G. Darwin, showed that such a sharp deflection could come only from a collision of a heavy particle with another of comparable mass, and at such a small distance that the electrical force of attraction or repulsion was extremely great.

Such an observation was completely incomprehensible if one assumed, as Thomson had done, that the positive charge in the atom was spread out over the whole atom. The only sort of explanation which could be given was that the positive charge was very concentrated, in a minute nucleus, carrying all the mass, and yet so small that two nuclei could approach to a distance very small compared to atomic dimensions. Rutherford therefore concluded that the alpha particle, and the nuclei, must be essentially point particles, containing the whole mass of the atom, and with positive charges equal numerically to the atomic number times the electronic charge, so that the alpha particle would have a charge of two units. He used the theory of scattering which Darwin had worked out, assuming that the particles repelled each other according to the Coulomb law of electrostatics, with a force inversely proportional to the square of the distance between, and proportional to the product of the charges, and predicting how many alpha particles should be scattered through each angle. When this formula was compared with the experimental results of

Rutherford and his colleagues, it checked very satisfactorily, verifying the assumption that the charges on the nuclei were given by the atomic numbers.

This experiment, then, furnished the experimental proof of the nuclear atom. Rutherford at once was able to give a general picture of an atom. It consisted of a very minute nucleus, containing practically all the mass of the atom, and a positive charge equal to the atomic number times the magnitude of the electronic charge. For electrical neutrality, the nucleus would have to be surrounded by a number of electrons equal to the atomic number. The forces exerted between two nuclei were shown to be given by the Coulomb, or inverse-square, law, down to a very small distance, of the order of a small multiple of 10^{-13} cm; for the largest deflections of alpha particles were shown to come from encounters at a distance of this order of magnitude, and the scattering law, derived on the basis of the Coulomb law, held for these deflections. This deduction of the nuclear nature of the atom formed one of the most important discoveries of the century, in the field of atomic structure.

Two deductions from this postulate were obvious. In the first place, the atom as a whole must have some analogy to the solar system. There was a very heavy but concentrated nucleus, attracting the electrons according to the inverse-square law. They had a very much smaller mass, and would have to be assumed to be at a comparatively large distance from the nucleus. Thus, we have seen that the nucleus cannot be of dimensions larger than the order of 10^{-13} cm. On the other hand, atomic dimensions, as one can tell from a great variety of evidence, are of the order of magnitude of 10^{-8} cm. This evidence comes from many independent sources. For instance, from the kinetic theory of gases, it is possible to estimate the radii of molecules from measurements of the viscosity and thermal conductivity of gases, which depend on the mean free paths of molecules. The study of the properties of imperfect gases also leads to values of molecular dimensions. Much more direct evidence is available, however: in a liquid or solid, we may merely assume that the atoms fill up most of the space, and since we know how many atoms or molecules there are in a given volume, from Avogadro's number, we can immediately compute the molecular volumes. All these types of evidence agree in leading to atomic dimensions of the order of magnitude of 10^{-8} cm, as we have stated.

With such a small nucleus, and such a comparatively large atom, the resemblance to the planets moving around the sun is obvious. Since the nucleus is so heavy compared to the electrons, it must remain approximately fixed as the electron moves around it in its orbit; therefore its mass will be unimportant in the dynamics of the electrons, and only its charge, which produces the attraction between nucleus and electrons, and holds them in their orbits, will be significant in determining their motion. Hence, we see how the motion of the electrons is determined by the atomic number but not the atomic weight of the atom, so that we understand how it is that different isotopes can have the same chemical properties.

The other deduction is that the study of atomic structure must be divided into two quite separate parts: the structure of the nucleus, and of the outer electrons. This separation has persisted and has led almost to a complete separation of physics into two parts, nuclear and nonnuclear physics. The whole explanation of nuclear masses, energies, transformations, radioactivity and artificial radioactivity, and so on, forms one subject in itself. On the other hand, the whole behavior of the outer electrons is determined almost completely by only two properties of the nucleus, its charge and its mass (the latter being almost completely unimportant, so long as it is large enough compared with the electronic mass). It is these outer electrons which determine the ordinary properties of the atom with which we are familiar: its spectrum, its chemical properties, the behavior of the molecules and solids which it can form. And it is in the study of these problems of the outer structure of the atom that the striking progress was made in the years immediately following Rutherford's discovery of the nuclear atom.

Bohr's theory of the structure of the hydrogen atom came in 1913, only two years after Rutherford's discovery. The discovery of X-ray diffraction, and its application to the nature of crystals, as well as the X-ray spectra of the atoms, came at the same time. These led to Bohr's explanation of the periodic system of the elements, to the interpretation of atomic spectra, and finally to the discovery of wave mechanics by Schrödinger in 1926. This was a period of most intense activity in the study of the electronic structure of the atom, and as we have said, it made use of the properties of the nucleus only in the most elementary way. We shall now turn our attention to these advances, which have led to such a complete understanding of the dynamics of the electron, and the theory underlying all ordinary chemical problems. Then we shall go back, in Chap. 11, to the studies which were being made in the intervening period regarding the nature and structure of the nucleus, and which led up to the unsolved problems which hold the center of the stage at present—the nature of nuclear forces, and of cosmic rays.

PROBLEMS

4-1. Uranium disintegrates by a long series of processes into an isotope of lead. The series branches; the successive atomic species formed in one branch of the series are given below. The subscript to the left indicates the atomic number of each atomic species, while the superscript to the right indicates the atomic weight. Indicate what type of radiation must be given off in each process. (Often a gamma ray is given off along with a beta particle; you will not be able to deduce this from the information given.) $_{92}U^{238}$, $_{90}Th^{234}$, $_{91}Pa^{234}$, $_{92}U^{234}$, $_{90}Th^{230}$, $_{88}Ra^{226}$, $_{86}Rn^{222}$, $_{84}Po^{218}$, $_{82}Pb^{214}$, $_{83}Bi^{214}$, $_{81}Tl^{210}$, $_{82}Pb^{210}$, $_{83}Bi^{210}$, $_{84}Po^{210}$, $_{82}Pb^{206}$.

4-2. The isotope $_{83}Bi^{214}$ disintegrates not only into $_{81}Tl^{210}$ but also into $_{84}Po^{214}$. Either of these then disintegrates into $_{82}Pb^{210}$. Explain how this can be the case.

4-3. The isotope $_{92}U^{235}$ disintegrates in a series, called the actinium series, as shown below. Indicate the type of radiation given off in each process, as in Prob. 4-1. $_{92}U^{235}$, $_{90}Th^{231}$, $_{91}Pa^{231}$, $_{89}Ac^{227}$, $_{90}Th^{227}$, $_{88}Ra^{223}$, $_{86}Rn^{219}$, $_{84}Po^{215}$, $_{82}Pb^{211}$, $_{83}Bi^{211}$, $_{81}Tl^{207}$, $_{82}Pb^{207}$.

4-4. The element $_{90}Th^{232}$ disintegrates in a series in which the disintegrations are of the types given below. Write down the successive atomic species in this series of disintegrations. Alpha, beta, beta plus gamma, alpha, alpha, alpha, alpha, beta plus gamma, beta, alpha.

4-5. The law of disintegration for a radioactive species states that the fraction of atoms disintegrating per second is a constant. That is, if N is the number of atoms at time t, we have $dN/dt = -aN$. Find N as a function of time, assuming that there are N_0 atoms at time $t = 0$. Find the relation between the half-life, or the time at which N will equal $N_0/2$, and the constant a.

4-6. The half-life of $_{88}Ra^{226}$ is 1,580 years. What fraction of the atoms disintegrate per second? How many disintegrations per second will there be from a sample of 1 μg (10^{-6} gm) of radium?

4-7. It is observed that about 1.2×10^4 alpha particles are emitted per second from 1 gm of $_{92}U^{238}$ (if it is free from its disintegration products). Find the half-life of $_{92}U^{238}$. If it is assumed that 4×10^9 years have elapsed since the earth solidified, find what fraction of the $_{92}U^{238}$ present at that time still exists.

4-8. If atoms of a given atomic species are being produced at a rate A per second by disintegration of another species, and the atoms in turn are disintegrating, then the number N existing at time t is given by the differential equation

$$dN/dt = A - aN.$$

Find the number N at time t, if $N = 0$ when $t = 0$. Show that at large enough times N approaches the asymptotic value $N = A/a$.

4-9. The half-life of $_{90}Th^{232}$ is 1.5×10^{10} years. This is so long that in any laboratory experiment the rate of disintegration, and hence of production of its disintegration product $_{88}Ra^{228}$, may be treated as a constant. Assume that at $t = 0$ a sample of $_{90}Th^{232}$ is freed from its disintegration products, and that the $_{88}Ra^{228}$ starts to build up. Find the asymptotic amount of $_{88}Ra^{228}$ which will be present, per gram of $_{90}Th^{232}$, after waiting sufficiently long. The half-life of $_{88}Ra^{228}$ is 6.7 years.

4-10. Use the half-life of $_{92}U^{238}$ as determined in Prob. 4-7 to find the amount of $_{90}Th^{234}$ in equilibrium with $_{92}U^{238}$ after waiting long enough, proceeding as in Prob. 4-9. The half-life of $_{90}Th^{234}$ is 23.8 days.

CHAPTER 5

THE BOHR ATOM

5-1. Introduction. Rutherford's postulate of the planetary atom brought with it a great puzzle. We have seen, in Chap. 2, that an accelerated electron continually radiates energy. Yet atoms in their accustomed normal states certainly are not radiating all the time. In the Thomson atom, or the linear-oscillator model for the atom, Lorentz and Drude found a comfortable escape from this difficulty, for the lowest state of such an oscillator is merely that in which the electron is at rest. But the Thomson atom definitely disappeared from the scientific scene with Rutherford's discovery of the nucleus, and there was no apparent escape from the assumption that the electrons of the atom rotated about the nucleus, as the planets rotate about the sun. Why, then, do they not radiate all the time?

By studying the dynamics of a particle moving according to an inverse-square attraction, as we shall do in Sec. 5-4, we easily find that the orbit is smaller, and the frequency of rotation in the orbit greater, as the energy decreases. This seems a little paradoxical, for the kinetic energy increases as the orbit decreases in size, being inversely proportional to the radius; but the potential energy proves to decrease twice as fast as the kinetic energy increases. If, then, an electron rotating in such an orbit radiates energy away, it will move into orbits of successively smaller radii, successively higher frequency of rotation, and will continue to radiate more and more energy, of higher and higher frequency, until it falls into the nucleus. This catastrophe would have to happen to a classically constructed atom consisting of a nucleus and electrons. It clearly cannot be happening with the atoms of our experience. What prevents the catastrophe?

It was this puzzle which faced physicists immediately after Rutherford's discovery of 1911; and it was not long before an answer was provided. Rutherford was working at that time at the University of Manchester; he had not yet been called to the Cavendish Professorship at the University of Cambridge, where he ended his career as the successor of J. J. Thomson and Clerk Maxwell in that illustrious chair.

A brilliant young Dane, Niels Bohr, received a fellowship to work with Rutherford at Manchester; and in 1913 he produced his theory of the structure of the hydrogen atom, resolving the puzzle, and laying the foundation for all the later work on atomic structure. His answer, of course, was that the classical mechanics was not adequate to describe atomic structure, and that we must use the quantum theory instead. His imaginative use of the quantum theory, however, carried that theory far beyond the relatively limited range of problems to which it had so far been applied, and opened the way for its use in studying atomic dynamics of the most general sort.

Bohr's advance was really based on three sorts of foundations: the quantum theory, as we have studied its development in Chap. 3; the nuclear atom, whose discovery we have just described; and the experimental knowledge of atomic spectroscopy, which we have not so far mentioned. This last work, which up to that time had been only a fascinating but unexplained mass of experimental results, had been developing since the latter part of the nineteenth century, presenting a riddle whose solution was certain to disclose the nature of atomic structure, but a riddle which no one before Bohr had been able to penetrate. Let us start our discussion of Bohr's theory by an account of what was known about atomic spectra in 1913.

5-2. Atomic Spectra. Ever since the spectroscope was discovered, it was obvious that arcs or sparks gave spectra of extraordinary interest and complexity. They gave spectral lines of extreme sharpness, so that the wavelengths, or frequencies, could be measured with a precision of six or more figures. These lines were observed not only as bright lines emitted in the spectra of hot gases but also as absorption lines when light of a continuous spectrum passed through a cooler gas. Fraunhofer, in the early part of the nineteenth century, had found these absorption lines in the sun's spectrum, showing conclusively that the same sort of atoms existed in the sun as on the earth. There were even cases where the spectral lines of an element were first discovered in the sun or the stars; helium, whose spectrum was first found in the sun, is the classic example of this.

It was found that each type of atom had its characteristic spectrum, so that spectrum analysis became a powerful tool for chemical analysis. Two clearly distinguished types of spectra were observed: the line spectra, which were characteristic of the atoms, and band spectra, characteristic of molecules. Examples of spectra of the two sorts are shown in Fig. 5-1, and the distinction between their appearance is clear. The assignment of one type to atoms, the other to molecules, was verified without question in such cases as iodine vapor, where there is a chemical equilibrium between monatomic iodine atoms and diatomic molecules I_2; as the relative proportions of the two were changed, by varying pressure or temperature, the relative intensities of the two sorts of spectra varied in the expected way.

All these facts were interesting, but perhaps not very remarkable at first sight. More surprising, however, were the very striking regularities observed in some of the line spectra. The example shown in

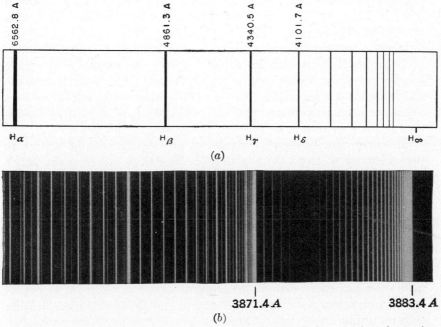

(a)

(b)

FIG. 5-1. Typical atomic and molecular spectra. (a) Balmer series of atomic hydrogen. The lines H_α, H_β, H_γ, H_δ, correspond to $n = 3, 4, 5, 6$. The wavelengths are given in Angstroms. H_∞ marks the computed position of the series limit, and the beginning of the continuous absorption spectrum. (b) Part of a molecular spectrum (CN), photographed with a diffraction grating. (*Courtesy of O. Oldenberg.*)

Fig. 5-1(a), which illustrates part of the spectrum of atomic hydrogen, certainly shows that there must be very simple laws governing the structure of the spectrum. This particular spectrum of hydrogen is simpler than any other; so simple, in fact, that Balmer, in 1885, had been able to show that the frequencies of the lines were given with extreme accuracy by the very simple formula

$$\text{Wave number} = 109{,}737 \left(\frac{1}{4} - \frac{1}{n^2} \right) \quad \text{cm}^{-1} \qquad (5\text{-}1)$$

where n is an integer, equal to 3, 4, . . . , and where the wave number, or reciprocal of the wavelength, is given instead of the frequency, to which it is proportional; the wave number proves to be a convenient quantity to use experimentally. This Balmer formula was so simple that physicists were convinced that if it could be explained, we should understand the structure of the hydrogen atom; but no suggestion as to how to explain it appeared until Bohr came along.

There were, however, other regularities observed in many spectra. Ritz, in 1908, had combined many of these regularities into a generalization called the combination principle. He found that the wave numbers of spectrum lines could always be written as the differences of two quantities, which he called terms. For example, the wave numbers given in the Balmer formula, Eq. (5-1), can be written as the difference of the term $109,737/4$ and the other term $109,737/n^2$; we note, when we write them this way, that the first term $109,737/4$ is merely the special case of the second obtained by setting $n = 2$.

Of course, merely the statement that any number can be written as the difference of two others is trivial. The thing which made Ritz's combination principle important is that in many cases a large number of spectral lines can be written as differences of a much smaller number of terms. If we have n terms, there will be $n(n - 1)/2$ differences, and this number can be very much greater than n. Spectral lines are not observed having the frequencies given by all these differences, but many of them are. Thus the combination principle becomes an important way of simplifying the results of spectroscopic measurements: we can merely tabulate the term values rather than the spectrum frequencies, and give the frequency of each line only by indicating the two terms whose difference gives the frequency. But at the same time the combination principle suggests that we have here an experimental fact which should find theoretical explanation.

Other regularities were found by Rydberg, in studying spectra of atoms other than hydrogen. In the language of Ritz's combination principle, Rydberg found that in many cases series of terms could be found of the form of $R/(n - d)^2$, where R was a constant, equal very closely to the value 109,737 which we have already given (and which is usually called the Rydberg number, in tribute to Rydberg's work), n is an integer, and d is a constant. The Balmer formula is the special case where d is zero. Rydberg's formula, for nonhydrogenic atoms, is far less accurate than Balmer's formula for hydrogen, but still it is accurate enough to be of great importance, and it is obvious, from the occurrence of the same Rydberg number in the spectra of many elements, that there is some widespread similarity between the theories of the spectra of various atoms.

5-3. Bohr's Stationary States. We have now seen the sort of information which Bohr had available when he started thinking about the theory of atomic spectra. What do the facts suggest to us? We observe exceedingly sharp spectrum lines coming out from atoms which, if they were governed by classical mechanics, would be continually changing their properties as the electrons fell into the nuclei, revolving more and more rapidly as they approached their catastrophic end. From our knowledge of the quantum theory, it seems plausible that the process of emitting one of the spectrum lines should consist of the emission of a photon, whose energy $h\nu$ equals the difference between the initial and the final energy of the atom. The atom, then, would have to lose its energy in finite jumps. It cannot take on any arbitrary energy, any more than a linear oscillator, as discussed in Chap. 3, could take on any arbitrary energy. It would, instead, have only a discrete set of energies which it can assume. We conclude from this line of argument that it must exist in stationary states, in which its energy remains constant, rather than radiating continuously as classical mechanics would require. Each of these stationary states would have a perfectly definite energy; and as it jumps from a state of energy E_2 to one of lower energy E_1, the frequency of the emitted photon will be given by the relation

$$E_2 - E_1 = h\nu \qquad (5\text{-}2)$$

In Eq. (5-2), we have a statement that the frequency of the photon is given by a difference of two values, equal to the energy of the corresponding stationary state, divided by h. Here, then, we have a most simple explanation of Ritz's combination principle: Ritz's term values are just the appropriate energy levels of the atom, expressed in units of wave numbers. From the observed spectrum of an atom, when interpreted in terms of its term values, we have a straightforward catalogue of the stationary states in which it can exist. In particular, for the hydrogen atom, we are led to assume that it can exist only in stationary states whose energies, energy levels as we call them, are given by the values R/n^2, in appropriate units. The Balmer series is observed when the atom changes from a term with $n = 3, 4, \ldots$, to one with $n = 2$. We shall see presently that the reasonable assumption is that the energy is $-R/n^2$, small n values corresponding to low energies, so that we assume that in the emission of the Balmer series, the initial state is characterized by $n = 3, 4, \ldots$, and the final state by $n = 2$.

With this information, it is inevitable that we should ask whether terms of hydrogen do not also exist for $n = 1$; and whether transitions do not occur in which the final state, instead of having $n = 2$, may not have some other value.   The experimental answers to both questions were available, and both were affirmative.   In fact, even Balmer had asked whether such lines would not be found in the spectrum. The American spectroscopist Lyman, working in the ultraviolet part of the spectrum, had found parts of the series of lines terminating in the state with $n = 1$ in 1906, and continued until this complete series was known.   The German Paschen in 1908 had found lines whose frequencies were given by $R(\frac{1}{3}^2 - 1/n^2)$.   It was obvious that the energy levels of hydrogen were given by $-R/n^2$, where n is any integer, and that transitions between any two values of n seemed to be possible.

From this information, it was also quite clear why the hydrogen atom did not have the catastrophe predicted by classical mechanics, the electron falling into the nucleus.   The existence of the sharp lines, the definite energy levels, showed that there were only certain definite energies which the atom could have, given by the values $-R/n^2$.   The lowest of these comes for $n = 1$, and is simply $-R$.   It was necessary to assume that these energy values were somehow prescribed by the quantum theory, and that the theory limited the values of n to integers, thereby allowing no lower energies than that for $n = 1$ (somehow, of course, the case $n = 0$ would have to be excluded).   Since this was the lowest energy level, it would be impossible for an atom in that state to lose energy and have a transition to any lower state.   This, in other words, must be the normal, or ground, state of the atom, the lowest energy level in which it could exist.   All other states would have higher energy.   They were excited states, to which the atom could be excited by absorption of photons of radiation, but from which it could fall back to the ground state by emission of the same photons.

Clearly this general picture was much broader than merely a theory of a hydrogen atom.   Bohr assumed that any atomic system could exist only in a variety of stationary states, each with its own energy. The lowest of these was the ground state, those of higher energy were excited states.   So long as the atom is in a stationary state, it does not radiate; the radiation comes only when it jumps from one stationary state to another, and in that case the frequency of the radiation is given by the frequency condition of Eq. (5-2).   If the initial state has higher energy than the final state, the photon is emitted, and the atom radiates; if the initial state has lower energy, the photon is absorbed.   Thus we explain the observation that the frequencies of emission and absorption lines are the same.   We can understand at the same time, however, why not all emission lines are observed in absorption; in a cold gas, the atoms will all be found in their ground states, and therefore only those frequencies can be absorbed which correspond to transitions from the ground state up to some excited state.

This general idea of stationary states also suggested a quite different type of experiment. It is known that a gas is rendered luminous when it forms an electric arc. In this arc, there are electrons wandering around having a considerable energy. The mechanism of excitation seems clear. An electron strikes an atom in its ground state. If the electron has enough energy, it can raise the atom to one of its excited states; to do this, the electron must clearly have an energy at least equal to the difference of energy between the ground state and the excited state, an amount called the excitation energy. The excited atom then can radiate and return to its ground state. Clearly, for example, for hydrogen, there will be a variety of excitation potentials, given by the values $R(1 - 1/n^2)$, where n is any integer greater than 1. Larger and larger values of n will correspond to higher and higher excited states, with the electron in larger and larger orbits. There is obviously a limit, when n becomes infinite; we shall see shortly that this corresponds to an infinitely large orbit, or a case in which the electron is entirely removed from the nucleus, or the atom is ionized. This limiting value R then corresponds to the ionization potential of the atom, the energy required for an electron to ionize it.

The suggested experiment, then, is one in which a gas, say atomic hydrogen, is bombarded by electrons of carefully controlled energy. If the energy is too small, no transitions of the atoms will be possible. The bombarding electrons cannot lose energy, and will have what we call an elastic collision; the gas will emit no radiation. As the energy is increased to become equal to the first excitation potential, many electrons will collide with atoms, losing just enough energy to raise them to the first excited states. We shall have what are called inelastic collisions; the bombarding electrons come away from the collisions with greatly reduced energies, reduced by just the amount which they have lost in exciting the atoms. At the same time, the atoms will start to radiate the line associated with the transition from the lowest excited state to the ground state. If the electron energy is raised still further, some bombarding electrons may be able to raise atoms to higher excited states. With still greater bombarding energy, electrons can ionize the gas, and we can measure an ionization potential, the minimum energy with which ionization is possible. Franck and Hertz, in Germany, started experiments of this sort immediately after Bohr's explanation of the nature of stationary states, in 1913. Their experiments resulted in a complete confirmation of these ideas, and a great deal of subsequent work of the same sort, by many physicists, has completely verified the idea of stationary states and of the transitions between them.

5-4. The Stationary States of Hydrogen. In the preceding section, we have outlined Bohr's theory of stationary states, its success in explaining Ritz's combination principle of atomic spectra, and its verification by the experiments on excitation and ionization potentials by Franck and Hertz. Next we go on to the more detailed part of Bohr's theory: his explanation of the stationary states of hydrogen. There must be some principle, not obvious at first, which determines the particular energy values characteristic of these stationary states. This principle must be analogous, for the planetary problem furnished by the motion of the single electron of hydrogen around its nucleus, to the rule which Planck set up: that the energy of a linear oscillator must be an integral multiple of $h\nu$, where ν is the frequency of the oscillator.

Let us put ourselves in Bohr's place, and see whether we cannot figure out what this rule is. We know that the energy of the stationary states, from the Balmer formula, is given by $-R/n^2$. But the dynamics of the motion of an electron in an inverse-square field are simple and familiar. Let us work backward, and find what are the characteristics of orbits having these energies. Of course, we know, from the theory of planetary motion, that particles moving under the action of an inverse-square attraction move in ellipses; the simplest orbits are circles. Let us for the moment think only of these circular orbits, which are so simple that we can work out their dynamical principles with great ease. Let us find the relation between the energy, radius, frequency, and other properties of such a circular orbit, and work backward from the Balmer formula to find which particular orbits must represent stationary states.

Let us consider an electron of charge $-e$ (we here use e for the magnitude of the electronic charge), moving in a circular orbit around a nucleus of nearly infinite mass compared with the electron, and charge $+e$. The mass of the electron is assumed to be m. The attractive force between the two particles, in electrostatic units, is e^2/r^2, where r is the distance between, which may be taken to be the radius of the circle on which the electron moves, since the nucleus will be almost precisely fixed. In mks units, the force is $e^2/4\pi\epsilon_0 r^2$, where $\epsilon_0 = 8.85 \times 10^{-12}$ farad/m. For the convenience of those who prefer mks units, we shall give our results in those units; to get electrostatic units, we omit the factor $4\pi\epsilon_0$ or replace ϵ_0 by $1/4\pi$. This force must equal the centripetal force, which, for a particle moving with velocity v in a circle of radius r, is mv^2/r. Thus, in mks units, we have

$$\frac{e^2}{4\pi\epsilon_0 r^2} = \frac{mv^2}{r} \quad i.e. \quad \frac{e^2}{4\pi\epsilon_0 r} = mv^2 \tag{5-3}$$

Since the potential energy is $-e^2/4\pi\epsilon_0 r$, and the kinetic energy is $mv^2/2$, this at once tells us that the potential energy is numerically equal to twice the kinetic energy, but of opposite sign, as we stated earlier. Expressing this differently, the energy equals the negative of the kinetic energy, or half the potential energy:

$$E = -\frac{e^2}{2(4\pi\epsilon_0)r} = -\frac{mv^2}{2} \tag{5-4}$$

We can, if we choose, rewrite this energy in still another form, by squaring the first expression of Eq. (5-4), dividing by the second, and find

$$E = \frac{-me^4}{2(4\pi\epsilon_0)^2(mvr)^2} \tag{5-5}$$

In Eq. (5-5), we have an especially interesting formula for the energy, for it expresses the energy as a negative constant, divided by the square of a physical quantity mvr, and this suggests the formula $-R/n^2$ which we are trying to establish. The quantity mvr, in fact, is just the angular momentum of the electron. If the energy is to agree with the term values demanded by the Balmer formula, in other words, we see that the angular momentum must be proportional to the integer n, capable of taking on only discrete values. This hint, then, suggests the direction in which we should look for our conditions determining the stationary states.

At this point, we may well look back, as Bohr presumably did at the same stage of his argument, to the way in which Planck had determined the stationary states of an oscillator, as we have described it in Chap. 3. Planck, we remember, set up a phase space, in which the coordinate and momentum of the oscillator were the two coordinates, and in which lines of constant energy were drawn. These lines were ellipses, for that case. Planck's condition determining the energy was that the allowed energy values were to be those for which the area inside the ellipse was an integral multiple of the constant h. This area proved to be E/ν, where E was the energy, ν the frequency, of the oscillator; so that the law stated that the energy had to be an integral multiple of $h\nu$.

Obviously this rule is one capable of extension. Suppose we have some other system, again described by a single coordinate and its momentum, and suppose we again draw lines of constant energy in the phase space, and demand that such a line enclose an area of nh, where n is an integer. We could always apply such a condition, which we might well call a quantum condition. It seems a plausible hypothesis to adopt this as the principle determining the states. Let us see what it gives for our hydrogen atom. The obvious coordinate to use here, since the particle is rotating like a wheel on an axle, is the angle of rotation, and the momentum related to this coordinate proves to be the angular momentum. The motion of the system is given by the simple statement that the angular momentum remains constant, while the angle continually increases. All angles will be contained within the range from zero to 2π. Thus in the phase space a representative point will move uniformly to the right along a horizontal line whose ordinate measures the angular momentum, as θ goes from 0 to 2π, then will start over again, at zero, and retrace the motion, and so on. The only thing which we can mean by the area of the curve of constant energy is the area bounded by the axis of abscissas, the lines $\theta = 0$ and 2π, and the line whose height measures the angular momentum. The area under this curve is 2π times the angular momentum. Thus this argument would suggest that the quantum condition for a rotating system like this should be

$$\text{Angular momentum} = \frac{nh}{2\pi} = n\hbar \qquad \hbar = \frac{h}{2\pi} \qquad (5\text{-}6)$$

Obviously, this condition is of the form which we have seen could lead to a Balmer formula; for that, we needed to have the angular momentum equal to an integer times a constant. At this point we can imagine Bohr, with considerable excitement, substituting numerical values in his formula. Clearly, from Eq. (5-5), the energy should be given by

$$E = -\frac{2\pi^2 me^4}{h^2(4\pi\epsilon_0)^2}\frac{1}{n^2} \quad joules \qquad (5\text{-}7)$$

so that the Rydberg number, expressed in energy units, should be $2\pi^2 me^4/h^2(4\pi\epsilon_0)^2$. In order not to keep the reader in suspense while we work out the numbers, let us say that Bohr made this substitution, the value agreed within experimental error with the observed Rydberg number, and theoretical physics had achieved the greatest triumph of detailed numerical agreement between theory and experiment since Maxwell had derived the velocity of light from purely electrical quantities in the middle of the preceding century.

To make it easy for the reader to make this same calculation, let us say a few words about the proper units to use in expressing this formula for the Rydberg number. If we use mks units, m equals 9.11×10^{-31}

kg, e equals 1.60×10^{-19} coulomb, h equals 6.625×10^{-34} joule-sec, and the energy from Eq. (5-7) comes out in joules. If this is set equal to $h\nu$, the frequency will be in cycles per second. The wave number, which we want for comparison with the Rydberg number R, equals the frequency divided by c, the velocity of light, which is 3.00×10^8 m/sec. If we convert to cm^{-1}, we have

$$R = \frac{2\pi^2 me^4}{h^3 c (4\pi\epsilon_0)^2} = 109{,}737 \text{ cm}^{-1} \text{ approximately} \qquad (5\text{-}8)$$

using the numbers which we have just mentioned. If we prefer to use electrostatic units, the Eq. (5-7) is easily seen to be replaced by $-2\pi^2 me^4/h^2 n^2$. In these units, $m = 9.11 \times 10^{-28}$ g, $e = 4.80 \times 10^{-10}$ esu, $h = 6.625 \times 10^{-27}$ erg-sec, and the energy of Eq. (5-7) comes out in ergs. Again we divide by hc and find R in cm^{-1}; the result is the same as in Eq. (5-8).

It is also sometimes interesting to have the energy corresponding to the Rydberg unit expressed in electron-volts; this represents the ionization potential of hydrogen. If we use mks units and take the energy $2\pi^2 me^4/h^2(4\pi\epsilon_0)^2$ in joules, we can set this equal to eV, where e is the magnitude of the electronic charge, and V becomes the energy in volts. Hence we have

$$\text{Ionization potential of hydrogen} = \frac{2\pi^2 me^3}{h^2(4\pi\epsilon_0)^2} = 13.60 \text{ ev} \quad (5\text{-}9)$$

This value of course can also be found from the cgs units, but this is a case in which the use of mks units is particularly convenient, since it leads at once to practical units.

Other quantities besides the Rydberg number and ionization potential can be found easily from the Bohr theory. For instance, it is very interesting to find the radii of the orbits of various n values. From Eq. (5-4), we find at once that

$$r = a_0 n^2$$

where $$a_0 = \frac{h^2(4\pi\epsilon_0)}{4\pi^2 me^2} = 0.53 \times 10^{-8} \text{ cm} = 0.53 \text{ A} \qquad (5\text{-}10)$$

The radius of the orbit in the ground state, about a half angstrom, is thus seen to be of the order of magnitude of 10^{-8} cm, but the orbits very rapidly grow larger as n increases.

Another interesting quantity is the frequency of rotation in the orbit. The angular frequency of course is v/r, and this is 2π times the frequency itself.   Using Eqs. (5-4) and (5-7), this is then

$$\text{Rotation frequency} = \frac{4\pi^2 me^4}{h^3 n^3 (4\pi\epsilon_0)^2} = \frac{2Rc}{n^3} \tag{5-11}$$

inversely proportional to n^3.   It is an interesting and remarkable fact, which Bohr used a great deal in setting up his so-called correspondence principle between classical and quantum mechanics, that there is a very close relationship between this classical frequency and the frequency of the emitted radiation in the quantum theory.   In fact, if we integrate the classical frequency with respect to n, from one integer n to another n', we find at once

$$\int_n^{n'} \frac{2Rc}{n^3}\, dn = Rc\left(\frac{1}{n^2} - \frac{1}{n'^2}\right) \tag{5-12}$$

which is just the emitted frequency as computed in the quantum theory.   If in particular $n' = n + 1$, the integral is just the average classical frequency averaged between the two stationary states in question.

5-5. Elliptical Orbits in Hydrogen.   The simple theory of the hydrogen atom, set up in the preceding section, showed a perfect agreement with the observed spectrum, and such quantities as the size of the atom, though less susceptible of exact check, seemed very reasonable.   The theory is obviously incomplete, however, for we have considered only circular orbits, whereas classical mechanics would permit elliptical orbits as well.   The extension of the theory to elliptical orbits was made in 1916, by Sommerfeld, the German physicist.   The mathematics of his method is somewhat too complicated to take up here, but the ideas underlying it are simple.   Sommerfeld set up the problem of the motion of the electron in polar coordinates, r, θ.   He introduced the momenta, p_r and p_θ, associated with these coordinates.   Of these, the quantity p_r is the ordinary component of momentum along the radial direction, and p_θ is the angular momentum.   This angular momentum stays constant during the motion, and the quantum condition for it in every case, just as for the circular orbits, is that it should be a constant times $h/2\pi$.   When we introduce this value for p_θ, we can then write the radial momentum p_r in terms of r and the energy, or can set up a two-dimensional phase space, with r and p_r as variables, and can set up curves of constant energy in this phase space.   These curves are not simple ellipses, or anything of that sort.   Nevertheless, we can still use the same type of quantum condition used earlier, namely that the area of one of these curves must equal an integer times h.

Sommerfeld worked out the value of this area and applied the quantum condition, finally deriving the value of the energy for an elliptical orbit. The quantum number associated with p_θ, measuring the angular momentum in units of $h/2\pi$, is usually called the azimuthal quantum number, and is denoted by k. The quantum number associated with p_r is called the radial quantum number, and is denoted by n_r. Sommerfeld's formula for the energy was then

$$E = -\frac{R}{(n_r + k)^2} \qquad (5\text{-}13)$$

expressed in wave numbers. In other words, he found just the same formula as Bohr, if we replace the integer $n_r + k$ by Bohr's quantum number n. It is interesting, however, to see what are the characteristics of the elliptic orbits of Sommerfeld's theory.

One can prove that the ratio of minor to major axis of one of the elliptical orbits is equal to k/n; n is called the principal quantum number, since it determines the energy. Since $n = n_r + k$, the circular orbit corresponds to $n_r = 0$, in which case there is no radial motion, and $k/n = 1$. All other orbits of the same n value, and hence the same energy, prove to have the same major axis; the nucleus is in each case at one of the foci of the ellipse. For a given value of n, k can take on the values $n, n - 1, n - 2, \ldots, 1$; it cannot be zero, for in that case the electron would go through the nucleus. We shall find the nature of these various orbits to be of great importance when we take up more complicated atoms, but for the moment they are not of great consequence, since they merely show that Bohr's calculation of the spectrum of hydrogen was correct, even though he disregarded the possibility of elliptical orbits.

Sommerfeld carried his arguments further, and set up the problem not only in polar coordinates in a plane but in spherical polar coordinates in three-dimensional space. He then applied three quantum conditions, to the three variables. His final result was extremely interesting. The energy and the shape of the orbits, of course, were the same as before, since we can hardly expect the problem to be altered when we consider it in different coordinates; the orbit still lies in a plane. But Sommerfeld found that the plane in which the orbit could be located could have only certain definite orientations in space. They could be described as follows: the component of the angular momentum vector, whose magnitude is $kh/2\pi$, along the axis of the coordinates, could have only one of the integral values $m_k h/2\pi$, where m_k could take on the values $k, k - 1, \ldots, -k$.

This orientation of the orbit in space was called space quantization.

It became paradoxical when there was no special feature distinguishing the axis of coordinates; it is hardly reasonable to say that the orbit must be oriented in a particular way with respect to a direction in space which has no special significance; and the application of space quantization in such a case is one of the many features in which this simple Bohr theory was not adequate. If there is an external field along a given direction, however, such as a magnetic field, then the space quantization must be carried out with respect to this field; and in this case it becomes very significant, and in fact leads to the theory of the Zeeman effect.

The Zeeman effect arises because an electron rotating in an orbit has a magnetic moment on account of its orbital motion, so that the energy depends on the orientation of the orbit with respect to the magnetic field. The theory is so elementary that we can work it out at once, in simple cases. First let us find the magnetic moment of the electron in its orbit; we carry out the calculation only for circular orbits, and shall merely state without proof the result for elliptical orbits.

Let an electron rotate with velocity v in an orbit of radius r. Its period of rotation will equal the circumference of the orbit, divided by the velocity, or $2\pi r/v$. The electron is equivalent to a current circulating around the orbit. The magnitude of this current is, of course, equal to the charge flowing per unit time, or to e divided by the period, which is the time during which a charge e flows around the circuit. Using the value of the period which we have just found, this means that the current is $ev/2\pi r$. Next we note that a current circulating in a closed loop is equivalent to a magnetic dipole, whose magnetic moment equals (in mks units) the magnitude of the current multiplied by the area of the loop. Since this area is πr^2, the magnetic moment is $evr/2$. This, however, can be rewritten $(e/2m)(mvr)$; and since we remember that mvr is the angular momentum, we find that the magnetic moment is $(e/2m)$ times the angular momentum. A similar treatment in Gaussian units gives a magnetic moment of $(e/2mc)$ times the angular momentum.

This relation, that the magnetic moment equals $e/2m$, or $e/2mc$, times the angular momentum, proves to hold for elliptical as well as circular orbits, though we shall not carry through the argument for that case. Hence, since in every case the angular momentum is $kh/2\pi$, where k is the azimuthal quantum number, we find that the magnetic moment is $k(eh/4\pi m)$ in mks units, or $k(eh/4\pi mc)$ in Gaussian units. The quantity $eh/4\pi m$ or $eh/4\pi mc$, depending on units, is called the Bohr magneton. It is a unit of magnetic moment, which proves to have wide application to the discussion of the magnetic properties of all sorts of materials. The ratio of magnetic moment to angular momentum, $e/2m$ or $e/2mc$ depending on units, is often called the gyromagnetic ratio, and proves to be important in problems of magnetic resonance which are now of great experimental interest.

In a magnetic field, the atom will have a magnetic energy equal to the magnetic field times the component of magnetic dipole moment in its direction. In mks units, where we measure B in webers per square meter (1 weber/sq m = 10^4 gauss), this magnetic energy is then $m_k(eh/4\pi m)B$. Expressed in wave numbers, this is $m_k(e/4\pi mc)B$. If we put in e in coulombs, m in kilograms, c in meters per second, and B in webers per square meter, we get the wave number in m^{-1}. The corresponding numerical quantity in cm^{-1}, the more usual spectroscopic unit, and with B in gauss, is

Magnetic energy in wave numbers = $m_k(4.67 \times 10^{-5})B$,

$$\text{(in gauss)} \quad (5\text{-}14)$$

Since the magnetic field is at most a small multiple of 10,000 gauss, in ordinary experiments, this means that the magnetic contribution to the energy is a fraction of a wave number, which, compared with the Rydberg number of 109,737 wave numbers, shows that the Zeeman effect is a very small thing. Still it is interesting on account of the information which it gives about atomic magnetic moments.

We expect, then, that in a magnetic field each of the energy levels of Bohr's theory will be split into a number of levels, the splitting being proportional to the magnetic field. In a transition between two electronic states, if m_k changes, there will be a magnetic contribution to the frequency of the emitted line which, expressed in wave numbers, will equal $\Delta m_k(e/4\pi mc)B$ in mks units. We shall see in a later section that there is a law, called a selection principle, which states that Δm_k can take on only three possible values, 0 or ± 1. Thus we can expect that in a magnetic field each spectrum line will be split into three components, one of which is undisplaced, the other two displaced from this one by $\pm(e/4\pi mc)B$. Now the remarkable fact is that this is exactly the same result which Lorentz, very early in the century, had derived from classical mechanics, and which we mentioned in Chap. 2. We notice the very interesting way in which Planck's constant h has canceled out of the final answer, so that it is possible for a classical theory to arrive at the same result.

In spite of the simplicity of this result for the Zeeman effect, it does not prove to be correct for hydrogen, for reasons which we shall go into later. In fact, the detailed study of the Zeeman effect for many atomic spectra proved, in the years from the beginning of Bohr's theory to 1926, to be one of the most powerful tools for disclosing the puzzling aspects of quantum mechanics. We shall come back to it in detail in later chapters; but at the time of Bohr's original theory, and Sommerfeld's space quantization, these questions were not properly understood, and we shall not go further with the Zeeman effect at the moment.

Sommerfeld's contribution, at this point in the development of quantum theory, was to treat the various degrees of freedom separately, to introduce a quantum condition for each one, and correspondingly to introduce as many quantum numbers as there were degrees of freedom. He stated the quantum conditions in the form of an integral relation

$$\oint p_i \, dq_i = n_i h \tag{5-15}$$

Here q_i is one of the generalized coordinates, p_i its conjugate momentum. In a two-dimensional phase space in which q_i and p_i are plotted, the integral $\oint p_i \, dq_i$ measures the area enclosed by a curve in which p_i is plotted as a function of q_i, for constant energy. The symbol $\oint$ is taken to indicate an integral around a closed path so that it gives the area of the closed curve. Sommerfeld's statement of Eq. (5-15) tells us that this area should be an integer n_i, which is called a quantum number, times Planck's constant h. Thus this quantum condition is really identical in principle, though stated in different language, with the quantum conditions used earlier by Planck for the linear oscillator, and by Bohr for the circular orbits in hydrogen.

There is one feature in Sommerfeld's quantum conditions, however, which goes beyond these earlier cases, and which in fact disclosed almost immediately a shortcoming of the type of quantum theory used by Bohr. An expression like that of Eq. (5-15) has a meaning only if each of the p_i's can be written in terms of the corresponding q_i, and of the total energy. It is rather an accident when this is possible, however. Much further study of the mathematical basis of such expressions was given by Sommerfeld, Born and Jordan, and others, in the ten years following Sommerfeld's suggestion of his quantum conditions in 1916. It was gradually made clear that only mechanical problems of a type called separable could be handled by this method: problems in which the different variables could, so to speak, be separated from each other. The mechanical motions in such cases were shown to be of a type called multiply periodic. But most mechanical motions are not of this type. Hence it was clearer and clearer, as time went on, that the type of quantum mechanics which we have described in this chapter was limited to very simple systems; it could not even be adapted rigorously to an atom of helium, with two electrons. It is only the wave mechanics, and Schrödinger's equation, which have avoided this difficulty; we shall see in Chap. 9 that the wave mechanics leads to a modified form of Sommerfeld's quantum conditions for separable problems, but leads to valid results as well for nonseparable cases, which could not be treated at all by Bohr's theory.

5-6. Transition Probabilities and Planck's Law. Bohr's original theory of the hydrogen spectrum merely predicted the energy levels, and said that radiation was emitted or absorbed when atoms had transitions from one level to another. But there is another side to the problem, which is of great practical importance: what is the probability of transition from one level to another? We can formulate the question in mathematical language, which Einstein used in a paper in 1916 in which he discussed the black-body radiation law.

Einstein assumed that we were dealing with two states: a lower energy level which we can denote by the index 1, a higher one denoted by the index 2. If, then, an atom is in the state 2, it will have a certain probability of spontaneously jumping back to state 1, emitting a photon as it falls. Einstein denoted this probability as A. That is, if we start with N_2 atoms in state 2, the number falling from state 2 to 1 in a time dt will be $AN_2\,dt$. It is easy to show that if no other probabilities of transition are present, the number of atoms in state 2 will fall off exponentially with the time. Similarly, if we are dealing with atoms in the lower state 1, they can absorb radiation, and be lifted to the higher state 2. The probability of absorption will naturally depend on the density of radiation present, having the frequency ν required to produce the transition. If the energy density of this radiation is u_ν, Einstein assumed that the number of atoms being raised in time dt from state 1 to state 2 would be $Bu_\nu N_1\,dt$, where B is a constant, N_1 the number of atoms in state 1.

Einstein asked whether there would not have to be some relation between A and B. Surely we expect such a relation. If A is large, a transition will be likely in which radiation is emitted, and the corresponding spectral line will be strong. Similarly if B is large, absorption will be likely, and the absorption line will be strong. Kirchhoff had shown, in the latter part of the nineteenth century, that thermodynamics demands that the emission and absorption of a given system for light, at a given frequency, must be proportional: a good absorber is a good radiator, as the law is often stated. Hence a proportionality between A and B is to be expected.

Einstein derived this relationship by asking the following question:

Suppose we have a certain number of atoms, in equilibrium at a temperature T according to the Maxwell-Boltzmann law. That is, the number of atoms having energy E will be proportional to $\exp(-E/kT)$, so that if the energies in states 1 and 2 are E_1 and E_2, the numbers N_1 and N_2 in this case will be proportional to $\exp(-E_1/kT)$ and $\exp(-E_2/kT)$. Suppose these atoms are surrounded by black-body radiation of temperature T, so that the energy density u_ν at the frequency which can be emitted and absorbed by the transition from states 1 to 2, will be given by Planck's law. Then the general principles of thermodynamics tell us that the atoms and radiation will be in equilibrium; that is, as much energy will be emitted per second in the transitions from state 2 to 1 as is absorbed in the transitions from state 1 to 2.

The first thing which Einstein found, when he imposed this condition, is that there is a form of transition probability which we have so far disregarded, which must actually be present. We can see this by considering the limiting case of very high temperature, in which u_ν is exceedingly great, and N_1 and N_2 are almost exactly equal to each other. In this limit, it is clear that the number of transitions from state 1 to state 2 with absorption of energy, which is $Bu_\nu N_1\,dt$, will be much greater than the number of spontaneous emission transitions from state 2 to 1, which is $AN_2\,dt$. The reason for this is that A and B are assumed to be constants, N_1 and N_2 approach equality at high temperature, but u_ν increases without limit as the temperature increases, whereas there is no such factor in the probability of spontaneous emission. The only way out of this dilemma is to assume that there is an additional probability of emission, proportional to the radiation density. Einstein assumed such a probability, calling such a process an induced emission, and assumed that the number of such transitions in time dt was $Bu_\nu N_2\,dt$, proportional to the number of atoms in the excited state, and to the density of radiation. Later work, based on wave mechanics, has verified the real existence of this induced emission.

Einstein's assumption, then, was that the number of atoms going from state 2 to 1 in time dt was $(A + Bu_\nu)N_2\,dt$, and the number going from state 1 to 2 was $Bu_\nu N_1\,dt$. Now let us assume that we are at a moderate temperature, where N_1 and N_2 are not equal to each other. These two numbers of transitions must equal each other, for thermal equilibrium. If we equate them, and set

$$\frac{N_2}{N_1} = \exp\left[-\frac{(E_2 - E_1)}{kT}\right]$$

as is required by the Maxwell-Boltzmann distribution, we can derive u_ν. We note that $E_2 - E_1 = h\nu$, where ν is the frequency involved in the transition between the two states in question. Then we have

$$(A + Bu_\nu) \exp - \frac{h\nu}{kT} = Bu_\nu$$

$$u_\nu = \frac{A}{B} \frac{1}{\exp (h\nu/kT) - 1} \tag{5-16}$$

We see that Eq. (5-16) will be identical with Planck's law, provided

$$\frac{A}{B} = \frac{8\pi h\nu^3}{c^3} \tag{5-17}$$

Einstein had thus derived the relation between the two constants A and B, and had shown that the general type of analysis which he and Bohr had used for the transition probabilities between stationary states was compatible with thermodynamics.

5-7. Bohr's Correspondence Principle and Selection Rules. From this analysis of Einstein, it was obvious that the quantities A and B, measuring the probabilities of spontaneous emission and absorption, had a fundamental significance; but from Bohr's original work there was no way to calculate them. Yet this was very important. Empirically, some spectrum lines proved to be strong, some weak. Of course, part of the reason for this was the question of the numbers N of atoms in the appropriate stationary states; but it was clear that the A's and B's must vary greatly from one transition to another. Bohr attempted to solve the problem of finding these A's and B's from a principle which he called the correspondence principle. This was never completely satisfactory; it could not be made entirely quantitative in most cases, and it has since been supplanted by exact calculations which can be made by the wave mechanics. Nevertheless it was very useful, and it led to some very definite predictions, in the form of selection rules. These rules were statements that the A's for certain transitions should be exactly zero, so that such transitions would be forbidden or would never occur. Such selection principles are very widespread, and it is quite impossible to understand the observed spectra without making use of them.

Bohr's general line of argument was to look for parallels between the radiation which would be emitted by a system classically, and the corresponding emission on the quantum theory, reasoning that somehow the quantum theory must reduce to the classical theory in the limit of large quantum numbers, and that the parallelism might persist to some extent even for small quantum numbers. We can see his general approach by thinking of a linear oscillator. An electrified particle, vibrating sinusoidally according to classical mechanics, with a frequency ν, will emit radiation of this frequency ν, gradually losing energy until it comes to rest. In the quantum theory, however, we know that the oscillator has an infinite set of energy levels, given by the formula $nh\nu$, where n is the quantum number. If we start with a system in a highly excited state, with a large value of n, it will find lower levels whose energy is less by $h\nu$, $2h\nu$, $3h\nu$, etc. It could, then, in the absence of a selection principle, make transitions to the states whose energy was lower by each of these values. The emitted photons would then have energies $h\nu$, $2h\nu$, $3h\nu$, etc., so that the frequencies of the emitted lines would be ν, 2ν, 3ν, etc.

This, however, would be contrary to the classical behavior of the oscillator, in which only the frequency ν is omitted. Bohr assumed, therefore, that there must be a selection principle operating in this case, which would make the probability of transition, or the quantities A and B, equal to zero, for any transition in which the quantum number n changes by more than one unit. According to this selection principle, in other words, the oscillator emits only the frequency ν in the quantum theory, just as it would do classically.

Suppose now that we have an oscillator which is not quite linear; the restoring force may be given by a power series in the displacement, the first and leading term being proportional to the displacement, but with small terms of higher power. Classically, one can show in this case that the vibration of the oscillator is still periodic, but not exactly sinusoidal. It is shown in mathematics that any such periodic motion can be analyzed into a Fourier series; that is, a series of sinusoidal terms of frequency ν, 2ν, 3ν, etc. That is, if x is the displacement of the particle, Fourier's theorem states that we can write x in the form

$$x = \Sigma(n)(a_n \cos 2\pi n\nu t + b_n \sin 2\pi n\nu t) \qquad (5\text{-}18)$$

where n takes on all integral values, and the a_n's and b_n's are constants, which one can call Fourier amplitudes. The term corresponding to $n = 1$, vibrating with frequency ν, is called the fundamental, and those with larger values of n are called harmonics. One then finds that, in the case of the oscillator whose restoring force is not quite linear, we shall have not only the fundamental, which would represent the complete motion for a linear oscillator, but also small components of frequency 2ν, 3ν, etc., the amplitudes of these higher harmonics going to zero as the departure from linearity gets smaller and smaller. Bohr assumed that in the corresponding quantum case, the probabilities of transitions in which n changes by 2, 3, etc., units would be determined by the magnitudes of these classical Fourier amplitudes of frequency 2ν, 3ν, etc.

The frequencies emitted in the quantum theory would not be exactly twice, three times, etc., times the frequency emitted when n changed by unity; for in a nonlinear oscillator, the energy levels are no longer given by $nh\nu$, but deviate from these values. The frequency of the classical motion depends on energy, and the whole situation is much more complicated than with the linear oscillator. Nevertheless, Bohr could show that there are close relations between the classical frequencies of the various Fourier components of motion, and the corresponding frequencies emitted in the quantum theory. We saw, in discussing the hydrogen atom, that there is a remarkable relation between the average frequency of motion in a classical and quantum frequencies.

We can state Eq. (5-12), in words, in the following way: in a transition from a state of quantum number n' to a quantum number n, the frequency emitted on the quantum theory equals $(n' - n)$ times the average frequency which would be emitted by a corresponding classical system, averaged between the initial and final states. What Bohr showed was that this same relation holds for any quantum-mechanical problem, not merely for the hydrogen atom; it depends on very fundamental laws of mechanics. In other words, in a jump of one unit in the quantum number, the quantum-mechanical frequency equals the average classical frequency; in a jump of two units, twice the average classical frequency; and so on. Or stating it in terms of the harmonics or Fourier components, which we have just been discussing, the quantum-mechanical frequency emitted in jumping by m units in the quantum number is the averaged frequency of the mth harmonic of the motion, averaged between the initial and final states.

In the limit of very large quantum numbers, where we should expect in a sense to be approaching the classical mechanics, we note that a jump of a few units in quantum number will make a small relative change in the energy, so that the classical frequency will not vary much between the initial and final state. In this limit, the averaged classical frequency will not differ much from the classical frequency in the initial (or final) state, and we can say that the quantum-mechanical frequency emitted in a jump of m units in the quantum number approaches the classical frequency of the mth harmonic in the motion.

Bohr then assumed that the intensity emitted in the quantum theory in a jump of m units would be closely connected with the corresponding intensity of the mth harmonic in the classical motion. In fact, he could set up the amplitude of this mth harmonic, from a Fourier analysis of the classical motion, or an analysis into sinusoidal functions of time, and was then able to derive plausible formulas for the Einstein

.A coefficients in terms of the squares of these amplitudes. These formulas became exact in the limit of large quantum numbers, where classical mechanics became very accurate. For small quantum numbers, his formulas were only suggestive, not exact, but they proved to be qualitatively correct, in cases where the A's were different from zero. And in case the classical amplitudes were zero, he could prove many selection principles, which turned out to be verified by experiment.

Let us state some of the important selection principles, for the cases we have already discussed. The azimuthal quantum number k has a very important selection principle: transitions are only allowed in which k changes by ± 1. This is fundamental to the whole spectroscopy of more complicated elements than hydrogen. The quantum number m_k, often called the magnetic quantum number on account of its appearance in the theory of the Zeeman effect, can change only by ± 1 or 0; this is the rule which we mentioned in Sec. 5, where we were discussing the theory of the Zeeman effect. These, in addition to the selection principle for the linear oscillator, according to which n changes only by ± 1, are the ones encountered in the problems we have treated so far.

At the same time, there are interesting qualitative results of the determination of the A's, in cases where there are no selection rules. There is no selection rule for the principal quantum number n, in the hydrogen case, but the values of the A's very rapidly decrease, as the difference of n values increases. Thus, for instance, suppose we have a collection of hydrogen atoms in their ground state, $n = 1$. They can have transitions to states of higher n values, but these transition probabilities decrease very rapidly with n. In the absorption spectrum of such a collection of hydrogen atoms, the successive absorption lines will get very rapidly weaker, as we go up in the series; this is observed experimentally, and is indicated in Fig. 5-1(a). It is also interesting to note that in this case of hydrogen there is a continuous spectrum, starting at the limit of the discrete spectrum. This continuous spectrum arises from electrons which are raised, by action of the radiation, to states of positive energy; that is, ionized states, in which the electron is entirely removed from the positive nucleus. This is really a sort of photoelectric effect, and such photoelectric absorption, with a continuous absorption spectrum, is observed at the limit of every spectrum series.

5-8. Bohr's Theory for Atoms of Higher Atomic Number. Bohr's theory can obviously be extended, in a practically trivial way, to one-electron atoms with higher atomic number than unity. For instance, the singly charged helium ion has one electron; and so does the doubly charged lithium, and so on. All we have to do to make the change is to replace the nucleus of charge e by a nucleus of charge Ze, where Z is the atomic number. This makes the following changes in the results which we have so far given: the energies become Z^2 times as great, the radii of the orbits are $1/Z$ times as great, the frequencies of rotation in the orbit are Z^2 times as great. The spectrum of ionized helium was known at the time Bohr's theory was set up, but it was generally ascribed incorrectly to hydrogen. Bohr was immediately able to show that it was a helium spectrum, and this was later verified experimentally. Other spectra of the same series are now known.

The more important application of this case, however, comes from the study of the X-ray spectra, which we shall take up in the next chapter. We shall find there that the electrons of a heavy atom still have orbits resembling in many ways those of hydrogen, but under the influence not of a nuclear charge of e, or even of Ze, where Z is the true atomic number, but rather of a so-called effective nuclear charge $Z_{eff}e$, where Z_{eff} varies from almost the true atomic number for the innermost electrons, down to approximately unity for the outermost electrons. The whole theory of X-ray spectra is based on a study of the energies, and orbital dimensions, of electrons in the field of such effective nuclear charges. We shall go on to these questions next and shall find the first indications of how Bohr's theory is to be extended to the study of atoms with many electrons.

PROBLEMS

5-1. Find the wavelength of the first line in the Balmer series; in the Lyman series. Find the maximum wavelength of light required to ionize the hydrogen atom.

5-2. Draw the orbits for hydrogen, $n = 3$, $k = 1, 2, 3$. In constructing the ellipses, remember that the geometrical description of an ellipse states that the sum of the distances from the two foci to every point of the ellipse is the same, and that the nucleus is at one focus.

5-3. Prove that, for a given k, the closest approach of an elliptical hydrogen orbit to the nucleus approaches $a_0 k^2/2$ as n becomes large. (*Hint:* Use the properties of the ellipse given in Prob. 5-2, and the facts stated in the text about its major and minor axes.)

5-4. Make a diagram of the energy levels of the hydrogen atom, plotting energy vertically, representing each energy level by a horizontal line at the appropriate height. In one column show the levels for $k = 1$, in the next column for $k = 2$, then $k = 3$, and so on. Indicate the transitions allowed by the selection principle for k by drawing arrows between the initial and final levels of each transition.

5-5. If atoms are surrounded by black-body radiation at temperature T, obeying Planck's law, show that the probability Bu_ν of absorption or induced emission is small compared to the probability A of spontaneous emission, provided the frequency ν is large compared to the frequency for which the Planck distribution u_ν has its maximum value, but that the reverse is the case if the frequency is low compared to that for which u_ν has its maximum.

5-6. Show that certain lines in the spectrum of ionized helium agree in frequency with some lines in the hydrogen spectrum.

5-7. An electron in a Bohr atom in a magnetic field can have a transition in which only its quantum number m_k changes, the other quantum numbers n and k remaining unchanged. Find the emitted frequency, and compare it with the frequency of classical rotation of a free electron in the same magnetic field.

CHAPTER 6

X RAYS AND CRYSTAL STRUCTURE

6-1. Introduction. During the years between 1895, when X rays were discovered, and 1912, it had become rather clear that they were similar to ordinary light, but had wavelengths of the order of a few tenths of an angstrom unit, thousands of times smaller than the wavelength of ordinary light. This was clear, partly from photoelectric experiments, partly from some rudimentary diffraction experiments which had been performed. But almost nothing was known about the spectroscopy of X rays, on account of the lack of a suitable spectrometer. The two commonest types of spectrometer in the visible spectrum are the prism and the grating spectrometer. The prism was impractical in the X-ray region, for the index of refraction of all ordinary materials was found to be almost exactly unity, so that no appreciable refraction or dispersion took place. As far as diffraction gratings were concerned, it would be quite out of the question to rule gratings with lines as close together as would be indicated by the very short wavelengths suspected.

This limitation, we might say here, has been removed since then, and gratings can now be used for determining X-ray wavelengths. The way this is done is to let the X rays strike the grating, not at normal incidence as with the spectroscopy of the visible, but almost at grazing incidence. Then the X rays effectively see the rulings greatly foreshortened, appearing to be much closer together than they actually are, and appreciable diffraction results. Furthermore, the index of refraction for X rays, though very close to unity, is actually slightly less than unity, which results in a critical angle for total reflection from air to glass near to grazing incidence. In other words, at grazing incidence all the X rays are reflected, so that one gets a very good intensity for the diffracted beams. Thus the diffraction grating for X rays is now usable, though not very convenient, and very accurate absolute measurements of X-ray wavelengths have been made in this way, comparing them with the spacing of the rulings, and hence with fundamental physical constants. There is now no more question about the wavelengths of X rays, and the nature of their spectrum, than there is in the visible part of the spectrum.

In 1912, however, these developments had not been made, and in that year the German von Laue had a very ingenious idea, which simultaneously opened up two fields: X-ray spectroscopy and the structure of crystals. It occurred to von Laue that the distance between the atoms of a crystal, which of course was approximately known because one knew both the mass of the individual atoms and the

FIG. 6-1. X rays diffracted by an iron crystal; Laue photograph. (*Courtesy of G. L. Clark and O. Oldenberg.*)

density of the crystal, was of the same order of magnitude as the probable length of the X rays. If, then, a beam of X rays passed through a crystal, the radiations would be scattered by the various atoms, and the scattered wavelets would interfere with each other. He convinced himself that if the interference pattern were examined, one should see a pattern of spots, coming from the diffracted peaks coming off in different directions. This experiment was tried by Friedrich and Knipping, with the result that the predicted spots were found. These Laue spots, as they were called, and as they are shown in Fig. 6-1, opened up a whole new field. They showed a beautiful regularity of arrangement, which must be characteristic of the structure of the crystal. It was necessary, then, to study two things simultaneously: the nature of the atomic arrangement in the crystal which was being used to produce the diffraction pattern, and the nature of the spectrum producing the pattern.

It soon appeared that Laue's experimental arrangement was not the ideal one for making the experiments. The English father and son, W. H. and W. L. Bragg (later Sir William and Sir Lawrence Bragg), very shortly suggested another arrangement which proved much more practical, both as a spectrometer and as a device for investigating crystal structure. The X-ray crystal spectrometer which they devised is still the most convenient method of investigating X-ray spectra, much more practical than the ruled grating. At the same time, the Braggs started the study of crystal structures using X-ray diffraction. The study of X-ray crystallography, which they started, has now gone so far that the positions of the atoms in very large numbers of crystals have been determined, and X-ray diffraction methods can now be used not only to investigate perfect crystals but even to study such things as thermal vibrations, the order-disorder transformations going on in some crystals composed of mixtures of elements, and many other detailed properties of the solid state.

One of the first facts which the Braggs discovered, when it was possible to study X-ray spectra, was that X rays consisted of two sorts of radiations: a continuous spectrum, similar to white light, and a line spectrum, similar to the optical line spectra. The continuous spectrum, sometimes called by the German name *Bremsstrahlung* (or collision radiation), was assumed to result from the radiation emitted by the electrons which produced the X rays as they were decelerated to rest in the target; the X rays of course are produced by bombarding a target with a beam of fast electrons. We have already seen, in our discussion in Chap. 3, that there will be a high-frequency limit to this spectrum. An electron, in coming to rest in the target, must emit one or more photons, and the largest photon which it can radiate, corresponding therefore to the highest frequency found in the spectrum, will correspond to the total kinetic energy of the electron, assuming it is completely stopped in the target, and delivers all its energy to a single photon.

The line spectrum, on the contrary, must correspond to definitely atomic phenomena. The frequencies of the emitted lines were very soon found to satisfy the Ritz combination principle, so that the X-ray term values could be found; and by our discussion of the preceding chapter, we know that this means that the atoms have definite sta-

tionary states, and that the radiation is emitted when the atoms have
transitions from one stationary state to another. In the X-ray
spectra, then, one has means for studying the stationary states corresponding to energies much greater than those met in the hydrogen
spectrum.

It had already been found, by rough use of photoelectric and other
methods, that each atom had several series of lines, one of shortest
wavelength which was named the K series, one of longer wavelength

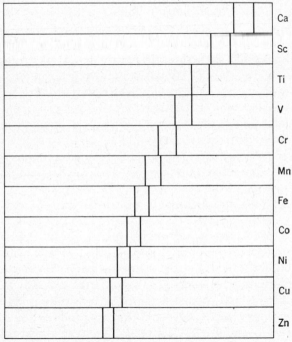

Fig. 6-2. K X-ray lines of a number of successive elements, as obtained by Moseley
and later workers.

called the L series, and several others. But now at last these series
could be quantitatively investigated, and the first work of this sort
was done by the young Englishman Moseley, who was killed in the
First World War very shortly afterward. Moseley observed the
spectra of a number of elements and found the very striking sort of
regularity shown in Fig. 6-2 when the atoms were arranged in order of
their atomic numbers. Here, clearly, was a much more regular
dependence of properties on atomic number than one sees in the
optical spectra, where one observed the very strong tendency to a
periodic behavior which is shown also in chemical properties. For

instance, all the alkali metals have similar optical spectra, all the alkaline earths, and so on.

Moseley not only measured the wavelengths of X-ray lines; he was able to develop a law expressing their dependence on atomic number, which led to an immediate interpretation of their origin in terms of Bohr's theory of the hydrogen atom. What he found was that the line of highest frequency in the K series corresponded rather accurately in frequency to that predicted by Bohr's formula for hydrogen, for the transition from the state given by $n = 2$ to $n = 1$, with an atom whose nuclear charge was Z, the atomic number; more accurately, it seemed to correspond to a value of Z somewhat smaller than the real atomic number, and called the effective atomic number. Similarly, the lines of the L series were found to be closely related to transitions in hydrogenlike atoms. Here was an obvious clue to the structure of the inner part of the atom.

It clearly seemed that a heavy atom must contain electrons much like those of a hydrogenlike atom, and that they could have similar transitions. This clue led to the whole concept of shells of electrons in the atom. Gradually it became clear that a heavy atom has electrons within it in orbits corresponding to a number of the types of Bohr orbits. These orbits cannot be very different from those in a hydrogenlike atom with nuclear charge Ze, as is shown by the resemblance of Moseley's laws giving the frequency to the Bohr theory. There is room inside the atom for many such orbits. We remember that the radius of an orbit in a hydrogenlike atom of atomic number Z is only $1/Z$ times as large as the corresponding orbit in hydrogen, which makes the orbits of small n values very small in heavy atoms, leaving plenty of space for them inside the atom. It became clear that the lines of the K series were associated with transitions to the orbits of $n = 1$, the L series with transitions to orbits of $n = 2$, and so on; and as a result of this, the electrons with $n = 1$ in the atom are often referred to as the K shell of electrons, those with $n = 2$ as the L shell, those with $n = 3$ as the M shell, and so on. We shall see later more precisely how the transitions are supposed to occur which lead to the sharp X-ray lines.

Before we go on to describe these happenings more in detail, we should point out one thing which the study of X rays and crystal structures has done: it has provided an accurately known scale of atomic dimensions, involving practically no hypotheses at all. The procedure is the following: With a ruled diffraction grating, one can make a very accurate measurement of the wavelength of one of the sharp lines in an X-ray spectrum. One can then observe this same line by means of crystal diffraction.   As we shall see in the next section, this gives us an equally accurate measurement of the distance between the planes of atoms in the crystal, or of the interatomic spacing.   Hence we know interatomic distances with very high precision, and can calculate with equal precision the number of atoms in unit volume, or, using the measured density, in unit mass.   This in turn gives us a measurement of Avogadro's number, which we have already mentioned, quite independent of the measurement by means of Millikan's oil-drop experiment and the charge of the electron.   These two determinations agree within the error of experiment, which by now is very small.   At present, by such methods, atomic dimensions are not matters of speculation but of experimental determination with a very high precision.

6-2. The Bragg Law.   Laue used a very straightforward but rather complicated type of analysis to set up a theory of the scattering of X rays by a crystal.   The Braggs, shortly afterward, saw that the theory could be expressed in alternative and much simpler language, and we shall include their discussion; it can be made the basis of just as complete a treatment as that of Laue, though we shall not give all the analysis here.   The basis of the Braggs' treatment is that they consider the scattering of X rays, not by the individual atoms, but by planes passing through all the atoms.   Before studying it, we must look a little into the basis of crystallography.

Long before the days of X rays, the crystallographers had come to some definite conclusions about the structure of crystals, merely by studying their external behavior and physical properties.   They had concluded that the essential feature in their structure was that they were composed of repeating elements, atoms or molecules, or groups of molecules, repeated time and again like the pattern on a wallpaper. They had studied the geometry of three-dimensional structures which had this property of repeating and had found that the most fundamental concept regarding it was that of the unit cell.   One must have a three-dimensional volume of such a form that many of these volumes can stack together to fill all space; each such volume is like each other, and each one contains a certain definite number of atoms in a definite arrangement, the atoms in each such volume of course being proportional to the number of atoms in a molecule, as given by the chemical formula of the substance.   These volumes are called unit cells.   Furthermore, the crystallographers and geometers had shown that the unit cells can always be chosen in the forms of parallelepipeds, determined by three vectors, representing their edges, though this way of choosing them is not unique.

In some cases, like simple crystals in which the unit cells are cubes, such a structure is obvious. There are other cases, however, where we might be tempted to doubt the validity of this theorem. For instance, a honeycomb is an obvious example in which space is filled with volumes which are not parallelepipeds, but rather hexagonal solids. But even in such a case we can, if we choose, pick unit cells of the form of a parallelepiped. This possibility is shown in Fig. 6-3, the two-dimensional example of the hexagons which can fill space. We have indicated one of the diamond-shaped parallelograms which form the unit

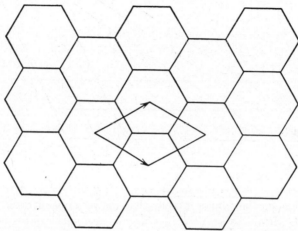

FIG. 6-3. Two-dimensional structure formed from hexagons with a diamond-shaped unit cell. The vectors shown by the arrows represent the fundamental vectors of the unit cell.

cells, and have also shown the two vectors representing the edges of the unit cell. It is obvious that the periodic nature of the crystal can be expressed by the statement that if the crystal is displaced through either of these vectors, or any linear combination of them with integral coefficients, it will coincide with itself.

Clearly, then, to investigate the structure of a crystal, we must do two things: find the shape and size of the unit cell, and find the locations of the atoms in this cell. The first of these tasks is much simpler than the second, except in very elementary cases where there are only one or two atoms in the unit cell. Let us now return to the method of the Braggs, that of considering the scattering by planes of atoms rather than individual atoms. In Fig. 6-4 we show a two-dimensional example of a crystal and show one atom at an equivalent position in each unit cell. We also show three sets of planes which are so chosen that one of the planes passes through each of the atoms in the crystal. Such a set of planes can be chosen in an infinite number of ways, and

the first part of the theory of X-ray diffraction deals with a classifica-
tion of the types of planes; but we do not need to have to go into this,
for our present purpose.   The essential point, at the moment, is that
if we know the geometrical nature of the various sets of planes, we can
work backward from them and determine the unit cell.   Furthermore,
as one can prove by more elaborate methods, we can handle the scattering of X rays as if they were scattered by one or another of these sets

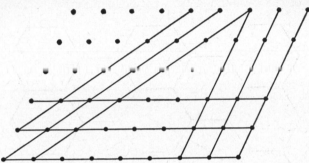

FIG. 6-4. A two-dimensional set of atoms, one per unit cell, with three sets of
planes passing through the atoms.

of planes, just as if the atoms, or scattering material, were uniformly
distributed over the planes rather than being concentrated at points.
   If we are willing to grant this, then we can carry out a very simple
discussion, following Fig. 6-5.   Two planes of atoms are shown,
separated by a distance d.   A beam of X rays strikes the crystal; two

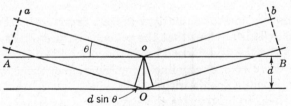

FIG. 6-5. Figure to illustrate Bragg's law of diffraction.

of the incident rays are shown in ao and AO, making an angle θ with
the plane of the atoms (this is the so-called glancing angle of incidence).
The Braggs assumed (and it can be proved easily) that the beam would
be reflected by the planes, according to the ordinary law of reflection,
making equal angles of incidence and reflection; thus the reflected
beam has rays indicated by ob and OB.   But there is an additional
condition, given by the requirement of interference of the wavelets
scattered by the atoms, which make up the reflected beam.   The ray
AOB is reflected from the lower plane of atoms, the ray aob by the

upper plane; and it is clear from the geometry that the ray AOB has traveled further than aob, by a distance $2d \sin \theta$, from a wave front aA, indicated by one dotted line, to another wave front bB, indicated by another dotted line. In the whole scattered beam, then, we shall have many different rays, whose paths differ by integral multiples of this distance.

We may now expect that these rays will interfere destructively unless these path differences are integral multiples of a wavelength. In other words, we have a condition which states that

$$n\lambda = 2d \sin \theta \qquad (6\text{-}1)$$

where n is an integer, λ the wavelength. Equation (6-1) is Bragg's law. It states that we shall not get scattering unless there is a particular relation between the wavelength and the scattering angle. The integer n, which tells how many wavelengths' difference of phase we have between successive scattered rays, is called the order of the reflection. We can now use the Bragg law to analyze the type of reflection or scattering to be expected with different types of experiments.

Let us start with Laue's original experiment. In this case a beam of X rays having a continuous spectrum is allowed to fall on a crystal. It passes through, and the emerging beam consists of a set of separate rays, which strike a photographic plate, at some distance from the crystal, in a pattern of spots. In the crystal, any given set of planes, like one of those shown in Fig. 6-4, will have a fixed angle θ to the beam. Hence, according to the Bragg law, scattering by this set of planes will occur for X rays of an appropriate wavelength, and since we are dealing with a continuous spectrum, this wavelength may very likely be found in the incident beam. Each of the Laue spots, then, will represent a beam scattered from a particular set of planes, and from the positions of the spots, the angles of orientation of the planes can be found. By use of this set of angles, the shape and size of the unit cell can be worked out.

Much better for quantitative purposes is a procedure using monochromatic X rays. In general, no set of planes in the crystal will happen to lie at the correct angle to allow diffraction by radiation of the given wavelength. However, in this scheme, the crystal is slowly rotated mechanically, so that all angles will successively be available. Each set of planes, then, will at some instant have the correct angle for scattering. When this occurs, a beam will be scattered in a given direction and will fall on a photographic plate. The pattern on this plate, then, will have spots corresponding to many sets of planes. From the angle of each, and the known wavelength, one can use Eq.

(6-1) to find the spacings between the planes, and work backward more conveniently than in the Laue method to get the unit cell.

Still another method, the so-called Debye-Scherrer, or powder, method, was worked out a few years after the two fundamental techniques which we have described, and has the advantage that it can be used for powders and materials which cannot be obtained in large crystals. The fragments of the powder are very minute single crystals, and they will be found oriented by chance in all possible directions. Thus, with the same monochromatic beam as before, some crystal grains will always be found to reflect each of the types of

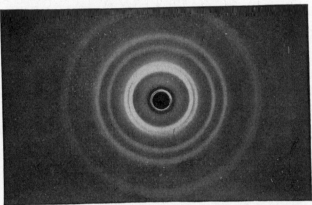

FIG. 6-6. X-ray powder pattern taken with monochromatic X rays incident on aluminum powder.   (*Courtesy of B. E. Warren and O. Oldenberg.*)

beam, and as before, each of these beams can be photographed on a plate, resulting in a pattern of circular rings, like that shown in Fig. 6-6. Here again the pattern can be analyzed to obtain the properties of the unit cell.

6-3. Determination of Atomic Positions. The positions of the various spots, in any of these experimental arrangements, are determined by the shape and size of the unit cell, and conversely the unit cell can be determined from the positions of the spots. The remaining problem, that of finding the atomic positions within the cell, is solved by using the intensities of the spots. We can give a general idea why this is so, though an exact treatment is quite complicated. It is obvious that the more atoms there are in a set of planes, the more it will scatter, and hence the stronger the corresponding spot will be; so that surely the intensities will give some information about the distribution of atoms. We can go much further than this simple idea, however.

In the first place, we note that the nth-order reflection, in Eq. (6-1), could equally well be considered the first-order reflection by a set of planes with spacing d/n. Now let us consider the way the density of scattering material will vary, as we go from one plane of the type shown in Fig. 6-4 to another parallel plane. The X-ray scattering is produced by the electrons in the atoms; we remember that this was mentioned in our discussion of the Thomson scattering formula in Chap. 4. The physical reason is that the electrons are set into vibration by the incident X rays, and in turn scatter spherical wavelets; the nuclei cannot scatter, for they are too heavy to be set into vibration. Any plane parallel to those in Fig. 6-4 will cut through a certain amount of electronic density; if x is a variable at right angles to the plane, we could determine the amount of charge between two planes located at x and $x + dx$, an infinitesimal distance apart, and divide by dx, to get such a density. This density must be a periodic function of x, with a period d; for we know that the whole crystal repeats its properties periodically. Then Fourier's theorem, which we have already met in Sec. 5-7, tells us that it can be written as a sum of sinusoidal functions, one with wavelength d, one with wavelength $d/2$, then $d/3$, etc. If we knew the amplitudes of all these sinusoidal components, we could synthesize the Fourier series, and find the exact density, as a function of x.

When we now go into the scattering theory more completely, we see that the intensity of the nth-order scattered spot from this set of planes, which we have seen can be considered to be reflected from a set of planes with spacing d/n, is proportional to the square of the amplitude of the Fourier component of wavelength d/n. In other words, by measurement of these intensities, we can directly get the amplitudes of the Fourier components. It would seem, then, that we could synthesize the Fourier components, and hence find the actual variation of density along the direction x normal to the set of planes in question. We could do this again for each other set of planes in the crystal; and by superposing all this information, we should be able to find completely how the density varied from point to point within the crystal.

This program, unfortunately, cannot be carried out as completely as this would indicate. The reason is that experiment gives us the amplitude of each of these Fourier components but does not give the phase; it does not tell us whether we are dealing with a sine or a cosine, in an expression like that of Eq. (5-18). Much ingenuity has been devoted to the problem of how to find these phases. Sometimes symmetry information will give them, sometimes there are additional rather powerful mathematical theorems which are too complicated to go into here, sometimes one must merely guess. But the workers in the field have found ways to find the phases, though sometimes with great difficulty. Once they are known, then we really can carry through the program of synthesizing the information given by the X rays, to get a true picture of the density of electrons in the crystal. The final synthesis can be done by simple arithmetical operations or by complicated computing machines which are now available for such purposes. The result is a contour map of charge density, such as is shown in Fig. 6-7, which not only locates the atoms but even provides

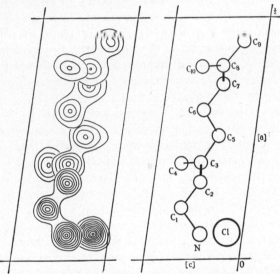

FIG. 6-7. Projection of the molecule, and Fourier section, for geranylamine hydro-chloride. (*Courtesy of G. A. Jeffrey and Proceedings of the Royal Society.*)

information about the distribution of electronic charge within them. These X-ray methods provide the closest thing which we have to being able actually to see the atoms in the crystals.

We shall not go further in the present chapter in describing the sorts of results obtained in this way about the structure of actual crystals. This would carry us into chemical problems, into the structures of molecules and solids, and we prefer to postpone these questions until Chap. 10, which will deal with molecular and solid-state problems. It is obvious from what we have said already, however, that information of very great value can be obtained about the structure of atoms, molecules, and solids by X-ray diffraction methods.

6-4. X-ray Spectra. By the methods we have just outlined, the structures of many crystals have been determined, and with that knowledge, the procedure can be reversed, and essentially the same device can be used as a spectrometer. Suppose we pick a crystal whose structure has been determined, and which can be obtained in a very perfect form (for perfection of the crystal is as necessary here as perfection of a diffraction grating is in ordinary spectroscopy). If then we let a single monochromatic wavelength of X rays pass through a set of slits and fall on the crystal, and go through the same sort of procedure described in Sec. 6-2, we can arrange our apparatus so as to obtain lines like those of Fig. 6-2, from which, working back from the lattice spacing, which is now assumed known, we can find the wavelength. Thus we have the essentials of a spectrometer. If several wavelengths are present, of course several lines will be seen in place of each one observed with monochromatic X rays. We shall not go into the technical details of how actual X-ray spectrometers are made, but they have been developed to a high degree of perfection, so that the wave lengths can be determined with great accuracy.

We have already seen the sort of results which Moseley found for X-ray spectra, in the very first work in this field. Further workers, in particular the Swedish physicist Siegbahn, and others, in the years following Moseley, determined the X-ray spectra of all the elements with great accuracy and found the term values. These spectra are so much simpler than the spectra found in the visible part of the spectrum that they were much more completely analyzed, even in the early days of X-ray spectroscopy. It was obvious almost immediately what was the general explanation of these spectra, in terms of the Bohr model; and consequently we shall describe them in terms of the theory from the beginning. There were certain complications, however, which the theory was not able to explain at first, and in fact which did not become clear until the theory of atomic spectra was worked out, as we shall describe it in Chap. 8. We shall therefore merely give a general description here and shall come back to these details later in Chap. 8.

We must assume in the first place that an atom contains electrons with different values of n, the principal quantum number of Bohr's theory. We know that the radius of the orbit is proportional to n^2/Z, where Z is the nuclear charge, so that the smallest orbits will be those of lowest n. An electron will not be exposed to the full attraction of the nucleus, for if we have a more or less spherical distribution of charge, we can use a well-known theorem of electrostatics, and say that a charge at a distance r from the center will be attracted effectively by all that charge within a sphere of radius r, while the charge outside that radius exerts no net force. Suppose we let s represent the number of electronic charges inside a sphere of radius r, where r is the radius of the orbit in question. Then the effective charge inside this radius, which then is the charge resulting in the Bohr orbit, should be $Z - s$ units; this quantity $Z - s$ is called the effective charge, and s the shielding constant. Clearly s must be greater, and $Z - s$ smaller, for large orbits, or orbits of large n value, than for small orbits, for more electronic charge will be contained within them.

We may assume, then, that in fact the radius of the orbit with a given n is given approximately by $n^2 a_0/(Z - s)$, where a_0 is the radius of the first Bohr orbit in hydrogen. Similarly we should assume that the energy of this orbit is given approximately by the formula $R(Z - s)^2/n^2$, where R is the Rydberg energy. As a matter of fact, closer examination shows that the shielding constant s should not be just the same for computing the radius and the energy; but this is a minor matter which does not affect the main argument. The quantity s, we remember, should increase with increasing n.

To remove one of the electrons from the atom, then, should require an energy $R(Z - s)^2/n^2$. If we bombard the atom with electrons whose energy is greater than this amount, they can knock electrons out of the atom. It is assumed that this is done in the process of generating X rays. The X rays are then assumed to be emitted when an electron originally in one of the outer orbits in the atom falls into the vacancy left in the inner shell by the removal of the electron by electronic bombardment. After this transition, there will of course be a vacancy left in the outer shell from which the electron fell. In other words, the initial term value, or energy level of the atom, should be the energy $R(Z - s)^2/n_1^2$, where n_1 is the quantum number of the electron originally knocked out of the atom, and the final term value should be $R(Z - s)^2/n_2^2$, where n_2 is the quantum number of the electron missing in the final state. This is in accordance with Moseley's observation, which we mentioned in Sec. 6-1, that the first line in the K series corresponded approximately to the energy $RZ^2(1 - \frac{1}{4})$, corresponding to $n_1 = 1$, $n_2 = 2$; insertion of the shielding constants s in the two term values improves the agreement of this simple formula with experiment.

As we have said before, the terms resulting from knocking an electron with $n = 1$ out of the atom are called K terms; those from knocking an electron with $n = 2$ out are the L terms; for $n = 3$, the M, and so on. The various lines of the K series of X rays come when an electron is first knocked out of the orbits with $n = 1$, called the K shell, and an electron with higher n value falls down into the vacant space in the K shell. Similarly the L series is emitted when an L electron is knocked out and an electron falls in from a higher orbit, and so on. One correlation is to be expected from this explanation: the minimum electron energy required to excite the lines of the K series should equal the K term value, and similarly for the other series. These correlations prove to be accurately fulfilled by experiments.

We now are ready to see how closely these expectations agree with experiment. Moseley's law, which he found from his first experiments, stated that the frequencies of the lines of a given series, for a set of elements of different Z values, should be proportional to $(Z - s)^2$, or that

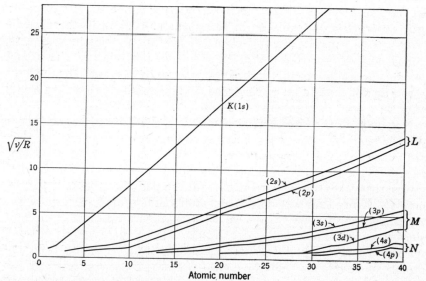

Fig. 6-8. Square root of X-ray term value (divided by Rydberg number) as function of atomic number. Designations $1s$, $2s$, etc., refer to spectroscopic notation, explained in Chap. 8. The low-frequency values are partly taken from optical rather than X-ray data.

the square roots of frequencies should be a linear function of atomic number. Bohr and Coster suggested that it was useful to plot the terms in the same way. In Fig. 6-8, we show a tabulation of much of the experimental data, in the form of the square root of the frequency (divided by the Rydberg constant R) plotted against the atomic number. The general straight behavior of the curves is a good verification of Moseley's law, and shows that our explanation of the origin of the X-ray spectra is correct, in its general outlines. We should expect furthermore that the slope of the curve for the L series should be half that for the K series; that for the M series, one-third that for the K series; and so on. This is likewise approximately fulfilled. Finally, the lines should lie progressively lower for the higher n values, as the shielding constants get larger; and this is also true.

When we look at the curves more carefully, however, we see that there are a good many features in which they are more complicated than this simple explanation would suggest, and this leads us further into our knowledge of atomic structure. One conspicuous feature is the way in which the curves of higher n values behave, in the case where they correspond to low energies. In the first place, each curve starts out at a quite definite atomic number; terms of a given n value are not observed until we reach this atomic number. Thus, as an illustration, the M levels begin to appear at sodium in the periodic table. This suggests that M electrons are not present in very light atoms, and N electrons not until we reach fairly heavy atoms, and so on. Something of this sort of course is to be expected, for the light atoms do not contain many electrons, and it is unlikely that they would have all quantum numbers represented.

Not only do the curves start out at fairly definite places, but near their beginning, where they correspond to small energy values, they are very far from obeying Moseley's law. Rather, the curves show peculiar discontinuities of slope, and when we examine these carefully, we see that they can be correlated with the periodic system of the elements. Every time we come to an alkali metal, for instance, we repeat the same sort of behavior, as we see by comparing Li and Na. This suggests a very important generalization. The energy levels of small term value correspond to outer electrons, easily removed from the atom. We conclude that these electrons are strongly affected by the chemical nature of the atom, whereas the K and L electrons, which are much further within the atom, are almost unaffected by the chemical nature. Put in another way, if we could understand the behavior of the outer electrons, we should be in a position to understand the chemical properties of the atom. The conviction that this must be true gradually deepened in the decade following the original discovery of the X-ray energy levels, and as they were investigated more in detail, so that curves such as those of Fig. 6-8 became available. It is the explanation of the periodic table in terms of electron shells which we shall treat next; and this is in part an outgrowth of the study of X-ray spectra, of the sort which we have taken up in this chapter.

There are further complications in the curves of Fig. 6-8, which do not fit in with a very simple theory. Experimentally, one finds three L terms, five M terms, and so on, of which we have shown two L's, three M's. Where do these come from? If we had a hydrogenlike spectrum, all the levels should coincide. We can see a simple explanation as to why there should be several levels, however. Thus, we know that there are two types of Bohr orbits for $n = 2$: one for $k = 2$, a circular orbit, and one for $k = 1$, an elliptical orbit. In hydrogen, these have the same energy. However, the elliptical orbit, which has the nucleus at its focus, will penetrate closer to the nucleus than the circular orbit of the same n value; we remember that the diameter of the circular orbit is equal to the major axis of the ellipse, for hydrogen. As the ellipse penetrates further, however, it will be less shielded by the action of the other electrons. Hence we should expect a smaller shielding constant s for the elliptical orbit than for the circular one, and hence a lower energy. We shall find in the next chapter that the same sort of effect is very striking in the optical spectra. Such an explanation could show us why the L shell should have two levels, and similarly why the M shell should have three, the N shell four, as we have shown in Fig. 6-8, and so on. But really the L shell has three, the M shell five, and so on. This was a standing mystery for many years after it was discovered; and it was not explained until the discovery of the electron spin in 1925. In fact, it was one of the important facts leading to this remarkable discovery, which we shall take up in Chap. 8. The X-ray spectra, to sum up, fell in in a general way with our expectation from a model with hydrogenlike orbits of different n values; but they deviated enough from these expectations to give a great deal to think about in the years after they were discovered.

PROBLEMS

6-1. The principal line of the K series of X rays, called $K\alpha$, arises when an electron falls from the state $n = 2$ to the state $n = 1$. Moseley found empirically that the frequency ν of the line, as a function of atomic number Z, is given by the equation

$$\nu = 0.248 \times 10^{16}(Z - 1)^2 \qquad \text{cycles/sec}$$

Show how this equation can be approximately justified from Bohr's theory.

6-2. The line $K\beta$ arises when an electron falls from the state $n = 3$ to the state $n = 1$. Find the wavelength of the $K\alpha$ and $K\beta$ lines of copper from approximate use of Bohr theory, and compare with the values 1.549 and 1.402 A, respectively, observed by Moseley.

6-3. It is observed that, when continuous radiation falls on a copper sample, those wavelengths shorter than 1.377 A are absorbed much more than the longer wavelengths. This wavelength is called the K absorption edge. How can you explain this and its relation to the wavelengths of $K\alpha$ and $K\beta$ given in Prob. 6-2?

6-4. It is observed that the lines $K\alpha$ and $K\beta$ of copper appear when a copper target is bombarded with electrons whose energy is greater than about 8,970 ev, but do not appear for lower voltage. How would you explain this fact, with reference to the result of Prob. 6-3?

6-5. The crystal of NaCl consists of an array of Na^+ and Cl^- ions, at the corners of a simple cubic lattice, the atoms alternating in type as we go from one lattice site to another along either the x, y, or z directions. The distance from one atom to its nearest neighbor is found to be 2.814 A. A beam of continuous X rays is shot at a crystal along the x axis. A diffracted beam is observed emerging along the y direction. What wavelength will this beam have according to Bragg's law?

6-6. Using the NaCl crystal as in Prob. 6-5, with a beam of continuous X rays striking the crystal along the x axis, there will not only be the diffracted beam along the y axis, as in Prob. 6-5, but many other diffracted beams in the xy plane. Find the angles of these beams and the wavelengths of X rays forming the various beams.

6-7. A monochromatic beam of Cu $K\alpha$ radiation falls on a crystal of NaCl, along the x direction. The crystal, which was originally oriented with its lattice directions along x, y, and z, is rotated slowly about an axis in the z direction. Certain diffracted beams will emerge in the xy plane, when the crystal reaches suitable angles. Find the angles which these various emergent beams make with the x axis.

6-8. Atoms are located at the lattice points of a simple cubic lattice, at $x = n_1 a$, $y = n_2 a$, $z = n_3 a$, where the n's are integers. Show that all atoms are contained in the planes $h_1 x + h_2 y + h_3 z = pa$, where h_1, h_2, h_3, and p are integers. Find the direction cosines of the normal to these planes and the spacing between successive planes.

6-9. Use the description of the planes given in Prob. 6-8 to discuss the cases taken up in Probs. 6-6 and 6-7.

CHAPTER 7

ATOMIC SPECTRA AND THE PERIODIC SYSTEM OF THE ELEMENTS

7-1. Introduction. If one considers the important dates in physics, one notices that the years following Bohr's theory of the hydrogen atom in 1913, and the development of X-ray spectroscopy at the same time, seem to have few significant developments. Sommerfeld's theory of elliptical orbits, which we mentioned in Chap. 5, came in 1915; but it was an exception. We do not need to use very much imagination to tell why this was so: The next years were those of the First World War, and it was all that one could hope to have the theories kept alive, quite aside from making new developments in them. When the war was over, however, progress started rapidly again. The former foes soon became friendly again in a scientific way, and Germany, England, and, to a rapidly increasing extent, America, took up again the problems of atomic theory where they had been largely dropped in 1914.

These years, from the end of the war until the discovery of Schrödinger's equation in 1926, were dominated in a remarkable way by a book: Sommerfeld's "Atombau and Spektrallinien." The first edition of this remarkable work appeared in 1919, right after the war. Successive editions came out every two years or so, each time with most remarkable additions since the previous one. Graduate students in those days had to buy each new edition as it appeared; for Sommerfeld seemed peculiarly able to grasp the significance of the new developments and to weld them into a consistent whole. From each new edition, one got the impression of an increasing body of knowledge, but of increasingly great puzzles, which were only solved in 1925 and 1926, with the discovery of the electron spin, the Pauli exclusion principle, and finally of wave mechanics. Those were stimulating years for the physicist, years witnessing extraordinary inductive efforts, leading from fragmentary theories into a complete understanding of the laws governing those parts of the atom outside the nucleus.

We shall close this volume by remarking that the present years, including the year when this text is being written (1955), seem to the author to stand in much the same situation with regard to the understanding of nuclear structure, as the years from 1919 to 1926 stood in the theory of the outer part of the atom. Past years have been exciting ones for physics; but we must look around us, and realize that they were no more exciting than the ones we live in. Let us hope that successive editions of this book, if they should ever be called for, will be as different from this one, in their last chapters, as successive editions of Sommerfeld's book were.

Sommerfeld's book, of course, had chapters treating the matters which we have discussed in the preceding pages, and in much the same way, though it was a more advanced and mathematical text than this one is. But then it plunged headlong into atomic spectroscopy; for that was the greater preoccupation of the early 1920's. There is something of a tendency now to ask why one should be interested in atomic spectra. If, for instance, our major interest is the physics of solids, why bother with atoms? The answer is obvious. If it had not been for the great effort put in in understanding atomic spectra, we should never have discovered the electron spin, the exclusion principle, and wave mechanics; we should never have understood the periodic table of the elements; we should never have had a theory of solids. It was a puzzle of the very highest order to find these principles, and it is highly doubtful whether the puzzle would ever have been solved, if we had not had a problem relatively as simple as atomic spectra, with a body of data as rich as that of atomic spectroscopy, to point the way. Atomic spectra formed the guide to the discovery of the principles; and they can equally well form the guide to their understanding.

The spectrum of hydrogen, of course, had been understood experimentally since the preceding century, and Bohr's theory had explained it completely. Other elements all had much more complicated spectra; but there were a number which were simple enough so that much progress had been made in their study. In particular, the alkalies and alkaline earths were found to have rather simple spectra, and series of terms were picked out in them, showing considerable similarity to the Balmer series. The combination principle was verified, and the term values were shown to be given rather closely by the formula $R/(n - d)^2$, where n is an integer, d a constant; this is Rydberg's law, mentioned in Sec. 5-2.

Much work was done by the practical spectroscopists in studying such spectra, and by the early 1920's a number of them were well worked out. The German spectroscopist Paschen, and a number of others, had classified the terms into series, which they called the sharp, principal, diffuse, and fundamental series, the terms of each being given by Rydberg's law, but with different values of d. It gradually became clear that these series were connected with orbits, similar to the Bohr hydrogen orbits, with different values of the azimuthal quantum number k, the sharp series having $k = 1$, principal series $k = 2$, diffuse series $k = 3$, and fundamental series $k = 4$. This led to a general idea regarding the shape and size of the orbits connected with the various term values. It also led to a notation for atomic energy levels which has persisted ever since: the levels from which the sharp series originates were called s levels, those of the principal series p levels, the diffuse series d levels, and the fundamental series f levels. We speak, for instance, of a $3d$ electron as an electron with its principal quantum number n equal to 3, and its azimuthal quantum number k equal also to 3.

It was obvious, of course, that an electron in a heavy atom could not have a hydrogenlike orbit. We have already seen, in our study of X-ray levels, that surrounding the nucleus there must be a cloud of electrons, so that the field, at a distance r from the nucleus, would be that produced by the nuclear charge, and by those electrons within the sphere of radius r (assuming that the cloud was spherically symmetric, a very natural assumption). It seemed much more reasonable, then, not to compare the orbits with those of hydrogen, but rather to investigate the quantum theory of an electron in a spherically symmetric field, such as that arising from the nucleus and an electron cloud.

This problem, fortunately, can be carried through with not much more difficulty than the hydrogen problem. We find that in this case, just as with hydrogen, we have the principal and azimuthal quantum numbers, and, as with hydrogen, the angular momentum of the orbit is still given by $kh/2\pi$. Again as in hydrogen, there is just the same space quantization: the component of angular momentum along a fixed axis is $m_k h/2\pi$, where m_k is an integer taking on any one of the values between k and $-k$. The difference between this case and hydrogen comes in the energy; and here, as we shall show in Sec. 7-3, one can find that the energy should be given approximately by the Rydberg formula $R/(n - d)^2$, so that we have a good deal of assurance that this is the correct sort of explanation for the atomic spectra.

When we come to consider these energy levels and orbits concerned in the optical spectra, we immediately start to ask the same sort of question which was being asked in the early 1920's: How do these energy levels, and orbits, fit in with the X-ray levels? We have already seen that those X-ray levels correspond, according to Moseley's

law, to inner orbits in a central-field problem; and now we see that the
optical levels correspond to outer orbits in the same problem.   Can
one fit them together?   How many electrons of each type do we really
have in an atom?   How many electrons are there in the K shell, how
many in the L shell, and so on, and how many are left over in the outer
part of the atom, to take part in optical spectra?   How, in turn, does
this tie in with the known facts of chemistry?   There is every evidence
that, for instance, the inert-gas atoms—helium, neon, argon, krypton,
and xenon—form particular stable structures.   The elements which
follow immediately after them, the alkalies—lithium, sodium, potassium, rubidium, and cesium—act chemically as if they easily lost one
electron, forming singly charged positive ions, which have the same
number of outer electrons as an inert gas.   On the other hand, the
elements preceding the inert gases, the halogens—fluorine, chlorine,
bromine, and iodine—seem to like to pick up an electron and form a
negative ion, again having the same number of outer electrons as an
inert gas.   Can these questions not be tied in with the structure of the
atom?

For a while, there seemed to be a great gap between the thinking of
the chemists and the physicists on these questions.   In the years
between 1916 and 1921, the German Kossel and the American chemists
Lewis and Langmuir had constructed atomic models, intended to show
the chemical properties, which had no resemblance at all to Bohr
atoms.   They noticed particularly the obviously great importance of a
shell of eight electrons.   Thus, in going from helium, with atomic number 2, to neon, with atomic number 10, eight electrons are added, and
we go from one inert-gas atom to another.   They assumed that this
shell of eight electrons formed a stable structure, and Langmuir, in
particular, called this by the name of an octet and postulated that the
eight electrons forming it were located at the corners of a cube.   For a
few years, one had pictures of atoms with successive shells of electrons,
each formed in such a cubical way.   This picture of the octet, however,
had trouble as soon as one met the group of elements starting with
potassium and calcium; for between argon, which is the inert gas just
before potassium, and krypton, just before the next alkali rubidium,
there are eighteen electrons added, not eight.   And of course the
geometrical atom proposed by the chemists had the much more severe
restriction, that it had no connection with the Bohr atom, which certainly was very close to the truth.

We have sketched the sort of thinking that was going on in the early
1920's: the beginning of understanding of the atomic spectra, the confusion regarding their relation to the X-ray spectra, the puzzle as to

how any sort of atomic model satisfactory to the physicist could be reconciled with the chemical evidence. This was the situation in which Bohr, in the years from 1921 to 1923, made a new contribution to atomic theory, almost as significant in its way as his original explanation of the hydrogen atom. He undertook to study the whole formation of the periodic system of the elements. He imagined that one would start with a bare nucleus, and then would allow one electron after another to be bound to it. He asked what sort of orbits and energy levels they would enter; and in so doing, he set up a theory of the periodic system of the elements. This theory was far from complete. He lacked some of the fundamental ideas which we now know are needed for such a theory: the exclusion principle and the electron spin. In some important respects, as a result of this, his theory was actually wrong, though it was only a short time before it was corrected. Nevertheless, in its boldness, correlating the facts of X-ray spectroscopy, atomic spectra, and chemistry, Bohr's theory of the periodic system ranks as one of the very important syntheses in the history of scientific thought. In this chapter, we shall treat this theory of the periodic system, together with the facts of spectroscopy which led up to it.

7-2. The Spectra of the Alkalies. The spectroscopists had found out long ago that the alkalies had the simplest spectra, as we mentioned earlier. The reason seemed fairly clear, in the light of the thoughts of the chemists about the periodic system. Clearly the alkali atoms had only one outer electron, outside rather stable closed shells having the configuration of an inert gas. One could reasonably guess that only this outer electron was concerned in ordinary atomic spectra, and that the inner electrons were concerned in the X-ray spectra. An alkali atom, then, in some sense, would act like a one-electron atom, and might be supposed to be simple. An alkaline earth would be like a two-electron atom, and as we add more outer electrons, we should expect the problem to become much more complicated. Experimentally, this was the case. Elements of the iron group, for instance, had spectra so complicated that for a long time they seemed almost hopeless to unravel. We shall see in the next chapter that the analysis of these complex spectra formed one of the experimental triumphs of the 1920's and at the same time furnished the keys necessary to unlock the secrets of the exclusion principle, the electron spin, and quantum mechanics. The alkalies, however, were simple, and they provided all the information needed for working out the explanation of the periodic system.

In Fig. 7-1, we show the term values of the various s, p, d, and f

levels in the sodium spectrum, with the hydrogen values for comparison. These are not very complicated sets of levels; and we should hope to be able to find out something from them. In the first place, let us give some of the experimental evidence which led to the assumption that these levels were associated with values of the azimuthal quantum number equal to 1, 2, 3, and 4, respectively. The most striking evidence came from a selection principle. It was possible to prove, by Bohr's correspondence principle, that transitions were only allowed in which k increased or decreased by one unit. This selection principle proved to be strictly verified, in the spectra. Transitions were found

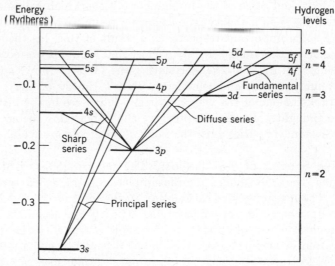

FIG. 7-1. Term values of s, p, d, f levels in the sodium spectrum. Hydrogen levels are shown for comparison.

to occur between levels of one type and those in an adjacent row in the scheme, but not otherwise. In fact, as shown in Fig. 7-1, the observed spectral lines fell into the following series: the principal series, in which an electron fell from a p level to a lower s level; the sharp series, in which an electron fell from an excited s level to a lower p level; the diffuse series, in which an electron fell from an excited d level to a lower p level; and the fundamental series, in which an electron fell from an excited f level to a lower d level.

Additional evidence for the correctness of the interpretation came from the intensities of the lines and their relation to the theories of intensities derived from the correspondence principle. That principle showed that a transition in which k decreased was much more probable than one in which k increased. In agreement with this, the principal, diffuse, and fundamental series were found to be more intense than the sharp series, in which k increased.   In fact, the reason why the principal series was so named was its large intensity, correlated with the correspondence principle.   The names of the sharp and diffuse series arose from the appearance of their lines (for reasons that can now be understood in terms of the fine structure of the lines).   The fundamental series, with $k = 4$, is not fundamental at all, but it was so named, before the theory was understood, because its levels had almost exactly the hydrogenlike values, as we see from Fig. 7-1.   We shall later see the reason why this is the case.

This sort of evidence had correctly determined the azimuthal quantum numbers of these lines, in the early days of the application of Bohr theory to the alkali spectra.   A greater puzzle, however, came when one tried to assign principal quantum numbers n.   We have already stated that the term values are given approximately by the Rydberg formula $R/(n - d)^2$, where n takes on a series of integral values, and d is a quantity, called the quantum defect, approximately independent of n.   It is obvious that from this law, which at first was purely empirical, we cannot determine the value of n for any particular term; for by choosing a value of d a unit greater, all the n's would be found to be a unit greater as well.   We cannot get further with determining the n values, without more understanding of the significance of the Rydberg formula, and of the whole structure of the atom.   We shall go on now to consider the nature of the energy levels of an electron in a central field, and this will give us valuable hints as to the proper values to choose for n.   But it is an interesting fact that, even with such hints, the principal quantum numbers are given incorrectly in the edition of Sommerfeld's *Atombau* published as late as 1924.   It was not easy to figure out just the nature of these orbits, and their connection with the X-ray levels.

7-3. The Central-field Model of the Atom.   During the years from 1921 to 1926, it became gradually clear that a good description of the spectra of the alkalies could be given by the sort of model we have described in earlier sections: an electron moving in a central field, such as would be produced by the nucleus, and a sort of spherically averaged charge resulting from the other electrons of the atom.   One of the first physicists to work along these lines was Schrödinger, whose later work on wave mechanics was much more famous.   A later worker along the same lines was Hartree, whose theory of the self-consistent field, introduced several years after the development of wave mechanics, was really merely a rephrasing of these same ideas in the language of wave mechanics.   The effort of these earliest workers was along a simple and direct line: to find, if possible, a spherically symmetric potential in which the energy levels of an electron would agree with the empirically determined levels found in an alkali atom, as illustrated in Fig. 7-1 for sodium.   They found that this could be done, with a good deal of accuracy; and the results of such calculations were in Bohr's mind when he proposed his theory of the periodic system.

The theory of the motion of a particle in a spherically symmetric field is a simple piece of mechanics, which these workers were all familiar with.   Let us examine this problem enough to understand its general features.   We can proceed as in treating the hydrogen problem.   First, let us write down the energy in polar coordinates, as is appropriate for a central-field problem.   We shall consider the problem in a plane, not treating space quantization (which can be handled in the general case as it is for hydrogen).   If our polar coordinates are r and θ, there will be two components of momentum, one along the radius, the other along the direction at right angles to the radius.   Rather than using this component of momentum at right angles to the radius, however, we use the angular momentum, which is equal to the component of momentum at right angles to the radius, times the radius vector.   If we let the radial momentum be p_r, the angular momentum p_θ, then the contribution of radial momentum to the kinetic energy is $p_r^2/2m$, and that of the angular momentum is $p_\theta^2/2mr^2$.'   We can verify these facts at once.   The radial momentum p_r equals mv_r, where v_r is the component of velocity along the radius; thus $p_r^2/2m$ equals $\frac{1}{2}mv_r^2$, which is certainly the contribution of the radial motion to the kinetic energy.   Similarly p_θ equals mrv_θ, where v_θ is the component of velocity along the direction of increasing θ, so that $p_\theta^2/2mr^2$ equals $\frac{1}{2}mv_\theta^2$.

The total energy is then given by the expression

$$E = \frac{p_r^2}{2m} + \frac{p_\theta^2}{2mr^2} + V(r) \tag{7-1}$$

where $V(r)$ is the potential energy.   We now observe that the angular momentum is constant, which of course follows because there is no torque, or because the potential energy $V(r)$ is independent of θ.   The quantum condition for θ then tells us, just as in hydrogen, that the angular momentum equals $kh/2\pi$, where k is an integer, the azimuthal quantum number.   We can now insert this fact in Eq. (7-1), and obtain the equation

$$E = \frac{p_r^2}{2m} + \frac{k^2h^2}{8\pi^2mr^2} + V(r) \tag{7-2}$$

This is exactly like the energy expression for a one-dimensional problem in which r is the variable, and in which the potential energy is $k^2h^2/8\pi^2mr^2 + V(r)$. The term $k^2h^2/8\pi^2mr^2$ is a fictitious potential energy of the centrifugal force. We can now solve the problem of the motion of a particle in this potential, by well-known methods of mechanics.

For the radial quantum condition, we must find the momentum p_r as a function of r. This can be done immediately from Eq. (7-2); we have

$$p_r = \left[2m \left(E - V - \frac{k^2h^2}{8\pi^2mr^2} \right) \right]^{1/2} \tag{7-3}$$

If we call $V + k^2h^2/8\pi^2mr^2$ the effective potential energy, we see that p_r is real when the energy E is greater than the effective potential energy, imaginary when it is less. In Fig. 7-2, we show the effective potential energy as a function of r, for different k values, for sodium, using a potential function which leads to results in close agreement with experiment. We show lines at various heights, such that the integral $\oint p_r\, dr$ is an integer times h; that is, for the various stationary states. We label these energies by the symbols $1s$, $2s$, etc., indicating the principal quantum number and the azimuthal quantum number, where we remember from the hydrogen case that the principal quantum number equals the sum of the azimuthal quantum number k, and the radial quantum number, which is $\oint p_r\, dr$ divided by h.

In Fig. 7-3, we now show p_r, plotted against r, for the s states, from Fig. 7-2. These curves are the lines of constant energy in a phase space representing the radial motion; they are the curves whose areas are h, $2h$, $3h$, . . . , respectively, and correspond to the elliptical lines of constant energy in phase space for a linear oscillator. It is clear that we can get the energy levels, as shown in Fig. 7-2, by computing the area $\oint p_r\, dr$ under the curves of Fig. 7-3 (carrying out the integration numerically, if $V(r)$ is a complicated enough function so that it cannot be done analytically), doing this as a function of the energy E, and picking out those energies for which the area equals $n_r h$, where n_r is an integer.

In either Fig. 7-2 or Fig. 7-3 we can get information about the orbit; for from either of them we can find the minimum and maximum values of the radius. We see that for the $1s$ and $2s$ orbits, both minimum and maximum lie well inside the atom (the approximate boundary of the charge cloud of inner electrons comes at about one atomic unit). The $1s$ orbit, belonging to the K shell, lies far inside the atom, while the $2s$, belonging to the L shell, extends out to about the boundary of the inner core of the atom. On the other hand, the $3s$ and higher members

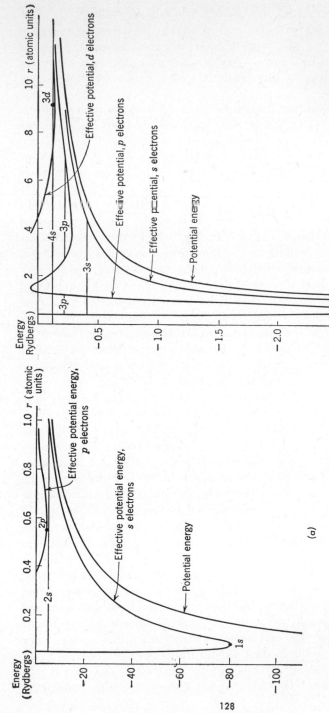

FIG. 7-2. (a) Effective potential energy of an electron in the sodium atom, as function of internuclear distance, for s and p electrons (k = 1 and 2). Orbits of 1s, 2s, 2p electrons occur at radii and energy shown. Scale chosen to show inner electrons. (b) Same as (a), scale chosen to show outer electrons. The situation according to which there appear to be two regions where the 3p orbit would be located is a peculiarity which appears in this type of theory, but which is absent in wave mechanics; it does not seem to correspond to any actual feature of the structure of the atom, and one cannot answer the question as to which region the 3p orbit is located in.

of the series extend far outside the atomic core. The minimum distances, however, for each of the s orbits, fall well inside the core of the atom. These are what are called penetrating orbits. In Fig. 7-4 we show the nature of the actual orbits in such a case. Far from being

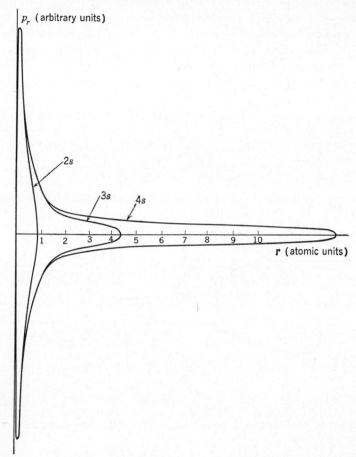

Fig. 7-3. Momentum p_r as a function of r, for 2s, 3s, 4s orbits in sodium.

ellipses, they are rather rosettelike orbits, the inner part resembling a small ellipse, the outer part a large ellipse. Similarly from Fig. 7-2 we can see that the $2p$ orbit, belonging to the L shell, lies well inside the atom, but the $3p$ and further members of the series do not. For the d and f electrons, the situation is quite different: none of the orbits penetrate the core, but they lie rather almost entirely outside the atom. In this outer region, the inner electrons shield the nucleus enough so that there is only one unbalanced charge, and the field is like

that of a hydrogen atom.   It is not surprising, then, that the energy
of these orbits is almost exactly hydrogenlike, as is consistent with the
value of Fig. 7-2.

From the analysis which we have given, we can see why the Rydberg
formula holds approximately for the optical energy levels.   In Fig. 7-3,
the curve of p_r vs. r, in the phase space, for an outer orbit, resembles the
corresponding hydrogen curve.   When the electron penetrates the
core, however, there is an additional high peak in the curve, contributing a large amount to the phase integral $\oint p_r\, dr$, which is almost
independent of the quantum number.   Thus the phase integral, for a

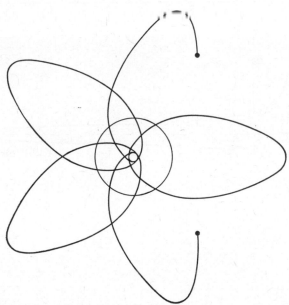

FIG. 7-4. A few turns of the orbit of the 3s electron in sodium.   The actual orbit
never closes on itself, and has infinitely many turns.   The circle shows the approximate size of the inner core.

given energy, equals approximately the hydrogenic value, plus a constant.   Now the hydrogenic value has a simple form, which we can
deduce by working backward from the known energy formula for
hydrogen.   We know that the energy is $-R/(n_r + k)^2$, where $n_r + k$
is the same as the principal quantum number n, and we have expressed
the energy in terms of the Rydberg energy.   In other words, the radial
phase integral, which equals $n_r h$, must equal $[(-R/E)^{\frac{1}{2}} - k]h$.   In the
alkali case, however, we have seen that the phase integral must equal
this value plus a constant: $n_r h = [(-R/E)^{\frac{1}{2}} - k]h + \text{constant}$.   If

we let this constant be dh, and solve for E, we have

$$E = -\frac{R}{(n_r + k - d)^2} \qquad (7\text{-}4)$$

which is Rydberg's formula. This simple proof, which was first given by Bohr, of course is not rigorous, but neither is the Rydberg formula exact.

From analysis of this sort, one can find the energies of the outer orbits in a problem such as we are discussing. The energies of the inner orbits are more nearly hydrogenlike, corresponding to atoms with effective nuclear charges $Z - s$. One can, as a matter of fact, solve for the energies of these inner orbits, and hence deduce approximate values for s. We see, then, that this model is capable of explaining the form of the energy both of the optical and of the X-ray energy levels, so that we can feel considerable assurance that it represents a fairly good approximation to the facts. We may anticipate, and say that the self-consistent field method, developed by Hartree after the discovery of wave mechanics, carries such arguments much further, in a quantitative way, and shows that if the field is properly set up, the energy levels derived from it form very accurate approximations to the observed X-ray and optical term values.

This is a picture, then, which can be used as a basis for a study of the periodic table. Bohr did not have as accurate potentials, and solutions for the X-ray and optical orbits, as we have now, and as we have described in this section, so that it was more of a feat for him to deduce the exact structure of the atoms than it might seem. Nevertheless, the reader has probably already thought ahead from the discussion we have given of the structure of sodium, to deduce for himself the principal quantum numbers of the optical levels and the way in which these correlate with the X-ray spectra.

7-4. Bohr's Theory of the Periodic Table. We have now become familiar with the sort of information which optical spectra can give regarding the potential field in which the electrons move. We see that it is possible to set up a potential such that the energy levels of an electron moving in it are good approximations to the observed term values. But the principal quantum numbers are uniquely determined from this potential, and this furnishes one of the pieces of evidence necessary to describe the structure of the atom. The other pieces of evidence come from the X-ray spectra, and from the chemical properties of the atom. Let us see the sort of argument which Bohr used, as applied specifically to sodium, the example we are using.

The atomic number of sodium is 11. It comes one unit beyond neon, with atomic number 10. This in turn is the inert gas coming beyond helium, with atomic number 2. The chemical ideas suggested very definitely that the two electrons of helium, and the eight additional ones added in neon, form very stable structures, and that sodium has in addition one outer electron, the valence electron, which is easily removed in forming a positive ion, and which also is responsible for the optical spectrum of sodium. When we combine this information with the X-ray evidence, it seems almost inescapable that the first two electrons, which are present in helium, form the K shell, the next eight form the L shell; the valence electron of sodium would be the first electron in the M shell.

This assumption, which certainly seems reasonable, is verified by our discussion of the preceding section. There we found that the 1s, 2s, and 2p orbits were located in the interior of the atom, while the 3s, 3p, 3d, and all orbits of higher principal quantum number, extended far outside the atom, and are easily removed. This is all consistent with the assumption that the 1s electrons form the K shell, the 2s and 2p the L shell, as we postulated earlier in the explanation of Moseley's law, and that the higher orbits in this case represent the various possible states of the single valence electron. We can now verify this assumption more accurately than could be done in the early 1920's, when Bohr was working out the theory of the periodic table, for we can calculate the energies of 2s and 2p levels from a potential such as we have used, compare them with the observed soft-X-ray energy levels, and find a very good agreement between theory and experiment. We conclude unmistakably, then, that the principal quantum numbers of the first members of the s and p series, in Fig. 7-1, are 3.

We can also conclude certain things regarding the number of electrons in each shell: we have seen that it seems highly plausible that there should be two electrons in the K shell, or in 1s orbits, and eight in the L shell, distributed between 2s and 2p orbits. By similar arguments applied to the higher alkali metals, Bohr concluded that the maximum number of electrons in the M shell must be 18, and in the N shell 32. These numbers—2, 8, 18, 32—formed an interesting progression: they were 2×1^2, 2×2^2, 2×3^2, 2×4^2. An obvious question was, how are the 8 electrons of the L shell distributed between 2s and 2p, how are the 18 of the M shell distributed between 3s, 3p, and 3d, and so on?

Here Bohr had practically no evidence to go on, and made a bad guess: he guessed that four of the L electrons were in 2s, four in 2p; six of the M electrons in 3s, six in 3p, six in 3d. Soon after, however, in 1924, the English physicist Stoner used certain detailed X-ray evidence which Bohr had not considered, and concluded that Bohr's assignment was wrong, and that rather we had two of the L electrons in the $2s$, six in the $2p$; two of the M electrons in $3s$, six in $3p$, ten in $3d$, and so on. Stoner's hypothesis has turned out to be correct, though there was very little evidence to go on at the time.   Therefore we shall assume it at once, and ask how the hypotheses of Bohr and Stoner go to explain the periodic system of the elements.

It became clear at once that several different assumptions were required to give a consistent statement of the principles underlying the structure of the periodic system.   We can see the nature of these assumptions now rather more clearly than Bohr and Stoner could see them in 1923–1924, but they were inherent in their work.   Let us state these assumptions clearly before we go on to describe their application to the periodic system.   There are really three assumptions, as follows:

1. The assumption of the self-consistent field (not clearly enunciated until Hartree brought it out several years after the development of wave mechanics, but clearly foreshadowed in the work of the period we are considering): the energy levels and orbits of an electron in an atom can be closely approximated by those of a single electron moving in a spherically symmetric field; and this field, in turn, is that produced, at least approximately, by the nucleus, and by all the other electrons in their orbits, the charge of these other electrons being averaged over their orbits, and over angles, so as to give a spherically symmetric charge distribution.

2. The number of electrons in a given shell is limited in number.   In particular, one can have only two electrons in an s orbit of any given principal quantum number; only six in a particular p orbit; ten in a particular d orbit; fourteen in a particular f orbit.   This was merely a postulate at the time, but it later developed into Pauli's exclusion principle, as we shall explain in the next chapter.

3. The available electrons in an atom will, in its ground state, fill the lowest energy levels, subject to condition 2; in excited states, one or more electrons can be raised from these levels to higher levels, and for optical excitation it is one of the outer electrons which is removed, while for X-ray excitation it is one of the inner electrons.

These three postulates, as applied in the light of the wave mechanics, have now shown themselves completely capable of describing the periodic system of the elements in all details.   Their results were deduced by Bohr, however, from available chemical and spectroscopic evidence, and we shall now give the sort of discussion which Bohr gave, showing the power of this method of analyzing atomic structure.   First

we give, in Fig. 7-5, the periodic system of the elements, in essentially
the form used by Bohr.

We start with hydrogen and helium, containing one and two 1s elec-

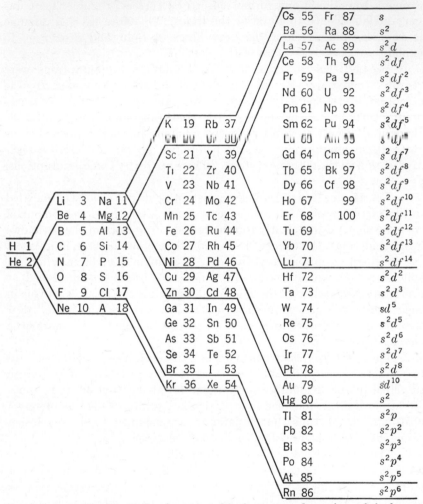

			Cs 55	Fr 87	s
			Ba 56	Ra 88	s^2
			La 57	Ac 89	$s^2 d$
			Ce 58	Th 90	$s^2 df$
			Pr 59	Pa 91	$s^2 df^2$
			Nd 60	U 92	$s^2 df^3$
			Pm 61	Np 93	$s^2 df^4$
	K 19	Rb 37	Sm 62	Pu 94	$s^2 df^5$
	Ca 20	Sr 38	Lu 63	Am 95	$s^2 df^6$
	Sc 21	Y 39	Gd 64	Cm 96	$s^2 df^7$
	Ti 22	Zr 40	Tb 65	Bk 97	$s^2 df^8$
	V 23	Nb 41	Dy 66	Cf 98	$s^2 df^9$
Li 3 Na 11	Cr 24	Mo 42	Ho 67	99	$s^2 df^{10}$
Be 4 Mg 12	Mn 25	Tc 43	Er 68	100	$s^2 df^{11}$
B 5 Al 13	Fe 26	Ru 44	Tu 69		$s^2 df^{12}$
H 1 C 6 Si 14	Co 27	Rh 45	Yb 70		$s^2 df^{13}$
He 2 N 7 P 15	Ni 28	Pd 46	Lu 71		$s^2 df^{14}$
O 8 S 16	Cu 29	Ag 47	Hf 72		$s^2 d^2$
F 9 Cl 17	Zn 30	Cd 48	Ta 73		$s^2 d^3$
Ne 10 A 18	Ga 31	In 49	W 74		sd^5
	Ge 32	Sn 50	Re 75		$s^2 d^5$
	As 33	Sb 51	Os 76		$s^2 d^6$
	Se 34	Te 52	Ir 77		$s^2 d^7$
	Br 35	I 53	Pt 78		$s^2 d^8$
	Kr 36	Xe 54	Au 79		sd^{10}
			Hg 80		s^2
			Tl 81		$s^2 p$
			Pb 82		$s^2 p^2$
			Bi 83		$s^2 p^3$
			Po 84		$s^2 p^4$
			At 85		$s^2 p^5$
			Rn 86		$s^2 p^6$

FIG. 7-5. Periodic table of the elements, with electron configurations of the lowest
states.   (The electron configurations do not in every case represent the absolutely
lowest state, but in every case the state indicated at least is very close to the ground
state.)   The lines are drawn to indicate chemically similar elements.

trons, respectively.   These are all the electrons the 1s, or K, shell can
hold, so that in the next element, lithium, the third electron must go
into a 2s level, where it is much more easily removed, and lithium is an
alkali, easily forming a positive ion.   Next we have beryllium, with

two $2s$ electrons, both fairly easily removed, but not so easily as with lithium.   We go on next adding $2p$ electrons, until at neon, with six $2p$'s, we have another inert gas.   Sodium, the next element, which we have used as our example, has one more electron, in a $3s$ state; magnesium has two $3s$'s, and as we go from aluminum to argon we add six $3p$'s.   We must assume—and we find, when we work out the self-consistent fields—that the $3s$ and $3p$ orbits are a good deal more strongly bound than the $3d$, so that the shell of $3s$ and $3p$ electrons in argon is again a stable configuration, another of Langmuir's octets. The reason why the $3s$'s and $3p$'s are more strongly bound than the $3d$'s is that their orbits penetrate further into the core of the atom, they are subject to greater attraction of the nucleus, and this decreases their energy.

In considering the elements beyond argon, we must take note of the fact that the $4s$ electrons, which penetrate strongly, are more tightly bound than the $3d$'s, as we have seen in sodium, in Fig. 7-1.   The elements potassium and calcium, which follow argon, have one and two $4s$ electrons, respectively, but no $3d$'s, in accordance with postulate 3; they form an alkali and an alkaline earth, similar to sodium and magnesium.   In scandium, the next element after calcium, we find that the $3d$ is definitely more tightly bound than $4p$, so that we start filling up the $3d$ shell.   This process continues through the elements titanium, vanadium, chromium, manganese, iron, cobalt, and nickel— the elements which are often called the iron group, or the $3d$ transition group.   These elements all contain partially filled $3d$ shells, and this shows itself in some of their important physical properties.   One finds that, though the $3d$ electrons are not very tightly bound, still their orbits are rather far inside the atom, so that they are well shielded from the outside.   With their partially filled shells, they have magnetic moments; we shall understand this better when we come to the next chapter.   It is for this reason that these elements are the ones showing paramagnetic and ferromagnetic properties.   Also electronic transitions are possible between these rather well-protected $3d$ electrons and other $3d$ levels of a type which we shall take up in the next chapter, and these transitions are responsible for the color of the ions of the transition-group elements in solution.

Though the $4s$ electron is more tightly bound than the $3d$, in the elements from scandium to nickel, there is very little energy difference between them.   This is shown in chromium, in which the lowest state is actually not that with four $3d$ electrons and two $4s$'s, but that with five $3d$'s and one $4s$, though the state with four $3d$'s and two $4s$'s lies only slightly higher.   In nickel, the state with nine $3d$'s and one $4s$ is only very slightly above the ground state, which has eight $3d$'s and two $4s$'s.   And in the next element, copper, the ground state, instead of having nine $3d$'s and two $4s$'s, has ten $3d$'s, and one $4s$; though the state with nine $3d$'s and two $4s$'s lies only slightly higher.   It is not surprising, therefore, that copper has some slight resemblance to an alkali metal, having one electron outside the complete shell of $3d$'s. The next element after copper, zinc, with two $4s$ electrons, slightly resembles an alkaline earth.

With the next element, gallium, which is quite similar in some ways to aluminum, we start adding $4p$'s, and this process is completed at krypton, the next inert gas.   Then we start the same process all over again   The $5s$, $4d$, and $5p$ electrons resemble closely the $4s$, $3d$, and $4p$ in their general energy relationship, and all are more tightly bound than the $4f$.   Thus, in the elements from rubidium to xenon, we go through another transition group, including such an important metal as molybdenum, in which the $4d$ electrons are being added.   The element palladium resembles nickel, and the element silver, with one $5s$, resembles copper.   After that we add electrons until we have a complete inert-gas configuration in xenon, with two $5s$'s and six $5p$'s.

Following after xenon, we add a $6s$ electron in cesium, and another in barium, similar to rubidium and strontium.   Then in lanthanum the first $5d$ electron is added.   But at this point, something new happens: the $4f$ level, which previously had been less tightly bound than the others, becomes more tightly bound, and we have a series of elements in which $4f$ electrons are added, one by one, with in each case three other electrons (two $6s$ and one $5d$, or one $6s$ and two $5d$).   These 14 elements are the rare earths.   Their outer electrons, which are mostly responsible for their chemical properties, are the same for each. They differ only in the number of $4f$ electrons, whose orbits are far inside the atom, even though they are not tightly bound.   It is for this reason that the rare earths are so hard to separate chemically.   Also, having partly filled inner shells, they have interesting magnetic and optical properties, like the iron group.   After the rare earths are completed, at lutecium, the $5d$ shell begins to be filled again, and we go through the elements from hafnium to platinum, similar to the group ending with palladium.   Gold, similar to silver and copper, comes next, with one $6s$ electron, and we go through another series of elements ending with the inert gas radon, with two $6s$'s and six $6p$'s.

Finally, we start to build up the $7s$ and $6d$ shells, radium having two $6s$ electrons, and being an alkaline earth.   Actinium has one $6d$ electron; but immediately beyond that point, the $5f$ electrons become more stable, as the $4f$'s did in the rare earths, and we start a new series of rare earths, which include thorium, protactinium, uranium, and the radioactive transuranic elements, neptunium, plutonium, and so on, stretching at the time of writing (1955) up to atomic number 100. This is as far as the periodic table goes; not for lack of electronic orbits, but because the nuclei become so unstable that they do not last long enough to be examined. It is likely that a few additional ones may be found; but there are good reasons for thinking that they will rapidly get more unstable. One feature of this instability is definitely electronic: the K shell has grown so small, by the time we come to these heaviest elements, that the K electron is practically colliding with the nucleus.

Here, then, we have the general outlines of the periodic system of the elements. We can now understand many features which were not clear before. For instance, in discussing X-ray spectra, we noted that each successive shell began to appear at a particular point in the periodic table. We now see that this is to be understood on the basis of the number of electrons present in each element. But we also see that the exact place where a shell appears is not very easy to define, for when electrons of a particular quantum number are first bound to an atom, as when the $3d$'s are first bound in scandium, they are easily removed, and are really optical rather than X-ray electrons. The X-ray spectroscopists are not likely to detect them by their techniques until they have become somewhat more tightly bound, as in somewhat heavier elements. All the available X-ray data, however, are entirely consistent with the structure of the periodic system, as we have described it.

It will make the periodic table somewhat more clear if we give some detailed experimental and theoretical facts about the elements. In Fig. 7-5, we indicate the number of electrons of each type in the ground state of each atom; this merely illustrates the discussion which we have just been giving. In Table 7-1, we give the term values corresponding to the various electrons in the lighter atoms. These term values are the energies required to remove the corresponding electron from the atom; they are the negatives of the energies of the electron in the central-field model which we have been discussing in the present chapter. These values are experimental, taken partly from X-ray data (which represent merely the tabulation of the information plotted graphically in Fig. 6-8), partly from optical data, partly interpolated between these. We see clearly from this table how the electrons of one or another type start, with light atoms, as loosely bound electrons (term values a fraction of a Rydberg unit), and eventually become tightly bound X-ray levels.

TABLE 7-1. IONIZATION POTENTIALS OF THE LIGHTER ELEMENTS (RYDBERGS)

Element	K	L		M			N			O
	1s	2s	2p	3s	3p	3d	4s	4p	4d	5s
H	1.00									
He	1.81									
Li	4.80	0.40								
Be	(9.3)	0.69								
B	(15.2)	1.29	0.61							
C	(22.3)	1.51	0.83							
N	(31.1)	1.91	1.07							
O	(41.5)	2.10	1.00							
F	(53.0)	2.87	1.37							
Ne	(66.1)	3.56	1.59							
Na	(80.9)	(5.10)	2.79	0.38						
Mg	96.0	(0.90)	3.7	0.56						
Al	114.8	(9.05)	5.3	0.78	0.44					
Si	135.4	(11.5)	7.2	1.10	0.60					
P	157.8	(14.2)	9.4	(1.40)	(0.65)					
S	181.9	(17.2)	11.9	1.48	0.76					
Cl	207.9	(20.4)	14.8	1.81	0.96					
A	235.7	(23.9)	(18.2)	2.14	1.15					
K	265.6	(27.8)	21.5	(2.6)	1.2		0.32			
Ca	297.4	(31.9)	25.5	(3.1)	1.9		0.45			
Sc	331.2	(36.2)	30.0	(3.6)	2.7	0.54	0.50			
Ti	365.8	(41.0)	33.6	(4.2)	2.6	0.51	0.50			
V	402.7	(46.0)	37.9	(4.8)	3.0	0.50	0.52			
Cr	441.1	(51.2)	42.3	(5.4)	3.1	0.61	0.50			
Mn	481.9	(56.7)	47.4	(6.7)	3.8	0.68	0.55			
Fe	523.9	62.5	52.2	6.9	4.1	0.60	0.58			
Co	568.1	(68.5)	57.7	7.6	4.7	0.63	0.66			
Ni	614.1	74.8	63.2	8.2	5.4	(0.68)	0.64			
Cu	661.6	81.0	68.9	8.9	5.7	0.77	0.57			
Zn	711.7	88.4	75.4	10.1	6.7	1.26	0.69			
Ga	765.6	(96.0	84.1	12.4	8.8	1.8	0.87	0.44		
Ge	817.6	(104.0)	89.3	13.4	9.5	3.2	1.39	0.60		
As	874.0	112.6	97.4	14.9	10.3	3.0	(1.6)	0.74		
Se	932.0	(121.9)	108.4	16.7	11.6	3.9	(1.7)	0.70		
Br	992.6	(131.5)	117.8	19.1	13.6	5.4	(1.9)	0.87		
Kr	(1055)	(141.6)	(127.2)	(21.4)	(15.4)	(6.8)	(2.1)	1.03		
Rb	1119.4	152.0	137.2	(23.7)	17.4	(8.3)	(2.3)	1.46		0.31
Sr	1186.0	162.9	147.6	26.2	19.6	9.7	2.5	(2.1)		0.42
Y	1256.1	175.8	159.9	30.3	23.3	13.0	4.7	2.9	0.48	0.49
Zr	1325.7	186.6	170.0	31.8	24.4	13.3	3.8	2.1	0.53	0.51
Cb	1398.5	198.9	181.7	34.7	26.9	15.2	4.3	2.5	(0.5)	(0.5)
Mo	1473.4	211.3	193.7	37.5	29.2	17.1	5.1	2.9	(0.5)	0.54

The ionization potentials tabulated represent in each case the least energy, in Rydberg units, required to remove the electron in question from the atom. Data for optical ionization are taken from Bacher and Goudsmit, "Atomic Energy States," McGraw-Hill Book Company, Inc., New York, 1932. Those for X-ray ionization are from Siegbahn, "Spektroskopie der Röntgenstrahlen," Springer-Verlag, Berlin. Intermediate figures are interpolated. Interpolated or estimated values are given in parentheses.

TABLE 7-2. RADII OF ELECTRONIC ORBITS IN THE LIGHTER ELEMENTS (ANGSTROMS)

Ele-ment	K	L		M			N	
	$1s$	$2s$	$2p$	$3s$	$3p$	$3d$	$4s$	$4p$
H	0.53							
He	0.30							
Li	0.20	1.50						
Be	0.143	1.19						
B	0.112	0.88	0.85					
C	0.090	0.67	0.66					
N	0.080	0.56	0.53					
O	0.069	0.48	0.45					
F	0.061	0.41	0.38					
Ne	0.055	0.37	0.32					
Na	0.050	0.32	0.28	1.55				
Mg	0.046	0.30	0.25	1.32				
Al	0.042	0.27	0.23	1.16	1.21			
Si	0.040	0.24	0.21	0.98	1.06			
P	0.037	0.23	0.19	0.88	0.92			
S	0.035	0.21	0.18	0.78	0.82			
Cl	0.032	0.20	0.16	0.72	0.75			
A	0.031	0.19	0.155	0.66	0.67			
K	0.029	0.18	0.145	0.60	0.63		2.20	
Ca	0.028	0.16	0.133	0.55	0.58		2.03	
Sc	0.026	0.16	0.127	0.52	0.54	0.61	1.80	
Ti	0.025	0.150	0.122	0.48	0.50	0.55	1.66	
V	0.024	0.143	0.117	0.46	0.47	0.49	1.52	
Cr	0.023	0.138	0.112	0.43	0.44	0.45	1.41	
Mn	0.022	0.133	0.106	0.40	0.41	0.42	1.31	
Fe	0.021	0.127	0.101	0.39	0.39	0.39	1.22	
Co	0.020	0.122	0.096	0.37	0.37	0.36	1.14	
Ni	0.019	0.117	0.090	0.35	0.36	0.34	1.07	
Cu	0.019	0.112	0.085	0.34	0.34	0.32	1.03	
Zn	0.018	0.106	0.081	0.32	0.32	0.30	0.97	
Ga	0.017	0.103	0.078	0.31	0.31	0.28	0.92	1.13
Ge	0.017	0.100	0.076	0.30	0.30	0.27	0.88	1.06
As	0.016	0.097	0.073	0.29	0.29	0.25	0.84	1.01
Se	0.016	0.095	0.071	0.28	0.28	0.24	0.81	0.95
Br	0.015	0.092	0.069	0.27	0.27	0.23	0.76	0.90
Kr	0.015	0.090	0.067	0.25	0.25	0.22	0.74	0.86

The radii tabulated represent the distance from the nucleus at which the radial charge density is a maximum, and are computed from calculations of Hartree and coworkers, in the *Proceedings of the Royal Society*, and elsewhere. Since only a few atoms have been computed, most of the values tabulated are interpolated. The interpolation should be fairly accurate for the inner electrons of an atom, but unfortunately it is quite inaccurate for the outer electrons, so that these values should not be taken as exact.

Finally in Table 7-2, we give numbers representing the sizes of the various orbits. These numbers, as a matter of fact, are derived from wave mechanics, and we look ahead to a later chapter in giving them. They are numbers which, for a Bohr circular orbit, would be the radius of the orbit; for elliptical orbits, they represent a sort of weighted average over the orbit. These numbers will become plainer after studying the chapters on wave mechanics. But it helps us in understanding the structure of the atoms to see the numbers at the present time. The striking feature is the way in which the size of each orbit gets smaller, as we go to heavier and heavier atoms. A result of this is that the very heavy atoms are not very much bigger than the lightest ones. They have many more electrons in them, but the electronic orbits are squeezed in so tightly that they do not extend out much further than with the light atoms. It is partly for this reason that successive elements of similar structure (such as the alkalies) can show such similar chemical properties. The outer electrons of these elements have orbits which have very nearly the same dimensions, and very nearly the same ionization potentials.

We have now sketched the sort of discussion which Bohr gave of the periodic system of the elements, and we see the clarification which this brings into the whole problem of atomic structure. We have used only some very simple principles of spectroscopy in carrying out this discussion; but atomic spectra really are very much more complicated than we have hinted at so far. In the next chapter we shall give some idea of this complication and of the conclusions to which its study led. It was through this study that physicists were led, in the years 1925 and 1926, to the discovery of the electron spin, the exclusion principle, and the wave mechanics—discoveries even more important, in their generality, than any of those which had come earlier in the century.

PROBLEMS

7-1. The observed energy levels of the states of the sodium atom in which the outer electron is in the 3s, 4s, 5s, . . . , states, respectively, are found to be 0; 25,740; 33,201; 36,373; 38,012; 38,968; 39,575; 39,983; 40,274; 40,483; etc., in units of reciprocal centimeters (cm^{-1}), such that the reciprocals of these numbers give the wavelengths in centimeters. These are referred to the ground state as a zero, as is customary in spectroscopic work. The series limit comes at 41,450 cm^{-1}. Try to fit these values with a Rydberg formula, finding how closely this formula fits the data.

7-2. Find the ionization potential of sodium, from the figures given in Prob. 7-2.

7-3. The well-known D line in the spectrum of sodium comes when a 3p electron has a transition to the 3s ground state. The wavelength is found to be about 5,890 A. Compute the term value associated with the 3p state. Assuming that a Rydberg formula holds for the p states, find the term value for the $4p$ state, and find the wavelength to be expected when a $4p$ electron falls into the $3s$ state. Compare with the observed value of about 3,300 A.

7-4. The energy levels in the Ca spectrum arising from configurations in which one valence electron is in the $4s$ state, and the second in the $4s$, $5s$, $6s$, $7s$ states, respectively, are 0; 33,317; 41,786; 44,276 cm^{-1}. Find the ionization potential, and compare with the observed value of 6.111 ev.

7-5. The atoms and ions, Na, Mg$^+$, Al^{++}, form what is called an isoelectronic sequence, each having the same number (11) of electrons. The term values for a singly ionized atom like Mg$^+$ are given by a Rydberg formula of the form $4R/(n - d)^2$, and for a doubly ionized atom like Al^{++} by a formula like $9R/(n - d)^2$. Explain why this should be the case.

7-6. The observed term values of the Mg$^+$ ion, for the cases where the outer electron is in the $3s$, $4s$, . . . , state, are 0; 69,805; 92,786; 103,198 cm^{-1}, respectively, and for Al^{++} the corresponding values are 0; 126,163; 170,636; 191,479 cm^{-1}, respectively. Check the Rydberg formula, as given in Prob. 7-5, for these two cases. Find the ionization potentials of Mg$^+$ and Al^{++}. Compare the quantum defects d found in these two cases with the value for Na found in Prob. 7-1.

7-7. Assuming a simple ionic structure, as is assumed in chemistry, what electrons will the K$^+$ and Cl$^-$ ions contain in KCl? The Cu$^+$ ion in CuCl? The Cu^{++} ion in CuCl$_2$?

7-8. Assuming a simple ionic structure, what electrons will the Ba^{++}, Ti^{++++}, O$^-$ ions contain in BaTiO$_4$?

7-9. What electrons will the ferrous and ferric ions contain? The Mn^{+7} ion, as in KMnO$_4$?

7-10. What electrons will the copper atom contain in the initial and final states leading to the X-ray transition Cu $K\alpha$?

CHAPTER 8

COMPLEX SPECTRA AND MOLECULAR SPECTRA

8-1. Introduction. By considering only hydrogen and the alkalies, we have tried to make atomic spectra look simple. Really, almost all of them are extremely complicated, and nothing resembling the regularities of the Rydberg series can be found in them. Instead, regularities of quite a different sort are conspicuous: the levels fall into rather closely spaced groups called multiplets, with spacings between the levels of a multiplet which follow simple laws to a rather good approximation. In a magnetic field, the various levels of a multiplet split in quite different ways, showing various types of Zeeman effects. In the study of these phenomena, the spectroscopists found a fascinating field for puzzling out regularities which at first were only empirical, gradually began to take on a theoretical aspect, and finally led to the understanding of some of the most complex but important problems of quantum theory. The German experimentalists Landé, Paschen, Back, and a number of others were the leaders in this study, which was carried on through the earlier 1920's.

The further these theories went, however, the more confusing the situation appeared. The general idea behind the explanation of multiplets was elucidated by Landé and the others. One had to assume that there were several different angular momentum vectors in an atom—perhaps the angular momenta of several electrons—which somehow were coupled together to form a resultant. Each of these angular momenta was assumed to have a quantized value, as in the simple theory of hydrogen; but it was assumed also that the resultant was quantized. This implied, then, that in a case where there were two such vectors, there were only specific relative orientations of the two vectors: they could be parallel, antiparallel, and at such other angles that the quantized resultant took on all integral multiples of $h/2\pi$ between these extreme values.

Somehow, the various levels of a multiplet were assumed to come from various relative orientations of these vectors with respect to each other. It was assumed that a torque acted between the vectors; it might well be, for instance, that each one acted like a little magnet, as in the elementary theory of the Zeeman effect, and that these magnets exerted torques on each other. The energy, then, would depend on the angle between the vectors; this would explain the energy separation between the various terms of a multiplet. If one made the simple assumption that the energy was proportional to the cosine of the angle between, as it would be for the interaction of two magnets, a simple law resulted for the spacing of the levels of the multiplet. The law, derived by Landé, was called the Landé interval rule, and proved to be satisfied with surprising accuracy by the experimental values.

The theory could go much further than this, by studying the Zeeman effect. The quantum number representing the vector sum which we have mentioned was called the inner quantum number, and this could be determined in a unique way from the Zeeman effect. Let the inner quantum number be called J, so that the total angular momentum of the atom was $Jh/2\pi$. Then in a magnetic field, this vector would be space-quantized, and would have components along the axis of the magnetic field equal to $Jh/2\pi$, $(J-1)h/2\pi$, . . . , $-Jh/2\pi$, or $2J+1$ orientations in all. These would have different energies in the magnetic field, and if the levels were observed, one could find the inner quantum number merely by counting them. In this way, the J's of the components of many multiplets were found, and working back from these, the magnitudes of the two vectors whose vector sum formed J could be found.

But this raised an obvious question: what did these vectors represent? The natural first assumption was that they were the angular momenta of different electrons. But this did not work. It would lead us to think, for instance, that an alkali, in which there was only one outer electron, would not have this type of multiplet structure, and yet it did: experimentally the levels of the alkalies were double. Other queer things came in, too. For one thing, these quantum numbers often turned out not to be integers, but to be half integers. In an alkali spectrum, which we should think would be the simplest possible sort, a p state proved to be double, with values of J equal to $\frac{1}{2}$ and $\frac{3}{2}$ for the two states; a d state was double, with J of $\frac{3}{2}$ and $\frac{5}{2}$; and so on. The s states were single, with J equal to $\frac{1}{2}$. For years the spectroscopists puzzled about such things, and about the much more complicated results of a similar nature coming from more complex spectra.

Other puzzles came from the Zeeman effect. In Sec. 5-5, where we discussed the theory of hydrogen, we found that the magnetic moment arising from the orbital motion of an electron in an atom was $e/2m$ times its angular momentum, and that this led to a Zeeman splitting of each level which gave a Zeeman effect agreeing with the classical theory, though we stated that this did not agree with experiment for hydrogen. In fact, when the Zeeman effects of actual spectra were measured, there were very few cases in which this simple theory worked. Each separate level seemed to have a different splitting, resulting from a different ratio of magnetic moment to angular momentum. It appeared that one would have to assume that the magnetic moment

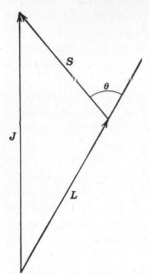

Fig. 8-1. Law of cosines for vector sum of L and S.

was actually $g(e/2m)$ times the angular momentum, where g, a numerical factor, was called the Landé g factor, from its discoverer. This g factor proved always to be a rather simple rational fraction; and gradually a theory was worked out which could predict it. One had to assume that, of the two vectors which combined to give the resultant J, one had the normal ratio $e/2m$ of magnetic moment to angular momentum, but the other had a ratio twice as great. One then took the components of both magnetic moments along the direction of the resultant, worked out the average ratio of magnetic moment to angular momentum, and the result proved to give the observed g value.

We have just said that one got the observed value in this way; but this is an exaggeration. There still was one change that had to be made. This change can be illustrated in the formula giving the Landé interval rule. If the two vectors whose vector sum gives J are called L and S, then in Fig. 8-1 we can see that we can get relations between J, L, and S by the law of cosines. In fact, we have $J^2 = L^2 + S^2 + 2LS \cos \theta$, where θ is the angle between L and S. Now the hypothesis on which the Landé interval rule is based is that the energy of interaction between the vectors L and S is proportional to the cosine of the angle between. In other words, the energy determining the separations of the multiplet levels should be proportional to

$$\cos \theta = \frac{J^2 - L^2 - S^2}{2LS} \tag{8-1}$$

But the formula which proved to agree with experiment gave the energy proportional to the quantity

$$\frac{J(J+1) - L(L+1) - S(S+1)}{2LS} \qquad (8\text{-}2)$$

The reason for this difference remained a puzzle until the wave mechanics was invented. One notes that $J(J+1) = [J + (\frac{1}{2})]^2 - (\frac{1}{4})$, and it was supposed that perhaps Eq. (8-2) pointed, as many other pieces of evidence did, toward half-integral rather than integral quantum numbers. But no real explanation of this formula could be suggested; and the formula for the Landé g factor proved to show an exactly similar discrepancy between the experimental formula and that suggested by theory.

All these puzzles led to a very confusing situation, for several years. Successive editions of Sommerfeld's book become more and more detailed, but more and more unsatisfactory. If one focused attention on the alkali spectra, it was supposed that one of the two vectors which coupled together to give J was the angular momentum of the valence electron, and perhaps the other was the angular momentum of the remaining core of the atom. Even this hypothesis was unsatisfactory, however. We have seen that, for an s state of an alkali, J was found to be $\frac{1}{2}$; for a p state, $\frac{1}{2}$ and $\frac{3}{2}$; for a d state, $\frac{3}{2}$ and $\frac{5}{2}$; and so on. These results came unambiguously from counting the number of Zeeman components in each level. These values clearly come by combining one vector whose magnitude is zero for an s state, 1 for a p state, 2 for a d state, and so on, with another vector whose magnitude is $\frac{1}{2}$. It was supposed for a short time that the vector $\frac{1}{2}$ came from the inner core of the atom, but this still left the puzzle as to why the vector representing the angular momentum of the valence electron had the value zero for an s state, 1 for a p state, and so on, just one unit less than k, which was 1 for an s state, 2 for a p state, and so on. This new vector, equal to $k - 1$, was given a symbol, called l; but no one had an idea as to what it meant.

This very confusing situation was resolved, in 1925, by a brilliant suggestion made by the two young Dutch physicists, Goudsmit and Uhlenbeck (later to settle in America). They suggested that the vector of magnitude $\frac{1}{2}$, concerned in the alkali spectra, had nothing to do with the atomic core, but that rather it represented something intrinsic in the valence electron. They suggested, in fact, that the electron had an intrinsic angular momentum of amount $(\frac{1}{2})(h/2\pi)$, just as if it were spinning around its axis like a top. In the alkali spectra, the vector J would represent the vector sum of this intrinsic angular momentum of the electron spin, and the angular momentum of the orbital motion; they still had no suggestion as to why the latter seemed to be $lh/2\pi$ rather than $kh/2\pi$, but had to postulate it. They further suggested that the ratio of magnetic moment to angular momentum was twice as great for the electron's intrinsic magnetic moment as for the orbital magnetic moment, and in this way they explained the peculiar g values which had been observed in the Zeeman effect. With a single hypothesis, they explained many, though not all, of the puzzling features which had confused the spectroscopists for a number of years.

Another related and complementary suggestion was made by Pauli at the same time, the so-called exclusion principle. Pauli did not actually state his principle in terms of the electron spin, for his paper was published before that of Goudsmit and Uhlenbeck; but his suggestion becomes so much more simple and comprehensible in terms of the spinning electron that we shall state it in that language.

Let us consider an s electron. According to the modification of the vector model which had been made, its orbital angular momentum seemed to be $lh/2\pi$, where $l = 0$. Thus, there was only one possible orientation of this orbit, in an external field: the component of angular momentum along the axis, $mh/2\pi$, could only be zero. The spin angular momentum, however, having a magnitude $(\tfrac{1}{2})(h/2\pi)$, could be oriented in two ways in a field with component $\pm(\tfrac{1}{2})(h/2\pi)$ along the axis. Thus we have two possible states for the s electron, under space quantization. For a p electron, with $l = 1$, there can be three orientations of the orbit, with $m = 1, 0, -1$, and each of these can be combined with each of the orientations of the spin, giving six arrangements in all. For a d electron, similarly, with $l = 2$, there can be ten arrangements of orbital and spin angular momentum, and for an f electron, with $l = 3$, there can be fourteen.

But these numbers are precisely those which we saw, in the last chapter, represented the maximum number of electrons which each of these shells can hold, in the periodic system of the elements. Pauli then postulated that the reason for this was that there was a principle in nature, which has come to be called the exclusion principle, which made it impossible for any two electrons to have the same set of quantum numbers. That is, if they have the same principal and azimuthal quantum numbers, they cannot simultaneously have the same component of azimuthal angular momentum along the axis (same m), and have the same component of spin angular momentum along the axis.

The combination of the suggestion of the electron spin, and of the exclusion principle, revolutionized spectroscopy. Hund, the German theoretical spectroscopist, started to apply these two ideas in new, detailed ways to a study of the effect of the exclusion principle on multiplet formation.   He found in particular that, as more and more equivalent electrons are added to a shell (by equivalent we mean having the same azimuthal and principal quantum numbers), the number of possible multiplets first rises, the maximum complexity coming when the shell is half full, then falls again, until when the shell is entirely filled, there is no remaining angular momentum, and we have a single state which does not take part in magnetic or other interactions with other electrons.   It is for this reason that in the alkali metals the inner shells of electrons are without effect on the vector model.

These ideas were carried further by the experimental spectroscopists. The American spectroscopists Russell, Saunders, and Meggers applied the principles to the analysis of several of the complex spectra in the iron group, found them entirely verified, and were able to show that the principles of the quantum theory, as then understood, were enough to analyze even these most complex spectra.   There was no doubt but that the essential features of atomic spectra were understood.   There were still a few puzzles left, however: why did we have to use a formula like Eq. (8-2) instead of Eq. (8-1); why did the angular momentum of orbital motion turn out to be $lh/2\pi$ instead of $kh/2\pi$, as Bohr's theory suggested?   And there were a number of other rather more serious puzzles, which we shall point out later.   These were seemingly small discrepancies; but to remove them, it was necessary to make the most striking theoretical advance since the discovery of the quantum theory, namely, the wave mechanics.   Fortunately this came almost immediately after the advances we have been describing, in 1926.   But it was such a profound step that we postpone it until the next chapter, devoting the rest of the present chapter to a description of the picture of atomic structure and complex spectra which was provided by the vector model, the idea of the electron spin, and the exclusion principle.

8-2. Russell-Saunders Coupling and Complex Spectra.   The spectrum of calcium was the first one in which the general ideas of complex spectra were tested out; its analysis by Russell and Saunders stands as a landmark in the understanding of atomic structure, and we can use it to illustrate the principles as well as any other.   This atom has two electrons outside the closed shells composed of the $1s$, $2s$, $2p$, $3s$, and $3p$ electrons.   From the principles which we have already mentioned, and which we shall discuss more in detail later, these inner electrons do not contribute anything to the problem of the vectors interacting in the atom.   We have, then, just two electrons, each with an orbital and a spin angular momentum.   Let us consider the problem of the coupling of the angular momentum vectors in such a two-electron atom.

The coupling of four vectors is obviously much more complicated than that of two vectors. But Russell and Saunders suggested that the coupling could be carried out in steps. First, we treat the orbital angular momentum vectors of the two electrons, which we may call l_1 and l_2, and assume that they are coupled to form a vector sum L. Similarly, we take the two spins, and assume that they are coupled to form a resultant S. Finally, L and S are coupled to give the inner quantum number J. The reason why this scheme seems reasonable is that, when the spectra are analyzed, using this description, we find that the energy separations of states with different L values, or different S values, are large, indicating that large torques act between two l vectors, or two spins; whereas the energy separations of different terms with the same L and S values, but different J's (that is, the different levels of a single multiplet), are much smaller. Hence it seemed reasonable to disregard entirely the coupling between the l's on the one hand, the spins on the other, as a first approximation, considering only the coupling between the two l's, and that between the two spins; and later to introduce the coupling between L and S as sort of a perturbation.

A certain amount of notation, which was introduced into spectral theory at the time these complex spectra were analyzed, helps in describing things. The vector L can take on orientations in an external field very similar to the l of a single electron. Therefore it proved convenient to use the same letters s, p, d, f, to describe $L = 0, 1, 2, 3$ which were used for a single electron; but to distinguish the many-electron case from the single electron, large letters were used, the states being denoted as S, P, D, F. We can easily find the L values arising from different simple combinations of l's. Thus, for instance, two s electrons will combine only to give an S term; for each has $l = 0$, and the vector sum must be $L = 0$ as well. An s and a p electron, having $l = 0$ and 1, respectively, will give only a P term, and so on. Two p electrons will give $L = 2, 1$, and 0, or a D, P, and S term. A p and a d electron, with $l = 1$ and 2, will give $L = 3, 2$, and 1, or an F, D, and P term. Clearly we run out of the letters S, P, D, F pretty soon; at that point the alphabet is continued, so that for $L = 4, 5, \ldots$, we have $G, H, \ldots$, terms.

With a single electron, the spin angular momentum is $\frac{1}{2}$ unit. If we used the symbol S for even the one-electron atom, we should have $S = \frac{1}{2}$. We have already seen that this means that J, for a one-electron atom, is equal to $L \pm \frac{1}{2}$, giving two levels. Such a spectrum is called a doublet spectrum. With two electrons, the two spins can be added to give $S = 1$, or subtracted to give $S = 0$. If $S = 1$, we have J equal to $L + 1, L, L - 1$; that is, we have three terms in each multiplet, and we say that we have a triplet. If $S = 0$, we have $J = L$, a single term, and we say that we have a singlet. We indicate the value of S by giving the multiplicity, expressing it as a superscript before the symbol indicating L. Thus a doublet P term would be indicated as ^2P; a triplet D, as ^3D. The symbol of a triplet to indicate $S = 1$ is used even for an S term, ^3S, though in this case there is but one term, since we are combining $L = 0$ and $S = 1$ vectorially (the confusion between S as representing the resultant of the spins, and S as representing a state of $L = 0$, is regrettable, but it is standard practice). It is customary to indicate the individual terms of a multiplet by using the value of J as a subscript following the symbol. Thus the two levels of a doublet P are written $^2P_{3/2}$, $^2P_{1/2}$ (read doublet P three-halves and doublet P one-half).

Let us recall how the terms are identified in a previously unanalyzed spectrum. First the terms themselves must be found, from the observed lines. Sometimes this can be done by inspection: by testing out sums and differences of observed frequencies, one can find a set of numbers, the terms, whose differences give the observed frequencies. In addition, however, the selection principles, which we have already mentioned in Chap. 5, can be of great use. For each term must be given its quantum numbers, L, S, and J, and there are certain selection principles associated with transitions of each of these quantum numbers, principles which were found to be verified experimentally, and at the same time which could be derived from the correspondence principle. These principles prove to be as follows:

1. In simple cases, L changes by ± 1 unit in a transition. (This is a special case of a more general rule, which we shall not go into, stating that the so-called parity of the term must change from even to odd in a transition, or vice versa.)

2. Transitions in which S changes are almost, but not quite, forbidden.

3. The quantum number J changes by ± 1 or 0 units; but the transition $0 \rightarrow 0$ is forbidden.

If the spectrum is not too complicated, it will be found by application of these principles that the levels are grouped into multiplets, the separations being given approximately by the Landé interval rule. Once we understand the principles underlying the theory of spectra, we know what sort of multiplets to expect; thus, in calcium, we expect to find singlets and triplets. In a magnetic field, each level will be split into a number of components, and this number equals $2J + 1$. By observing this number, we can find the J of each term. By seeing the J's grouped into a multiplet, we can at once deduce the L value of

the multiplet.   For instance, if we find a triplet consisting of three
levels, with $J = 0, 1$, and 2, we conclude at once that these must be
$^3P_{2,1,0}$, while if we find one with levels with $J = 1, 2$, and 3, we conclude
that it is $^3D_{3,2,1}$.   We can illustrate the operation of the selection principles by showing Fig. 8-2, giving the levels in these two multiplets, in a
schematic way, and showing the allowed transitions.   With practice,
the multiplet lines, as observed in the spectrum, become so familiar

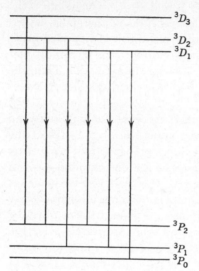

that in a simple spectrum a trained
spectroscopist can recognize the
multiplet he is dealing with almost
immediately.

We have illustrated the theory of
complex spectra by considering a
two-electron atom.   The same methods, however, hold for more complicated cases.   Again, the same
principle seems to hold: that the
various l vectors couple to give a resultant L, the various spins couple
to give a resultant S, and finally L
and S couple to give J.   We can
build up each atom from the case
of the atom with one less electron.
For instance, in a three-electron

FIG. 8-2. Allowed transitions between the levels of ^3D and ^3P
multiplets.

atom, like aluminum, we can first
find the resultant L and S of two
electrons, then add the third.   Con-
sidering S, for instance, we note that two electrons give $S = 0, 1$.   A
third electron, adding to $S = 0$, will give $S = \frac{1}{2}$; adding to $S = 1$, it
will give $S = \frac{1}{2}, \frac{3}{2}$.   We conclude, then, that a three-electron spectrum will have doublets and quartets.   Similar principles hold for
more and more complicated spectra.

In some spectra, particularly of the very heavy elements, the type of
coupling which we have described, which is called the Russell-Saunders
or L-S coupling, does not hold, and one has instead a type of coupling
called j-j coupling.   These are cases in which the energies of interaction
between the l and spin vectors of a single electron are large compared
with the coupling between different l's, or different spins.   In such a
case, the situation is described better if we assume first that each l and
its corresponding spin are coupled together to give a vector j; finally,
these j's are coupled together to give the resultant J.   In practice, one
seldom has pure j-j coupling, but there are many spectra in which one

has an intermediate situation between L-S and j-j coupling, with a resulting great complication of the spectrum. One can say, in general, that one has approximately pure L-S coupling if the separations between the levels of different J values in a multiplet are small compared with the distance between multiplets; but that, when the multiplet levels of different J values are spread almost as widely apart as the separation between multiplets, one has the complicated case of intermediate coupling.

We have now described the vector model of the atom and its complex spectrum. There is, however, a feature which comes in in these cases, which profoundly modifies the results, and this is the action of the exclusion principle. This has the effect of forbidding certain multiplets, in case we are combining two or more equivalent electrons; that is, electrons with the same principal quantum number and the same azimuthal quantum number. In the next section, we shall examine the analysis which Hund gave of the effect of the exclusion principle in forbidding certain multiplets.

8-3. The Effect of the Exclusion Principle on Multiplet Structure. When we consider the electron spin, a single electron can be represented by four quantum numbers: the principal quantum number n; the quantum number l, one unit less than Bohr's azimuthal quantum number k, but which we see from the vector model represents in some way the angular momentum of the electronic motion in the orbit; the quantum number representing the component of l along the axis of a magnetic field, which we can call m_l, and which can take on all integral values between l and $-l$; and a quantum number which represents the component of spin angular momentum along the axis of the field, which we can call m_s, and which can take on only the values $\frac{1}{2}$ and $-\frac{1}{2}$. If the electron is in a strong magnetic field, and if we disregard the torques coupling its orbital and spin angular momenta, each of the two angular momentum vectors, the orbital and spin, will be separately space quantized, and our quantum numbers m_l and m_s will be appropriate ones to use. Since m_l can take on $2l + 1$ values, and m_s can take on two values, there will be $2(2l + 1)$ combinations, representing the various stationary states possible for an electron of given n and l values. It is this number which gives us two states for an s electron, six for a p, ten for a d, and so on, and which, according to the Pauli principle, determines the number of electrons allowed in a given shell, in the periodic system of the elements.

Quite a different situation will arise if the external field is negligibly small, but if there is a large torque operating between the orbital and spin angular momenta. In that case, the orbital and spin angular momenta will be coupled to form the resultant angular momentum, whose magnitude equals the inner quantum number J times $h/2\pi$; this vector in turn will be space quantized. The first step in Hund's treatment was to show the relations between these two ways of describing the multiplet. This relation can be indicated by a simple table. In Table 8-1, we show the possible values of m_l and m_s for a p electron

TABLE 8-1. POSSIBLE VALUES OF m_l AND m_s FOR A p ELECTRON

m_l	m_s	M
1	$\frac{1}{2}$	$\frac{3}{2}$
1	$-\frac{1}{2}$	$\frac{1}{2}$
0	$\frac{1}{2}$	$\frac{1}{2}$
0	$-\frac{1}{2}$	$-\frac{1}{2}$
-1	$\frac{1}{2}$	$-\frac{1}{2}$
-1	$-\frac{1}{2}$	$-\frac{3}{2}$

We also show M, the sum of m_l and m_s. Since the resultant of L and S gives the angular momentum whose magnitude is given by J, we see that M represents the component of J along the axis: that is, the component of J must equal the sum of the components of L and of S, by simple vector rules. We note, then, that we have one level with $M = \frac{3}{2}$, two each with $M = \frac{1}{2}$ and $-\frac{1}{2}$, and one with $M = -\frac{3}{2}$. But this is just what we should expect, from the $^2P_{3/2}$ and $^2P_{1/2}$ states which we have in this case: $^2P_{3/2}$ will have states with M equal to $\frac{3}{2}$, $\frac{1}{2}$, $-\frac{1}{2}$, and $-\frac{3}{2}$; $^2P_{1/2}$ will have states with M equal to $\frac{1}{2}$, $-\frac{1}{2}$.

Hund showed that this parallelism existed in every case. He then proceeded to carry it further, for instance to a case of two electrons. In this case we start with the m_l's of the two electrons and combine them into M_L, the quantum number giving the component of L along the axis. Similarly we combine the m_s's to give M_S. Finally we combine these to give M. We can illustrate the simplest case by considering the problem of two s electrons, in which we have only the m_s's to combine (since m_l must have only the value zero). In Table 8-2, we

TABLE 8-2. POSSIBLE VALUES OF m_s FOR TWO s ELECTRONS

m_{s1}	m_{s2}	M_S
$\frac{1}{2}$	$\frac{1}{2}$	1
$\frac{1}{2}$	$-\frac{1}{2}$	0
$-\frac{1}{2}$	$\frac{1}{2}$	0
$-\frac{1}{2}$	$-\frac{1}{2}$	-1

give the four possible combinations. We see that we have three states, with $M_S = 1, 0, -1$, required for the $^3S_1$ state which should arise, and one, with $M_S = 0$, for the $^1S_0$. A similar comparison can be made in every case. There is one feature to be noted in making this comparison: there is no way in which we can identify one of the entries in the table, with one of the particular levels, in case we have more than one level with the same M_L and M_S. Thus, in Table 8-2, we cannot say that one of the states of $M_S = 0$ goes with the triplet, the other with the singlet. The only thing which has significance is to count the total number of levels with a given M_L and M_S. The reason for this only became evident several years after Hund's work, when these same problems could be treated by wave mechanics.

We are now ready to consider the case of equivalent electrons, for which this scheme gives new results; obviously in the cases we have considered so far, it does not tell us anything we did not know before. If the n's and l's for the two electrons are the same, then it is clear that we cannot simultaneously have the m_l's and the m_s's of both electrons the same. Hence, if our two s electrons are equivalent, we shall omit in Table 8-2 the states in which both m_s's are $\frac{1}{2}$, or both $-\frac{1}{2}$, or in other words the first and last entries in the table. Furthermore, if the electrons are equivalent, there is no difference between the electrons with subscripts 1 and 2. Thus, the second and third entries in Table 8-2, which differ only by interchanging the names of the electrons, are not really different, and only one should appear in the table. When we take account of these situations, we see that only one entry remains in Table 8-2, which describes the $^1S_0$ level. In other words, the remaining multiplet, the $^3S_1$, has disappeared on account of the exclusion principle.

This is the simplest example of the way in which the exclusion principle forbids certain multiplets in the case of equivalent electrons. We can carry out exactly analogous, though more complicated, calculations for further cases, finding in each case what multiplets remain after application of the exclusion principle.

In Table 8-3 we show the existing multiplets in the case of a shell of

TABLE 8-3. MULTIPLETS IN A SHELL OF EQUIVALENT p ELECTRONS

$$p: \ ^2P$$
$$p^2: \ ^3P, \ ^1S, \ ^1D$$
$$p^3: \ ^4S, \ ^2P, \ ^2D$$
$$p^4: \ ^3P, \ ^1S, \ ^1D$$
$$p^5: \ ^2P$$
$$p^6: \ ^1S$$

equivalent p electrons. First the number of p electrons is shown (the notation p^2 for two equivalent p's, p^3 for three, and so on, is widely used). Then we give the resulting multiplets. We observe a number of results from this table, which prove to be general, holding for other l values as well. First there is a sort of symmetry in the table. We have just the same set of multiplets for a given number of electrons in the shell, and a given number of vacancies or holes in the shell. Thus, a complete p shell holds six electrons. We then find the same set of multiplets for one and five p electrons, for two and four. The case of three p electrons, then, in which the shell is half filled, stands in the center. We notice furthermore that the highest multiplicity present rises as we add electrons, until the shell is half filled, being two for one p electron, three for two p's, and four for three p's; then, of course, the symmetry requires that the number fall again. Another general result is that with the shell half filled the state of highest multiplicity is always an S state (as in the case of the ^4S for p^3). Finally, the filled shell, in this case p^6, always has a ^1S state. That is, it contributes nothing either to the orbital or the spin angular momentum. This is the justification of the statement that we have made before, that a filled shell need not be considered in connection with the vector model of multiplets.

The way in which the number of allowed multiplets is decreased by the exclusion principle simplifies greatly the system of terms in many complex spectra. Thus, for instance, in the iron group, we have in each case a shell of several equivalent d electrons, and usually not more than one or two electrons outside the shell. To find the possible types of terms, we first use the table (similar to Table 8-2) for the allowed multiplets in a shell of equivalent d electrons. Then, starting with each of these multiplets, we add the orbital and spin angular-momentum vectors of the remaining electrons, according to the vector model, and find the resulting multiplets. It is in this way that the multiplets were predicted in such spectra as that of iron, whose analysis really verified in great detail the type of theory of complex spectra which we have been discussing in this chapter.

One application of the effect of the exclusion principle on the spectra of shells of equivalent electrons is found in the X-ray spectra. We have mentioned in Chap. 6 that in the L shell there are really three levels rather than the two which we should expect, in the M shell five rather than three, and so on. We can now understand these facts. An X-ray term arises when an electron is removed from an inner shell of an atom. In every case, a single electron is removed from an otherwise complete shell. From the principles which we have just been discussing, we see that the resulting shell, with one missing electron, has just the same type of multiplet that a single electron of the same sort would have. That is, with a missing s electron we have a ^2S state, with a missing p electron a ^2P, with a missing d electron a ^2D, and so on. The ^2S state really has only one level, but each of the others has two levels. We then see that with a K electron removed, we have but one level. With an L electron removed, it can be removed from the $2s$ shell, in which case we have a single level, but also from the $2p$, leading to a double level, or to three L levels in all. With an M electron removed, it can be removed from the $3s$ shell, leading to a single level, or from the $3p$ or $3d$, leading to two double levels, or five in all, and so on, in agreement with the observed facts from the X-ray spectra.

8-4. The Shortcomings of the Vector Model of Atomic Spectra. The vector model of atomic spectra, which we have been describing, had remarkable success in permitting the analysis of complex spectra, starting in 1925 when the essential ingredients of the theory were available. Nevertheless, there were serious shortcomings, which were not removed until the development of wave mechanics in 1926, and its extension to the theory of complex spectra in 1929. Some of these shortcomings are relatively minor, and we have already mentioned them. Why does the angular momentum seem to be given by $lh/2\pi$, one unit less than the Bohr value $kh/2\pi$? There really is a puzzle connected with this, for if l represents the real angular momentum of a Bohr orbit, then an s state, with $l = 0$, would have to represent an orbit passing through the nucleus. Why, again, do we have expressions like $J(J + 1)$ appearing in the Landé formula, instead of J^2? These relatively minor problems were removed in a very simple way by the wave mechanics when it appeared.

There were more fundamental puzzles, however. One of these came from the energy separation between different multiplets. The coupling energy between the L and S vectors seemed clearly to be magnetic. It is obvious that these vectors will be associated with magnetic moments, and ordinary magnetic theory gives interaction energies between different magnetic moments, proportional to the cosine of the angle between, as the energy of interaction of L and S was shown to be by the validity of the Landé interval rule. Moreover, approximate calculations of the expected magnitude of the magnetic coupling energy agreed in order of magnitude with the observed energies. However, the energies of interaction of the various l vectors to form L, and of the various spins to form S, proved to be of a much greater order of magnitude, much too large to explain by magnetic energies.

In the case of the l vectors, it was possible to get a hint as to why this should have been, though the hint was not exploited at the time.

Surely two planar orbits, in planes making an angle with each other, will have an energy which depends on the angle between the planes, for electrostatic reasons.   The central-field model of the atom assumes that the electrons act on each other only in a spherically averaged way, whereas actually an orbit in a plane will exert torques on other orbits in other planes.   Such an explanation could lead to large coupling energies between the l vectors, and to multiplets of different L values with widely differing energy, as was found.   But what about the spins?   There was no possible way, on the basis of such theories, to explain the large energy of interaction between spins on an electrostatic picture.   Yet these energies were there.   Two nonequivalent s electrons, for instance, led to multiplets ^1S and ^3S, the distinction depending only on the relative orientation of the spins; and these separations were very large, of the same order of magnitude as the energies depending on orientation of the orbital angular momenta.

More fundamental even than these questions was the foundation of the central-field approximation itself.   What possible justification could there be for treating the electrons in an atom as if they moved in a spherically symmetrical field, when actually we had a many-body problem to deal with?   The quantum theory was only adapted to dealing with multiply periodic motions—motions of a very special sort, of which the central-field motion was one, in which one could separate out the motions of the three coordinates and introduce quantum conditions.   Everything which one knew about classical mechanics indicated that the many-body problem did not have solutions of this sort.   We know that the three-body problem in astronomy is so difficult that it can hardly be solved except by very elaborate approximations.   The many-body problem must be very much worse, and it seemed hopeless to look for simplifications which would lead to solutions of the type which seemed to express the facts.   What about the penetrating orbits, coming in from the outer part of the atom, and penetrating close to the nucleus?   Why would they not completely perturb the inner X-ray electrons and spoil the simplicity of Moseley's law, like a comet coming into the orbit of an inner planet and perturbing its orbit?   The quantum mechanics in the form in which it had developed, up to the invention of wave mechanics, was powerless to answer these questions.   It was clear that it was leading the way to an answer, but it did not provide it.

A few attempts were made to carry through the mechanical principles rigorously, in simple two-electron cases.   Models of the ground state of helium were set up, in which two s electrons occupied the same orbit, moving at opposite ends of a diameter.   There is a periodic motion of the three-body problem having this form, and the quantum condition could be applied rigorously to it. The resulting energy bore no resemblance to the measured energy of the ground state of helium. Clearly these attempts to apply classical mechanics and a quantum condition rigorously were not the right approach. And yet the approach suggested by the theory of spectra—a sort of averaged field of all electrons but one, acting on that one, which would move as in a central field—did not represent a type of mechanics which could be made rigorous. This indicates the perplexing situation which faced the physicist in 1925. Similar puzzles were met in molecular theory, which we shall now briefly discuss.

8-5. The Spectra of Diatomic Molecules. In all our treatment of spectra so far, we have stressed atomic spectra, and have said almost nothing about molecular spectra. The reason is that it was the atomic spectra that pointed the way to the discoveries culminating in wave mechanics, while molecular spectra did not contribute very much; their value has come more in the years since the discovery of wave mechanics, when they have been very valuable in exploring the relation of quantum theory to chemical binding. Nevertheless interesting results were obtained on diatomic molecules in the years before 1925, and some of the information given by them was useful in a negative way, in showing that the type of quantum theory available before the wave mechanics was just as unable to explain molecules as it was to explain atoms.

The broad outlines of molecular theory were cleared up in the early days of the quantum theory, when the general nature of band spectra, the spectra of diatomic molecules, was explained. It was found in the first place that one had a number of electronic energy levels, as a function of internuclear distance. That is, it seemed as if, for any fixed distance between the nuclei, there were a series of electronic energy levels, just as there would be for an atom, but these energies were functions of internuclear position. There was no success, before the wave mechanics, in trying to identify these electronic energy levels with definite electronic quantum numbers, or anything of that sort. A pair of electronic energy levels for a typical diatomic molecule are shown in Fig. 8-3, and indicate the sort of energy levels which had to be postulated to explain the spectra. Let us first consider the nature of such curves and their significance, and then ask how they were found experimentally.

We consider the lowest level in Fig. 8-3, the ground state of the molecule. At infinite internuclear distance, the molecule reduces to two atoms, presumably in their ground states; the excited electronic levels generally go into excited levels of the atoms at infinite distance. The ground state of the molecule has a lower energy at smaller distances than at infinity; this is because the atoms attract each other as they approach. There is a minimum in the curve of the ground-state energy; the atoms will be in equilibrium at this position, so that the internuclear distance at the minimum indicates the actual size normally found in the molecule. The energy D, indicated in Fig. 8-3, the energy

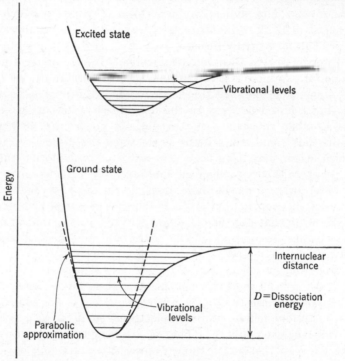

FIG. 8-3. Electronic and vibrational energy levels of a diatomic molecule.

difference between the minimum of the curve and the energy at infinite separation, is the energy of dissociation, the amount required to break the molecule apart into two separate atoms. This can often be found from independent chemical evidence, for it enters into the theory of chemical dissociation of the molecule in the gaseous state.

If, now, we have an energy curve like the lowest one of Fig. 8-3, we can regard this as a potential energy curve determining the motion of the nuclei. If the nuclei moved according to classical mechanics, they could be at rest at the minimum of the curve, or if their energy were greater, they could be vibrating and rotating. It is just as if we had two particles in classical mechanics, held together by an elastic force tending to restore the particles to the interatomic distance indicated by the minimum of the curve, provided they were displaced from this distance. If the restoring force were proportional to the displacement, the potential energy would be proportional to the square of the displacement, and we should have the parabolic potential energy shown by a dotted line in Fig. 8-3. We see that for small displacements, the actual curve does not differ greatly from this parabola.

Two classical particles held by such a restoring force, as we mentioned earlier, could vibrate and rotate. Their motion would be in a plane, and would consist of a rapid vibration in and out along the radial direction, and a much slower rotation. We are not dealing with classical mechanics, however, but with quantum mechanics. It turns out that approximately we can separate variables in the quantum-mechanical problem, and that we have separate problems for the vibration and the rotation. As far as the vibration is concerned, the problem is just like a linear oscillator for small enough amplitudes, so that the actual potential curve of Fig. 8-3 can be replaced by the parabola; for larger amplitudes, the deviations from the linear-oscillator problem can be handled analytically, and we can find the type of energy levels which result. To the approximation to which the linear oscillator is correct, we have a set of vibrational levels equally spaced in energy, the vibrational energy being $h\nu$, if ν is the vibrational frequency. The deviations from the linear-oscillator case result in the upper levels being somewhat more closely spaced, as is shown in Fig. 8-3, where a set of vibrational levels is indicated.

Superposed on this vibrational motion is a rotational motion, and this is handled much as in the hydrogen atom: the angular momentum proves to be quantized, equal to an integral multiple of $h/2\pi$. Unlike hydrogen, however, the radius of the orbit, and hence the moment of inertia, are approximately independent of the azimuthal quantum number. The reason is the large restoring force tending to bring the interatomic distance back to its equilibrium value, if it is displaced. As the molecule rotates faster and faster, having a larger and larger angular momentum, the internuclear distance tends to increase from the equilibrium distance, on account of the centrifugal effect, but the restoring force counteracts this, and keeps the internuclear distance nearly constant, independent of the rate of rotation. If this almost constant internuclear distance leads to a moment of inertia I, and if the angular momentum is p_θ, the kinetic energy of rotation is $p_\theta^2/2I = k^2h^2/8\pi^2I$, if k is the azimuthal quantum number related to the rotational motion. We find, then, a set of rotational levels whose energies are proportional to the squares of the azimuthal quantum

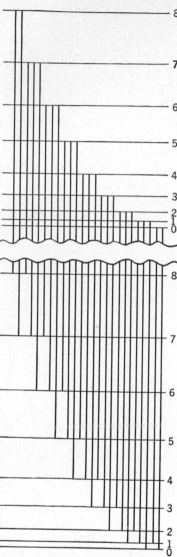

numbers. The rotational energy is added to the vibrational energy, so that the total energy is the sum of these, and we have a set of rotational and vibrational levels, indicated schematically in Fig. 8-4, for each of the electronic levels.

Transitions now occur from one level to another in an energy-level diagram of the type shown in Fig. 8-4. The ordinary optical band spectra come when we go from one electronic level to another, and when at the same time the vibrational and rotational quantum numbers change. There is a selection principle for the rotational quantum number: it changes by ± 1 unit or zero in the transition. This limits the number of possible transitions; and when we take it into account, we have the sort of transitions shown in Fig. 8-4. When we consider the spectrum produced by these transitions, we find that it has the form already shown in Fig. 5-1(b). This is a typical band spectrum; and it is by working backward from such a spectrum, as observed experimentally, that one gets back to the electronic energy levels, as shown in Fig. 8-3. The theory of the vibrations and rotations, and their interactions with each other, has been worked out in great detail, and the study of these levels has been carried to a high degree of perfection, so that the interatomic potential curves can be deduced from experiment with great certainty.

Fig. 8-4. Rotational energy levels associated with two vibrational states of a diatomic molecule, connected with different electronic levels. Allowed transitions are indicated. The breaks in the transition lines indicate a large energy gap between the two sets of levels.

There are other sorts of transitions which can be observed.   In the first place, one can have a transition from one vibrational level to another, without change in the electronic quantum numbers.   This corresponds to a much smaller energy jump, and consequently to a much lower frequency, or longer wavelength.   These transitions come in the infrared part of the spectrum, for this reason, and they are often observed, and check the same energy-level diagram which has already been determined from the optical band spectra.   Finally, one can have transitions from one rotational level to another, without change either in the electronic or vibrational quantum numbers.   The quantum of energy associated with such a transition is very small, and consequently the frequency very low; such radiation comes in the microwave part of the spectrum, and lines of this type are important in microwave spectroscopy.

From this sketch of band spectra, we see that they are well understood, as far as the vibration and rotation are concerned, and this interpretation had been made before the period of 1925, with which we are dealing in this chapter.   However, the explanation of the electronic energy was completely missing at that time.   There was no idea how one could apply quantum conditions to the electrons in a field of two attracting centers, such as one has there.   In the problem of the hydrogen molecule, as in the helium atom, attempts were made to set up simple models which would lead to periodic orbits.   For instance, a model was proposed in which the two electrons circulated at opposite ends of the diameter of a circle in a plane midway between two nuclei. This model leads to periodic orbits, and it could be quantized; but the results of the calculation bore no resemblance to the experimental energy level.   Here as in the problem of atomic spectra, it proved impossible to extend Bohr's theory to explain molecular structure. Clearly it would have been even more impossible to adapt this theory to the explanation of more complicated molecules, or of the motion of electrons in solids.   Something more was needed; and this was very soon provided, in wave mechanics in 1926, and in its application soon after to the theory of the hydrogen molecule, by Heitler and London. We now turn to this momentous improvement in quantum theory.

PROBLEMS

8-1. Using Eq. (8-2), prove Landé's interval rule: that in the levels of a multiplet the energy separation between two adjacent levels is proportional to the J value of the level with higher J.

8-2. Apply the result of Prob. 8-1 to the case of ^3P and ^3D levels, as illustrated in Fig. 8-2.   Assuming that the total width of the D multiplet is 20 per cent less than the total width of the P multiplet, work out the relative frequencies of the different spectral lines of the multiplet arising from the transition shown in Fig. 8-2, and show the spectrum graphically, as it would be observed in a spectrometer.

8-3. The formula for the Landé g factor can be shown to be

$$g = 1 + \frac{J(J+1) - L(L+1) + S(S+1)}{2J(J+1)}$$

Find the g factors for the various levels of a ^3P and ^3D multiplet, as discussed in Prob. 8-2.

8-4. Find the way in which the levels $^3D_3$ and $^3D_2$ are split up in a magnetic field, using the values of the g factors worked out in Prob. 8-3. Draw a diagram of the sublevels into which these two levels split, and indicate the allowed transitions, using the fact that the selection principle for m is $\Delta m = \pm 1, 0$. Find the relative frequencies of the various spectrum lines, and show the Zeeman pattern graphically.

8-5. Proceed as in Prob. 8-4, with the remaining five spectrum lines indicated in Fig. 8-2.

8-6. The D lines of sodium come from the transition $3p\ ^2P_{1/2,3/2} \rightarrow 3s\ ^2S_{1/2}$. Work out the Zeeman patterns for the levels, including the g values, and from this deduce the Zeeman patterns of the resulting spectrum lines.

8-7. Prove that two equivalent p electrons lead to the multiplets ^3P, ^1S, ^1D, as is stated in Table 8-3.

8-8. A diatomic molecule consisting of two like atoms can rotate about an axis which is the perpendicular bisector of the line joining the two nuclei. The quantum condition for the rotation is simply that the angular momentum equals an integer k times $h/2\pi$. If I is the moment of inertia about the given axis, show that the rotational energy is $k^2h^2/8\pi^2I$.

8-9. Consider a set of transitions between the various rotational levels connected with two vibrational levels in the spectrum of a diatomic molecule, as shown in Fig. 8-4. Assume that the moment of inertia of the molecule in the upper electronic level is I', that in the lower electronic level, I. Using the result of Prob. 8-8, show that the frequencies of the various lines connected with the transition are given by the formula $\nu = A \pm Bm + Cm^2$, where A, B, C are constants, m is an integer and the $\pm$ sign refers to transitions in which the rotational quantum number increases or decreases by one unit. Find B and C in terms of the quantities I and I'.

8-10. Take the formula for the frequency of band spectrum lines, as found in Prob. 8-9. Plot ν as a function of the integer m. Show that the frequencies so found lead to an appearance like one of the bands in Fig. 5-1(b); that is, the lines cluster together at one end at a point called the band head, and become more widely spaced as we go away from the band head.

CHAPTER 9

WAVE MECHANICS

9-1. Introduction. Physicists realized, during the years from 1924 to 1926, that something new was in the air. Wave mechanics was discovered by Schrödinger in 1926, and it was a great and startling achievement; but the time was ripe for it, and other developments had foreshadowed it. For some of these developments, we have only to look back at the events of the preceding two or three years; the spectroscopic advances which we have been describing in the preceding chapter suggested other things, for instance in the theory of dispersion, which definitely led to new attacks on quantum mechanics. These attacks blossomed out into the matrix mechanics of Heisenberg, a mathematical development of great complexity, which yet proved capable of formulating the quantum theory in quite a new way, and which later became incorporated into wave mechanics.

The more direct line of attack which led to wave mechanics, however, went far back in the quantum theory, to the early puzzle as to whether light was a wave motion or a motion of corpuscles. Einstein's explanation of the photoelectric effect, in terms of photons of energy $h\nu$, carrying the energy of the light beam, failed to appeal to a good many physicists, who felt that it was too extreme in its simple and straightforward form. It obviously carried no explanation of all the phenomena of interference and diffraction, on which the wave theory of light had been solidly based for a hundred years. The feeling gradually grew up that somehow both theories must be simultaneously right: that there must be some sort of radiation field, governed by electromagnetic theory, and showing the properties of interference and diffraction, but which did not itself carry energy, but merely served in some way to guide the photons.

There could obviously be some sort of statistical relation between the wave field and the photons. For instance, in the ordinary wave theory of light, we have Poynting's vector, a vector which measures the flux of energy, and we have the energy density, measuring the energy per unit volume in terms of the squares of the electric and

163

magnetic field.   It was fairly natural to assume that Poynting's vector did not measure the actual energy flux, but only the average flux of energy carried by photons; and that similarly the energy density measured only the average density of photons.   With such a theory, we could understand how the interference and diffraction patterns come about: according to the probability relation between the electromagnetic field and the photons, we should be likely to find photons at places where the wave theory tells us that we should have high intensity in the diffraction pattern, and should be unlikely to find them where the wave theory tells us there should be darkness.

Such a relationship becomes practically required, if we think about a problem like X-ray diffraction with weak intensities.   Such experiments are made now more often than they were in the 1920's, and we can describe an entirely practical experiment which illustrates perfectly this statistical relationship.   Let us consider X-ray diffraction by a crystal; for instance, suppose we have the arrangement leading to the Laue spots, as discussed in Chap. 6.   Suppose we detect the radiation, not by a photographic plate, but by a Geiger counter, which detects each individual photon; such counters are very often used at present to detect X rays.   If the counter is placed at a position of a Laue spot, we shall find many counts per second, while if it is placed in between the spots, we shall find hardly any counts at all.   If we observe enough counts so that the statistical fluctuations are ironed out, then the average intensity, as it varies from maxima at the spots to minima between, is found to be given perfectly by a wave theory. On the other hand, what we are observing is the behavior of individual photons, each of which carried enough energy to operate the counter.

Experiments like this convinced physicists of the reality of both the waves and the photons.   An experiment in 1923 had gone far toward convincing them that the photons were very fundamental: the Compton effect.   A. H. Compton, the American physicist, had found that, when X rays are scattered by a solid, some of the scattered radiation has a longer wavelength than the incident rays.   He measured the amount of the shift, and produced a theory which explained the experiments perfectly.   He assumed that the incident radiation consisted of photons, which had momentum as well as energy.   From the theory of relativity, one can find the relation between momentum and energy, and if the energy of a photon is $h\nu$, one can show that the momentum must be h/λ, where λ is the wavelength.   We note that, since $\lambda\nu = c$, the velocity of light, this means that the momentum must be $h\nu/c$, which is reasonable.   From Einstein's relation between mass and energy, a photon of energy $h\nu$ must be equivalent to a mass $h\nu/c^2$

(since the energy of any mass equals the mass times c^2). Then the momentum of this mass, if it moved with the velocity of light, should be c times the mass, or $h\nu/c$, as we have just assumed.

Compton treated the collision of a photon of energy $h\nu$, momentum $h\nu/c$, colliding with a free electron initially at rest, as if he were dealing with a collision of ordinary material particles. The electron will recoil, in order to satisfy simultaneously the laws of conservation of energy and of momentum, and the photon will be scattered in some definite direction. Since the electron after recoil has some kinetic energy, it is clear that the photon will have lost some energy, to satisfy conservation of energy. Since its energy equals $h\nu$, it is obvious that its frequency after scattering will be less than the original frequency. Compton worked out the details of the collision and found a formula for the frequency of the scattered radiation which exactly agreed with experiment.

This experiment, more than anything else, convinced physicists of the reality of photons, and of the necessity of bringing together the wave theory and the corpuscular theory. One attempt to do this was made, in 1924, by the author, in collaboration with Bohr and Kramers. In Bohr's original quantum theory, it was postulated that the whole process of emission of radiation was instantaneous, happening when the atom jumped from one state to another. This, however, was inconsistent with any sort of wave theory, for it is a fundamental principle of wave motion that the frequency of a wave cannot be sharply defined, unless the wave train contains many waves, so that it certainly cannot be emitted in a time shorter than many periods of the vibration. Accordingly, it was the suggestion of Bohr, Kramers, and the author that as soon as an atom entered an excited stationary state, it would start emitting waves, of an electromagnetic sort, of all the frequencies connected with transitions to lower stationary states. These waves would have intensities proportional to the Einstein A coefficients, which we mentioned in Sec. 5-6. The various waves would determine the probability of emitting photons of the various frequencies. When one of these photons was emitted, the atom would of course jump to another stationary state, and a new set of waves would be emitted.

An atom in its ground state would not emit any waves; but if external radiation fell on it, this radiation could induce electromagnetic oscillations in the atom, which would interfere with the incident wave in such a way that Poynting's vector would indicate that energy should be flowing into the atom; the rate of flow into the atom would determine the probability of absorption of a photon. These induced oscillators, in turn, would act like the oscillators discussed by Lorentz and Drude, in their classical electromagnetic theory, and would result in an explanation of the index of refraction of the material. Kramers and Heisenberg, at about the same time, derived from the correspondence principle a formula, called the Kramers-Heisenberg dispersion formula, giving the amplitude of these induced oscillators, and showing that they had a form almost identical with the linear oscillators of Lorentz and Drude. The quantum theory, by these steps, was coming very close to reconciling the wave theory and the theory of photons.

This sketch of the state of the theory of light, in the period just before 1926, will show that physicists were beginning to get used to the idea of a duality between waves and particles, with only a statistical relationship between them. But the decisive step to be taken was not in the theory of optics, but in mechanics. In his thesis in Paris in 1924, the French physicist L. de Broglie made the new suggestion that a duality between waves and particles existed in mechanics as well as in optics. He suggested that waves somehow accompanied electrons and other particles, just as they seemed to accompany photons; and by making this hypothesis, he was able to give the first plausible explanation as to why the quantum conditions existed. His idea was very simple. Suppose we have an electron moving around its orbit. If a wave accompanies it, going round and round, we shall have something like a standing wave. The condition of stability of a standing wave is that there be a whole number of wavelengths in the complete circuit, from one point back to the same point again, so that the wave can interfere constructively with itself. Why should not such a condition apply in mechanics, and why should not the quantum condition merely be the statement of the integral number of whole wavelengths demanded for this interference?

This argument was carried further by de Broglie, using rather complicated language on account of the fact that he used relativistic mechanics. Since then, it has been found that one can give just as convincing a form of the argument using classical mechanics, and we shall do so. Suppose, reversing the argument which we used in connection with the Compton effect, that we assume that the wavelength connected with a wave accompanying a particle of given momentum is found by the relation that the momentum equals h/λ. (De Broglie went through the justification of this assumption, in terms of the theory of relativity.) Suppose the wave circulates around the orbit of the particle. Then the number of waves in a small interval dq of distance around the orbit is equal to dq/λ, so that the total number of waves in the orbit is $\oint dq/\lambda$, where the integral is taken around the orbit. This, according to de Broglie's hypothesis, should be an integer. But $1/\lambda = p/h$, where p is the momentum, according to the hypothesis we have just described. Hence the condition for constructive interference of the waves is

$$\oint p \, dq = nh \tag{9-1}$$

or just the Sommerfeld quantum condition.

This simple explanation of the quantum condition was not carried further by de Broglie; it remained for Schrödinger, in 1926, to supply

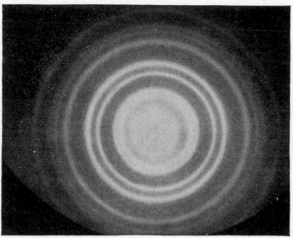

Fig. 9-1. Electron diffraction by gold foil—method of G. P. Thomson. (*Courtesy of G. P. Thomson and O. Oldenberg.*)

the additional suggestion needed to turn it into a complete theory. Justification for the hypothesis of de Broglie regarding waves accompanying particles, however, came very soon from a quite different source. Einstein pointed out, soon after de Broglie's paper, that if he were correct, particles such as electrons should show diffraction effects. It was possible immediately to find the wavelengths of the waves accompanying electrons of moderate energies, and it was evident that these wavelengths were of the same order of magnitude as X-ray wavelengths, so that one might expect to get electron diffraction by crystal lattices, just as one gets X-ray diffraction.

This prediction was very soon verified, in a very striking way. Davisson and Germer, American physicists, and G. P. Thomson in England, in experiments starting in 1925, showed that such diffraction actually occurred. The first experiments of Davisson and Germer were on single crystals of metals, those of Thomson on thin foils, and the diffraction effects observed were closely similar to those found with X rays. Thus we show in Fig. 9-1 a diffraction pattern obtained with electrons. Since then, this method of electron diffraction has been extended widely, and for certain types of structure work it is superior to X-ray diffraction. The differences between the two types of diffraction come principally because the electrons do not penetrate matter so well as X rays, so that electron-diffraction effects result from penetration only to small depths in the material. For this reason, electron diffraction has proved particularly useful in special cases, such as in investigating surface effects, and in studying diffraction by gaseous molecules, where a great deal of information has been obtained by such methods.

We have stated that de Broglie's suggested explanation of the Sommerfeld quantum condition was not carried further, until Schrödinger took up the problem in 1926. Schrödinger took seriously the suggestion that there might be a wave accompanying the particles, and he showed that if this were so, one could guess the form of the wave equation of the resulting wave motion practically uniquely, in a very simple way. Let us see how this is to be done, in a simple one-dimensional problem.

The student who is familiar with mathematical physics will realize that in any type of wave problem one can set up a differential equation, called the wave equation, describing the wave as a function of position and time. For instance, suppose one has a stretched string, stretched along the x axis, with a transverse displacement u, which is a function of x and t. That is, the function $u(x,t)$ regarded as a function of x, for a fixed t, tells us the instantaneous shape of the string, while the same function as a function of t, for fixed x, tells us how a particular point of the string moves. One then applies Newton's second law of motion to the motion of an infinitesimal element of length of the string. The force acting on it is provided by the tension in the string, and we set this force equal to the mass times the acceleration. The result can be stated in the form of a differential equation, which is

$$\frac{\partial^2 u}{\partial x^2} - \frac{1}{v^2}\frac{\partial^2 u}{\partial t^2} = 0 \qquad (9\text{-}2)$$

In Eq. (9-2), we use partial derivatives $\partial^2 u/\partial x^2$ indicating that we are differentiating u with respect to x, keeping t constant. The quantity v is the velocity of propagation of waves along the string, which can be written in terms of the tension and density of the string.

We shall not give the derivation of Eq. (9-2). The student familiar with mathematical physics will already have met it; the student who has not encountered it can either accept it on faith, or may be inspired to look up the derivation in any text on mathematical physics. We can, however, show very easily that the equation has solutions of the type which we should expect. In the first place, any wave, of any wave form, is a solution, provided it travels with a velocity v. That is, we can set u equal to any function $f(x - vt)$ of the variable $x - vt$. We note that this variable stays constant when $x - vt =$ constant, or when $x =$ constant $+ vt$; that is, it is constant at a point which moves along the axis with the velocity v. To prove that any such function is a solution of Eq. (9-2), we symbolize $x - vt$ by w, and use the formula for derivatives of a function of a function. We have $\partial u/\partial x = (df/dw)(\partial w/\partial x) = df/dw$, and similarly $\partial^2 u/\partial x^2 = d^2f/dw^2$. Again, $\partial u/\partial t = (df/dw)(\partial w/\partial t) = -v\, df/dw$, and $\partial^2 u/\partial t^2 = v^2\, d^2f/dw^2$, from which Eq. (9-2) is immediately satisfied.

One particular form of wave which is of great importance is the sinusoidal wave, $u = A \sin[(2\pi/\lambda)(x - vt)]$. Here λ is the wavelength, as we see from the fact that if x increases by λ, the sine comes back to its initial value, on account of the periodicity of the sine. It is generally convenient in mathematical physics, when considering a sinusoidal function, to write it in complex exponential form. Thus it is a well-known theorem that $\exp(iy) = \cos y + i \sin y$, where $i = (-1)^{1/2}$. Hence if we write an expression in such a complex form, the real or imaginary part will equal the cosine or sine, and we interpret the solution as being such real or imaginary part. We can then write the sinusoidal wave in the form $u = A \exp[(2\pi i/\lambda)(x - vt)]$, realizing that the real part is to be used in a physical problem. But on account of the exponential nature of this expression, it can be rewritten $u = A \exp(2\pi ix/\lambda) \exp(-2\pi ivt/\lambda) = A \exp(2\pi ix/\lambda) \exp(-2\pi i\nu t)$, where ν, which equals v/λ, is the frequency of oscillation. In this form, we see that the solution can be written as a product of a sinusoidal function of x, times a sinusoidal function of time.

Part of the importance of this possibility of writing the solution as a product of a function of x, times a sinusoidal function of time, arises because a similar thing is possible even in a more general case: the case where the properties of the string (for instance, its density) vary from point to point, so that the wavelength and velocity of propagation are functions of x. If we assume that u can be written as a function of x, times $\exp(-2\pi i\nu t)$, we find that $\partial^2 u/\partial t^2 = -4\pi^2\nu^2 u$. Hence we can rewrite Eq. (9-2) in the form

$$\frac{d^2u}{dx^2} + \left(\frac{2\pi}{\lambda}\right)^2 u = 0 \qquad (9\text{-}3)$$

In Eq. (9-3), we are regarding u as merely the part of the function depending on x, which must be multiplied by $\exp(-2\pi i\nu t)$ to get the whole function of x and t. We are defining λ by the equation $\lambda \nu = v$. Now the important feature of Eq. (9-3) is that if the wavelength varies from point to point, Eq. (9-3) still determines the space part of the displacement, and the time variation is still sinusoidal. This, then, furnishes a suitable starting point for setting up a wave function to describe wave mechanics.

We know that, in the case of de Broglie waves, $1/\lambda = p/h$. Furthermore, we can write p, at any point of space, in terms of the potential energy and total energy. Suppose the energy is E, the potential energy V. Then the conservation of energy tells us that E equals V plus the kinetic energy, which in turn is $p^2/2m$. That is, $p = [2m(E - V)]^{1/2}$, and substituting this in de Broglie's relation for the wavelength, and this in turn in Eq. (9-3), we have

$$\frac{d^2u}{dx^2} + \frac{8\pi^2 m}{h^2} (E - V)u = 0 \qquad (9\text{-}4)$$

In Eq. (9-4) we have Schrödinger's equation, for a one-dimensional problem. The quantity u measures what is called the wave function, the amplitude of the wave whose intensity gives the probability of finding the particle at a given point of space. For a three-dimensional case, analogy with the three-dimensional wave equation of mechanics, which holds for instance in the vibrations of an elastic solid, suggests that we have only to replace d^2u/dx^2 by the expression $\partial^2u/\partial x^2 + \partial^2u/\partial y^2 + \partial^2u/\partial z^2$.

This very simple procedure for guessing at a wave equation led to a mathematical formulation of quantum theory which has proved to be correct and complete. The theory of the solution of the wave equation is one of the best-explored parts of mathematical physics. Schrödinger found that, when he substituted for V the potential energy found in the hydrogen atom, the equation could be solved in terms of known functions, and the solution existed, or represented standing waves, only for discrete values of E, which were precisely those predicted by Bohr's theory. Similarly if one put in for V the value for a linear oscillator, he got the correct energy levels for this, and so on for other problems. In other words, here was a mathematical foundation which led to the same results as Bohr's theory, but in a much more reasonable and fundamental way. At the same time, the various problems raised by the Bohr theory of complex spectra were automatically resolved. For instance, in hydrogen, the quantum number l, equal to 0 for an s state, 1 for a p state, and so on, automatically entered in the correct way, and the other puzzles of the older theory were removed.

Schrödinger's equation went far beyond providing an alternative treatment of the same problems that could be attacked by Bohr's theory, however. For Schrödinger showed how it could be formulated for any mechanical problem whatever, so that it was not limited in any way to the multiply periodic problems to which alone Bohr's theory could be applied. He showed how to set it up for a many-electron problem. The mathematics became extremely complicated, so hard that we are still working on methods of solving it; but there was no doubt that the formulation was right. In the early days of wave mechanics, two celebrated problems which proved impossible for the older quantum theory were successfully attacked: the ground state of the helium atom, in which the Norwegian physicist Hylleraas provided an answer by elaborate mathematical methods, and the ground state of the hydrogen molecule, where a similar solution was given by the American physicists James and Coolidge. In each case, the energies computed from the solutions agreed with experiment within the experimental error. There is no question but that, for problems of the behavior of the electrons outside the atomic nucleus, Schrödinger's equation provides the fundamental and correct basis for the theory.

We shall now proceed to consider Schrödinger's equation. In the present chapter, we shall show how it leads to an alternative understanding of the simple problems in quantum theory to which the older quantum mechanics of Bohr had been applied. We shall also show the general method by which it can be applied to more complicated problems, and shall indicate how it reduces to ordinary classical mechanics in those limiting cases where we have used classical mechanics successfully for hundreds of years. Then in Chap. 10 we shall go on to some characteristically new results of wave mechanics, in problems of molecular and solid-state physics. We shall take up such problems as the relation of the electron spin to the theory of atomic multiplets, of the theory of chemical binding, and of ferromagnetism, problems which could not be even attacked by the earlier theories. Finally, in the last chapter, we shall go into recent knowledge regarding the atomic nucleus, a field where wave mechanics alone is not enough to give us all the answers, and where new developments are constantly being made.

9-2. Schrödinger's Theory for the Linear Oscillator. A simple and straightforward problem which can be easily treated by Schrödinger's method is the linear oscillator. If the restoring force on a particle of mass m, displaced a distance x from its position of equilibrium, is $-kx$, then its potential energy is $(\frac{1}{2})kx^2$. If we insert this value into Schrödinger's equation, Eq. (9-4), we have

$$\frac{d^2u}{dx^2} + \frac{8\pi^2 m}{h^2}\left(E - k\frac{x^2}{2}\right)u = 0 \tag{9-5}$$

This is not a very simple differential equation, but fortunately, as we have stated earlier, its solution is known. This solution is found to be

$$u_n = \exp\left(-\frac{v^2}{2}\right)H_n(v) \tag{9-6}$$

where
$$v = 2\pi x \left(\frac{mv}{h}\right)^{1/2} \tag{9-7}$$

in which the frequency v is the natural frequency of oscillation of the classical oscillator, or

$$v = \frac{(k/m)^{1/2}}{2\pi} \tag{9-8}$$

and where H_n is the nth of the so-called Hermite polynomials. The first few of these polynomials are

$$H_0 = 1 \qquad H_1 = 2v \qquad H_2 = 4v^2 - 2 \qquad H_3 = 8v^3 - 12v$$
$$H_4 = 16v^4 - 48v^2 + 12 \qquad \text{etc.}$$

and in general

$$H_n(v) = (2v)^n - \frac{n(n-1)}{1!}(2v)^{n-2}$$
$$+ \frac{n(n-1)(n-2)(n-3)}{2!}(2v)^{n-4} - \cdots \tag{9-9}$$

This solution, with subscript n, is for the nth stationary state, for which the energy proves to be

$$E_n = (n + \tfrac{1}{2})h v \tag{9-10}$$

We give this solution, not so much because the reader will want to study its mathematical form, but rather because it indicates that it is not a very complicated thing (being the product of an exponential and a polynomial), and to show that one can actually handle such problems mathematically. Much more interesting than the detailed mathematical form of the solution is its general appearance, which is indicated in Fig. 9-2, where the first few of the functions are plotted. These functions, called wave functions, show a wavelike nature. The first one, for $n = 0$, has one maximum; the second one, for $n = 1$, has a maximum and a minimum; and so on. In a general way we can say that the first one, then, has one wavelength in a round trip in which we go from one extreme of the orbit to the other and back again; the second one has two; and so on. Thus, we see the general significance of the quantum number. But clearly the problem is much more complicated than that of a wave on a string, and we shall have to come back to some of these complications later. At any rate, our solutions have the general character of standing waves, and the energy values, given by Eq. (9-10), have a close resemblance to the energy values $E_n = nh\nu$ given by the Sommerfeld quantum condition; except that we automatically are led to half quantum numbers for this particular

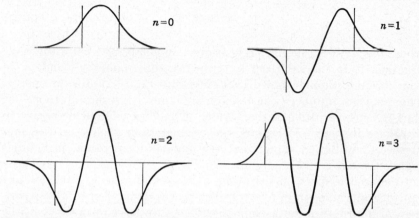

FIG. 9-2. Wave functions for the linear oscillator. Vertical lines show limits of the classical orbits.

problem. If we look back over the problems where we have used the quantum condition for a linear oscillator, we shall see that it is the differences of energy levels which we have used in every case, and agreement with experiment is not lost by the fact that the Schrödinger theory indicates that we should use half quantum numbers, not integral quantum numbers, for this particular problem.

9-3. Schrödinger's Theory for the Hydrogen Atom. Before we go on to describe more general properties of the solutions of Schrödinger's equation, we should like to have some more specific examples of its application; we therefore give next the case of the hydrogen atom, the most important test of its agreement with the Bohr theory, and one of the examples given by Schrödinger in his first paper in 1926. We take the problem of an electron of mass m moving in the field of a nucleus of charge Ze (by including Z, we can take care of the case of an arbitrary atomic number). The potential energy is $-Ze^2/r$ in cgs units, or $-Ze^2/4\pi\epsilon_0 r$ in mks units; we shall use the mks units, and the expression $4\pi\epsilon_0$ can be omitted in the answer to convert to cgs units. Then Schrödinger's equation takes the form

$$\frac{\partial^2 u}{\partial x^2} + \frac{\partial^2 u}{\partial y^2} + \frac{\partial^2 u}{\partial z^2} + \frac{8\pi^2 m}{h^2}\left(E + \frac{Ze^2}{4\pi\epsilon_0 r}\right) u = 0 \qquad (9\text{-}11)$$

Here again, as in the linear oscillator, the solution of this equation was known at the time of Schrödinger's work.

The solutions of Eq. (9-11) are most conveniently expressed in terms of spherical polar coordinates r, θ, ϕ. In the first place, it is found that solutions exist only for the discrete energy levels given precisely by the Bohr formula

$$E_n = -Rhc\frac{Z^2}{n^2} \qquad (9\text{-}12)$$

where the Rydberg number R is as given in Chap. 5. As for the wave function, it is characterized by two quantum numbers l and m, in addition to n, though they do not enter into Eq. (9-12) for the energy. The quantum number l can take on all values from zero up to $n - 1$; thus it behaves just like the l which it had been found necessary to introduce in place of the k of the original Bohr theory, and in fact further examination shows that the angular momentum, in Schrödinger's theory, is essentially measured by l. The quantum number m determines the space quantization, as in the Bohr theory, and can take on integral values from l to $-l$, just as was demanded by the experimental information on atomic spectra, as we have outlined it in the preceding chapter.

The wave function for a state of given n, l, and m, then proves to have the following form

$$u_{nlm} = \exp\left(-\frac{rZ}{a_0 n}\right) r^l \left[A_0 + A_1\left(\frac{rZ}{a_0}\right) + A_2\left(\frac{rZ}{a_0}\right)^2 + \cdots\right]$$
$$P_l^{|m|}(\cos\theta)\ \exp\ im\varphi \qquad (9\text{-}13)$$

where a_0 is the Bohr hydrogen radius, as given in Eq. (5-10); the A's are given in terms of A_0, which is arbitrary, by the recursion relation

$$A_s = -\frac{2}{n}\frac{n - l - s}{(l + s)(l + s + 1) - l(l + 1)} A_{s-1} \qquad (9\text{-}14)$$

The function $P_l^{|m|}(\cos\theta)$ is a well-known function, the associated Legendre function, given by the formula

$$P_l^{|m|}(\cos\theta) = \frac{\sin^{|m|}\theta(2l)!}{2^l l!(l - |m|)!}\left[(\cos\theta)^{l-|m|} - \frac{(l - |m|)(l - |m| - 1)}{2(2l - 1)}\right.$$
$$(\cos\theta)^{l-|m|-2} + \frac{(l - |m|)(l - |m| - 1)(l - |m| - 2)(l - |m| - 3)}{2.4(2l - 1)(2l - 3)}$$
$$\left.(\cos\theta)^{l-|m|-4} - \cdots\right] \qquad (9\text{-}15)$$

These general formulas for the wave functions are complicated, but the special cases for low quantum numbers are not. In Table 9-1 we give the wave functions for the states of $n = 1$, 2, and 3. We see

TABLE 9-1. WAVE FUNCTION FOR HYDROGEN, $n = 1, 2, 3$

$1s$: $u = \exp -\dfrac{rZ}{a_0}$

$2s$: $u = \exp \left(-\dfrac{rZ}{2a_0} \right) \left(1 - \dfrac{1}{2}\dfrac{rZ}{a_0} \right)$

$2p$: $u = r \exp \left(-\dfrac{rZ}{2a_0} \right) \begin{cases} \sin\theta \exp \pm i\varphi & \text{for } m = \pm 1 \\ \cos\theta & \text{for } m = 0 \end{cases}$

$3s$: $u = \exp \left(-\dfrac{rZ}{3a_0} \right) \left[1 - \dfrac{2}{3}\left(\dfrac{rZ}{a_0}\right) + \dfrac{2}{27}\left(\dfrac{rZ}{a_0}\right)^2 \right]$

$3p$: $u = r \exp \left(-\dfrac{rZ}{3a_0} \right) \left(1 - \dfrac{1}{6}\dfrac{rZ}{a_0} \right) \begin{cases} \sin\theta \exp \pm i\varphi & \text{for } m = \pm 1 \\ \cos\theta & \text{for } m = 0 \end{cases}$

$3d$: $u = r^2 \exp \left(-\dfrac{rZ}{3a_0} \right) \begin{cases} \sin^2\theta \exp \pm 2i\varphi & \text{for } m = \pm 2 \\ \sin\theta \cos\theta \exp \pm i\varphi & \text{for } m = \pm 1 \\ \cos^2\theta - \tfrac{1}{3} & \text{for } m = 0 \end{cases}$

that these are comparatively simple functions of the coordinates. One fact is to be noticed from our definitions of the wave functions: the dependence on angle is determined entirely by the quantum numbers l (which by 1926 was generally called the azimuthal quantum number, taking over the name from Bohr's quantum number k, which by then was pretty thoroughly discarded), and m; states of different principal quantum number n, but the same azimuthal and magnetic quantum numbers, differ only in the dependence of the wave function on r. To indicate this dependence on r, we show in Fig. 9-3 the radial dependence of the wave function, showing that for a given l and m value the radial wave function of the lowest state occurring for these l and m values has no nodes, the next one has one node, and so on. Furthermore, the wave functions extend out to rapidly increasing distances, as the principal quantum numbers n increase. One can show, in fact, that the radius of the outermost maximum of the wave function is closely related to the radius of the corresponding Bohr orbit, so that the Schrödinger theory leads to atoms of the same general size as the Bohr theory.

9-4. The General Significance of the Wave Function. We have shown the solutions of the problems of the linear oscillator, and the hydrogen atom, so that the reader will have some idea of the sort of mathematical problems encountered in solving Schrödinger's equation for simple cases; unfortunately, there are not many other problems whose solutions are as simple as these. Our main task, however, is not so much to ask how to solve Schrödinger's equation mathematically, as to inquire more deeply into the meaning of the wave function, the relation of wave mechanics to classical mechanics, the cases where the two are significantly different, and questions of that sort. Very important progress can be made, and has been made since 1926, along

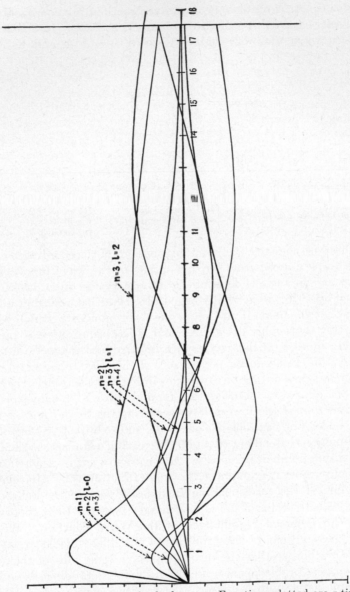

FIG. 9-3. Radial wave functions for hydrogen.   Functions plotted are r times the radial part of the wave function.

these lines, without having to go far in the direction of numerical solutions of Schrödinger's equation.

As for the general significance of the wave function, Schrödinger in his first papers was not very certain. He believed, in fact, that the intensity of the wave function (that is, the square of its magnitude) represented the actual density of charge in the atom. Max Born, the German physicist, however, very shortly made a study of scattering problems by means of wave mechanics, and was led to a statistical interpretation, along the lines of what we have described in Sec. 9-1. That is, Born assumed that the electrons or other particles described by wave mechanics were well-defined particles, as had always been supposed, and that the intensity of the wave function merely gave the probability of finding a particle at a given point of space.

This interpretation, in other words, fell in line perfectly with the thinking that had been going on in the preceding few years, regarding the relation of the wave theory and corpuscular theory of light. This point of view is generally accepted, and for that reason we now treat wave mechanics as being only a statistical theory, able to predict on the average what particles will do, but not predicting in detail the motion of an individual particle. It is not generally supposed that any detailed form of mechanics exists which can predict the precise behavior of an individual particle; though there have been physicists who have set up theories which do make such detailed predictions, and yet which reduce to the Schrödinger theory as regards the average behavior. It is impossible at this date to say whether the present view, that there is no precise way of predicting the behavior of particles, will persist permanently or not. For the present, however, it is a reasonable hypothesis.

This statistical relation between waves and particles, and the consequent impossibility of predicting precisely the behavior of a single particle, form the basis of the principle of uncertainty, which was set up by the German physicist Heisenberg, and discussed by him and Bohr, in the early days of wave mechanics. This principle is stated in the following way: it is impossible simultaneously to specify a coordinate, and its conjugate momentum, both with perfect accuracy. Instead, if a coordinate is specified with an uncertainty Δq, and its conjugate momentum is specified with an uncertainty Δp, then the product of the two uncertainties must always be at least equal to h

$$\Delta q \, \Delta p \geq h \tag{9-16}$$

The principle was demonstrated by setting up many examples of attempts to specify a coordinate and its momentum simultaneously,

and by showing in each case that the inequality, Eq. (9-16), was satisfied.   We shall give one of these illustrations, but we notice that the
principle has a very fundamental meaning when we consider the phase
space.   We remember, from the interpretation of the Sommerfeld
quantum condition first given by Planck, that the phase space can be
subdivided into small elements of volume h, and each of these elements
is associated with a unit increment in the quantum number.   The
uncertainty principle can be interpreted as saying that it is impossible
to define precisely the position of a representative point in the phase
space; the best we can do is to assign it to one of these cells, of volume h.

Let us look at an illustration of the uncertainty principle, and show
how closely it is associated with the wave nature of mechanics.   Suppose we have a beam of particles which are collimated so as to be

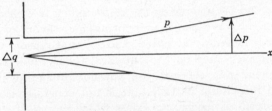

Fig. 9-4. Uncertainty principle in diffraction through slit. $\Delta p/p = \lambda/\Delta q$,
$\Delta p\,\Delta q = \lambda p = h$.

traveling parallel, and allow them to pass through a narrow slit, of
width Δq.   All the particles which come through the slit, then, were
located at the instant when they came through in a range of coordinates
Δq.   When they struck the slit, they all had the same component of
momentum transverse to the slit, or in the direction of the coordinate,
namely zero.

But the mere act of making them pass through the slit has interfered
with this situation.   For we remember that their motion is determined
by wave mechanics, and a wave passing through a narrow slit is
diffracted, as shown in Fig. 9-4.   It is broadened, according to diffraction theory, into a beam whose angular width is of the order of magnitude of the ratio of the wavelength to the slit width.   This means,
since the wave determines where the particles go, that some of the
particles will have a transverse component of momentum after going
through the slit.   An uncertainty Δp, in other words, has been introduced into the transverse momentum, by the process of limiting the
coordinate to a range Δq.   We can make a simple calculation of the
amount of this transverse momentum.   The total momentum of the
particle is h/λ, by de Broglie's relation, where λ is the wavelength.
The transverse component, by Fig. 9-4, is of the order of magnitude of

$\lambda/\Delta q$ times the total momentum. That is, Δp is of the order of magnitude of $(\lambda/\Delta q)(h/\lambda) = h/\Delta q$, just as the principle of uncertainty, Eq. (9-16), says it should be.

There are many other illustrations of the principle of uncertainty which could be given, but this one is sufficient to show the principles. It goes right back to the fundamentals of wave mechanics: an attempt to limit a wave to a region small compared to a wavelength causes the wave to spread widely on account of diffraction. Any attempt to limit the size of a wave too much is bound to defeat itself. This is seen when one tries to set up what is called a wave packet. One could let a beam of particles fall on a small aperture, as in the example we have just been discussing. If the aperture is not too small, a narrow ray or pencil of radiation will emerge from the aperture. One can then have a shutter, like a camera shutter, over the aperture, and open it for only a very small interval of time, so that only those particles which struck the aperture while the shutter was open will get through.

The wave which emerges, then, is limited to the cross section of the ray, and is limited front and back by the opening and shutting of the shutter, so that it occupies only a very small volume of space. It will travel forward much like an individual particle. All that wave mechanics can say about the motion of particles which have gone through the aperture is that they will move so as to stay somewhere within the wave packet, and where the packet has large intensity we shall be likely to find the particle; where it is weak we are unlikely to find it. We now find that if we have tried to make the packet too small, by making the aperture too small, it will immediately spread out, on account of diffraction. One can readily show, from the uncertainty principle, that the packet must always be fairly large compared to a wavelength, in order not to spread too rapidly; and this means that we cannot determine the position of a particle more closely than to distances of the order of magnitude of a wavelength.

Another closely related aspect of the principle of uncertainty connects the uncertainty in observing the time of an event and the uncertainty in its energy. If we carry out an observation within a time Δt, and use this observation to determine the energy of the system, the energy can be found only to an uncertainty ΔE, given by the relation $\Delta E\, \Delta t = h$. This relation on the one hand is tied up through the theory of relativity with the relation $\Delta p\, \Delta q = h$, for one can show that, just as the time forms a fourth variable closely related to the spatial coordinates q, so the energy forms the corresponding analogue to the momentum p.

On the other hand, our relation between energy and time goes back to very simple principles in physics. If we relate the energy E to a frequency ν, which we are trying to determine, by the relation $E = h\nu$, then in the statement of the uncertainty principle we can cancel out h, leaving $\Delta\nu\,\Delta t = 1$. But this merely says that the uncertainty in the determination of a frequency is of the order of magnitude of the reciprocal of the time taken to make the observation. This fact is familiar from any sort of wave motion. If we have a sinusoidal wave train, cut off after a time Δt, and analyze its spectrum into a sum of sinusoidal oscillations of all different frequencies, we find that the spectrum is broadened into a line of finite width, the width being of the order of magnitude $1/\Delta t$, so that the frequency cannot be determined, from observation of the spectrum line, to an accuracy much greater than this. This form of the uncertainty principle has an interesting application in the theory of broadening of spectrum lines in actual atomic spectra: the lines are broadened by the mere fact of having a finite lifetime in their stationary states, and anything which decreases this lifetime broadens the lines more.

9-5. The Limit of Classical Mechanics. The wave packet, which we have just been discussing, allows us to think about the limiting case of classical mechanics. In a classical problem, we determine the motion of a particle by giving its initial position and velocity or momentum; mechanics determines the subsequent motion of the particle. We can do the same thing in wave mechanics, by having a beam of particles whose momentum is adjusted as well as possible to the desired value, letting this beam fall on an aperture at the desired position, and opening a shutter for a short interval of time at the instant when we wish the particle to come through. We then allow a wave packet to emerge; and if any particles have been able to get through, they will travel so as to stay inside the wave packet. We see, then, from the principle of uncertainty, that we cannot precisely determine the position and momentum as in classical mechanics, but can determine them only to the extent allowed by the principle of uncertainty. There is another problem, however: to the accuracy to which wave mechanics can predict the motion of the particle, will the wave packet move according to classical mechanics? The answer is that it will; and this is the fundamental feature of the proof that wave mechanics reduces to classical mechanics in the limit which we are ordinarily familiar with.

One can easily set up formulas for the x, y, and z coordinates of the center of gravity of a wave packet. To do this, one has to assume that the square of the magnitude of the wave function $|u|^2$ measures the probability of finding the particle at the point in question, or corresponds to the intensity of the wave. Our problem, then, is just as if the mass within a volume $dx \, dy \, dz$ were $|u|^2 \, dx \, dy \, dz$. In such a case, we find in elementary mechanics that the center of gravity has an x coordinate equal to

$$(x)_{\text{av}} = \frac{\iiint x|u|^2 \, dx \, dy \, dz}{\iiint |u|^2 \, dx \, dy \, dz} \tag{9-17}$$

with similar formulas for the y and z coordinates. Now one can use Schrödinger's equation in the form involving the time (which we have not yet met, but shall describe shortly) to find the time rate of change of $(x)_{\text{av}}$; if we differentiate it with respect to time, we can differentiate under the integral sign in Eq. (9-17), and the result depends on the time rate of change of u, which is given by the form of Schrödinger's equation we have just mentioned. We differentiate twice to get the acceleration, and when we have done this, we find that the mass of the particle times the acceleration of the center of mass of the wave packet equals precisely the average external force, averaged over the wave packet. In other words, the center of gravity of the wave packet satisfies Newton's second law, and it will move according to classical mechanics.

In the ordinary problems of classical mechanics which we are used to, the wavelengths are so infinitesimal that we can disregard the size of the wave packet. Thus, a particle of mass 1 g, moving with a velocity of 1 cm/sec, will have a momentum of 1 g cm/sec. Its wavelength will be h (which is 6.6×10^{-27} erg sec) divided by the momentum, or will be 6.6×10^{-27} cm. Wavelengths of this order of magnitude, or smaller, are met in all ordinary mechanical problems. Thus, we can afford to make wave packets many wavelengths in dimensions, which will not spread appreciably at all, and yet which will be small compared to the accuracy with which we can really determine the coordinates, by any experimental methods at our disposal. These wave packets can then be treated as points, and they will move precisely as their centers of gravity move. This motion, as we have just seen, is according to Newton's laws of motion. Since the particle must be found within the wave packet, it will follow Newton's laws. We see, then, the reason why classical mechanics has been so successful.

If we ask what are the limits of applicability of classical mechanics, we ask, merely, under what conditions will the wavelength become comparable with the dimensions of the experiment? So long as the wavelength is negligibly small, Newtonian mechanics will be satisfactory. When we ask this, we see that we must be seeking problems with very small masses, very small velocities, or very small distances, in order that the product $\Delta p \, \Delta q$ should be small. The only practical case where we meet this limit is when we are dealing with atomic phenomena. Here the velocities are large, often much larger than we are used to in ordinary mechanics; but the masses and distances are both extremely small, and it is only in such cases that we need to use wave mechanics. This is the reason why we were able to get along with classical mechanics for so long.

It is interesting to ask why the wave packets travel the way that a classical particle would, according to Newtonian mechanics. We are accustomed to thinking of a ray as traveling in a straight line, and of radiation as traveling with a fixed velocity, and yet we know that particles in mechanics travel in curved lines (let us think, for instance, of a projectile fired in the air), with a variable velocity. The point in that the wavelength of the de Broglie wave, depending as it does on the momentum and hence on the kinetic and potential energy, varies from point to point. Our mechanical problem of wave propagation is analogous to that of a ray of light in a medium whose index of refraction varies continuously from point to point. Such a case is met, for instance, in the well-known example of the mirage, where the index of refraction of the air varies with height, on account of a peculiar variation of temperature with height. Then, as is well known, the rays of light are actually bent, and result in our appearing to see objects where they are not really located. Just such an effect goes on in the refraction of de Broglie waves. The variation of velocity with position, too, finds its explanation, once we have set up Schrödinger's equation in the form involving the time; as the index of refraction varies from point to point, the velocity of a wave packet correspondingly varies from point to point, in just such a way as to produce agreement with Newtonian mechanics.

9-6. Average Values of Various Quantities. In Eq. (9-17), we have found the average value of the quantity x, for a wave packet. The same formula holds, no matter whether we are dealing with a concentrated wave function, like a wave packet, or a more extended wave function. The reason is simple. The quantity $|u|^2 \, dx \, dy \, dz / \iiint |u|^2 \, dx \, dy \, dz$ measures the probability of finding the particle in $dx \, dy \, dz$, since the probability interpretation of the wave function indicates that the intensity (or square of the magnitude) of the wave function is proportional to the probability of finding the particle at a given point of space. The sum of the probabilities of finding the particle at all points must be unity; and by multiplying $|u|^2$ by $dx \, dy \, dz$, and dividing by $\iiint |u|^2 \, dx \, dy \, dz$, we have arranged things so that summing or integrating over all space we get unity. Then to find the average of a function like x, we multiply the x in a given volume element by the probability of finding the particle in that element, and add. In other words, we are finding a weighted mean, weighting each volume element by the probability of finding the particle in that element.

It is generally convenient to fix the absolute value of u so as to simplify these formulas. Schrödinger's equation has the peculiarity that if we find one solution, any constant times this solution is also a solution. We saw this fact, in discussing the hydrogen problem, where we left a constant factor undetermined. We can then choose this constant factor, in every case, so that

$$\iiint |u|^2 \, dx \, dy \, dz = 1 \tag{9-18}$$

This condition is called a normalization condition. We shall henceforth assume that wave functions are to be normalized, unless we state the contrary. In this case, the average value of x is simply $\iiint x|u|^2 \, dx \, dy \, dz$. More generally, we can find the formula for the average of any function of position, say, $F(x,y,z)$: it is

$$(F)_{\mathrm{av}} = \iiint F(x,y,z)|u|^2 \, dx \, dy \, dz \tag{9-19}$$

In Eq. (9-19), we have found the way to get the average of any function of position. For instance, we could find the average potential energy of any stationary state, in this way. We may reasonably ask another question, however: How would we find the average of a function of the momenta? How, for instance, would we find the average kinetic energy, or for that matter the average total energy of the system? We cannot merely take a function $F(x,y,z,p_x,p_y,p_z)$, involving the momentum components as well as the coordinates, and insert it in Eq. (9-19), and integrate; for the momenta do not appear in the wave function. In this respect, our statistical theory is very different from classical statistical mechanics, as discussed in Chap. 1. In that theory, we have a distribution function in a phase space: the probability of finding a system in the element $dx \, dy \, dz \, dp_x \, dp_y \, dp_z$ in the phase space can be expressed by a probability function $f(x,y,z,p_x,p_y,p_z)$ in the form $f \, dx \, dy \, dz \, dp_x \, dp_y \, dp_z$. And if we have a function such as F, above, whose average we desire, its value in classical statistical mechanics is

$$(F)_{\mathrm{av}} = \iiiiint F(x, \ldots , p_z)f(x, \ldots , p_z) \, dx \, dy, \ldots , dp_z \tag{9-20}$$

But such a definition is impossible in wave mechanics, for our probability function $|u|^2$, unlike the f of statistical mechanics, does not involve the momenta.

The way we get around this difficulty is one of the characteristic steps of wave mechanics, and appeared in the first work of Schrödinger.

Suppose we are finding the average of the momentum. Then Schrödinger postulated that its average value is found by the formula

$$(p_x)_{av} = \iiint u^* \frac{h}{2\pi i} \frac{\partial u}{\partial x} \, dx \, dy \, dz \qquad (9\text{-}21)$$

Here u^* represents the complex conjugate of u. That is, if u is a complex quantity, which we can write in the form $a + bi$, its conjugate is
by definition $a - bi$, where $i = (-1)^{1/2}$. Then u^*u represents the
square of the magnitude of u. This arises because

$$u^*u = (a - bi)(a + bi) = a^2 + b^2$$

the square of the magnitude of the quantity u.

In writing u in this way, we are implicitly assuming that it can be a
complex quantity; and we must in fact make this assumption. This
forms a great contrast to other branches of mathematical physics.
We stated, in Sec. 9-1, that an exponential solution for a wave equation
is often used, of the form $A \exp(2\pi i x/\lambda) \exp(-2\pi i\nu t)$, but that it is
only the real part of this which is assumed to have physical significance.
However, in wave mechanics, Schrödinger found that he had to use
the whole exponential function, in this complex form. If we form the
complex conjugate of such a function, it can be shown that this is
formed from the function itself by changing the sign of i to $-i$ wherever
it occurs. That is, if $u = A \exp(2\pi i x/\lambda) \exp(-2\pi i\nu t)$, the complex
conjugate u^* equals $A^* \exp(-2\pi i x/\lambda) \exp(2\pi i\nu t)$. When we multiply u by its conjugate, then, the exponentials cancel, and we find
merely that $u^*u = A^*A$, proportional to the square of the amplitude
of the wave.

We can understand, in terms of such exponential solutions of
the problem, why Eq. (9-21) is plausible. Suppose we take

$$u = \exp \frac{2\pi i x}{\lambda}$$

as far as its dependence on x is concerned; that is, we use the form
above, with $A = 1$, so that the function will automatically be normalized over unit volume, and we assume that we are dealing with unit
volume. Then in Eq. (9-21), $(h/2\pi i) \, \partial u/\partial x = (h/\lambda)u$. But h/λ is
the magnitude of the momentum, according to de Broglie's relation.
In other words, in this case, the expression of Eq. (9-21) would give
just the momentum, as computed from the plane wave. Schrödinger
postulated that Eq. (9-21) would hold in general. And the reason
why he had to assume the exponential form for the wave function is

that it is only in such a case that we have this simple method of finding the average value of the momentum.

It is then natural to generalize Eq. (9-21), and set up a formula for finding the average value of any function of coordinates and momenta. Suppose, as before, that we have a function $F(x,y,z,p_x,p_y,p_z)$, whose average we desire. Schrödinger postulated that we were to change p_x into the operator $(h/2\pi i)\,\partial/\partial x$, and similarly for p_y and p_z, wherever it appeared. Then we would allow this operator to operate on u, multiply it by u^*, and integrate. That is, we assume that

$$(F)_{\mathrm{av}} = \iiint u^* F\left(x,y,z, \frac{h}{2\pi i}\frac{\partial}{\partial x}, \frac{h}{2\pi i}\frac{\partial}{\partial y}, \frac{h}{2\pi i}\frac{\partial}{\partial z}\right) u \, dx \, dy \, dz \quad (9\text{-}22)$$

In writing such formulas, it is more convenient to use the quantity $\hbar$ (called h bar), introduced somewhat later by Dirac, and equal by definition to $h/2\pi$. Then in place of $(h/2\pi i)\partial/\partial x$, for instance, we can write $-i\hbar\partial/\partial x$.

As an example of the application of Eq. (9-22), let us calculate the average value of the energy. This has the form $(p_x^2 + p_y^2 + p_z^2)/2m + V(x,y,z)$, where the first terms express the kinetic energy, the last is the potential energy. But the operator $p_x^2/2m$, according to our rules, becomes transformed into $-(\hbar^2/2m)\partial^2/\partial x^2$. Thus, we have

$$(H)_{\mathrm{av}} = \iiint u^* \left[\frac{-\hbar^2}{2m}\left(\frac{\partial^2}{\partial x^2} + \frac{\partial^2}{\partial y^2} + \frac{\partial^2}{\partial z^2} \right) u + Vu \right] dx \, dy \, dz \quad (9\text{-}23)$$

where we symbolize the energy by H. Now, however, we begin to see the close relation of this method to the things we have been doing earlier. By Schrödinger's equation, Eq. (9-4), we see that

$$\frac{-\hbar^2}{2m}\left(\frac{\partial^2}{\partial x^2} + \frac{\partial^2}{\partial y^2} + \frac{\partial^2}{\partial z^2} \right) u + Vu = Eu \qquad (9\text{-}24)$$

Substituting this in Eq. (9-23), we see that $(H)_{\mathrm{av}}$ becomes equivalent to the energy E appearing in Schrödinger's equation, thereby verifying in this case our formula for finding the average of a function of coordinates and momenta.

Similar verifications can be carried out in all cases. As an example of a quantity whose value can be calculated in this way, we may mention the orbital angular momentum. One can set up the operators connected with x, y, and z components of angular momentum from the expressions in classical mechanics for these quantities. When we find the average values of these components, for the hydrogen wave functions, we find that the x and y components average to zero, and the z component averages to $mh/2\pi$, as we should expect. The reason for the zero average of the x and y components is that the component of angular momentum in the xy plane is as likely to be pointing in one direction as in another. To get the magnitude of the angular momentum, we can set up an operator representing its square. When we do this, we find that the average value of this quantity is $l(l + 1)(h/2\pi)^2$. This gives us a very interesting compromise between the value $k^2(h/2\pi)^2$ of Bohr theory, where $k = l + 1$, and the value $l^2(h/2\pi)^2$ which we should have been inclined to guess from the way in which the azimuthal quantum number proves to be l. Neither extreme is quite right; one must really make a compromise between them. This is one of the simplest cases in which the wave mechanics leads directly to quantities like $l(l + 1)$, where the Bohr theory led to quantities like k^2.

9-7. The General Formulation of Quantum Mechanics. In Eq. (9-24), we have an alternative statement of Schrödinger's equation, and this statement is in a form which can be readily generalized to all sorts of problems. What we do is to set up the energy H, according to classical mechanics. Then we convert each momentum component, when it appears, into an operator, by replacing it by $-i\hbar\partial/\partial q$, where q is the corresponding coordinate. This gives us an operator representing H. Schrödinger's equation is then

$$Hu = Eu \qquad (9\text{-}25)$$

where u is the wave function. This very simple statement seems to be perfectly general and precise.

We notice that this formula implies that u is a function of all the coordinates appearing in the problem, and that H involves differentiations with respect to all these coordinates. If there are N particles, and each has three coordinates, there will be $3N$ coordinates, so that u will represent a wave, not in ordinary three-dimensional space (as in the problem of one particle, which we have treated up to now), but in a $3N$-dimensional space. This need not frighten us; we do not have to try to visualize this space, and really we merely have to solve the equation for u, and use the function so obtained in the statistical interpretation of wave mechanics. The really frightening feature of the situation is not anything relating to the interpretation of the problem, which is straightforward; it is rather the extreme mathematical difficulty of solving such a differential equation as Eq. (9-25), in a many-dimensional space. Mathematical physics has not had to face such problems before, and a great deal of the work done on wave mechanics, ever since 1926, has dealt with the extremely hard problem of finding valid mathematical approximations to the solution of Schrödinger's equation.

We have stated that the interpretation of the Schrödinger wave function, even in its many-dimensional form, is not difficult, and this is true. If the coordinates are $q_1, \ldots, q_n$, so that u is a function of these variables, we merely assume that $u^*u \, dq_1, \ldots, dq_n$ is the probability of finding the coordinate q_1 in the range dq_1, q_2 in dq_2, and so on down to q_n. This gives us straightforward statistical information, and we could not have a statistical theory of this type unless u depended on all the coordinates.

Now that we know how to state Schrödinger's equation in a general case, it is simple to set it up for such a problem as a complex atom, or a molecule. We merely have to set up the energy, and the wave function, involving all the coordinates of the problem. For instance, in an atom, the energy operator involves the kinetic-energy operators of all the particles, the Coulomb attractions between all electrons and the nucleus, and the Coulomb repulsions between pairs of electrons. For a molecule, we need also the Coulomb repulsions between the nuclei. Such a Schrödinger equation, then, can be formulated for complicated problems to which the older Bohr theory could not even be approximately applied, and we are sure that the equation has solutions, so that it is merely a matter of mathematical difficulty to find the energy levels and wave functions of real atoms and molecules and solids. We have already indicated in Sec. 9-1 that, in the two problems of several particles to which it has been applied with great accuracy—the helium atom and the hydrogen molecule—the results agreed perfectly with experiment. We do not doubt that the same thing would hold in more complicated cases, if only the calculation could be made; but until the present, we have had to be content with approximate solutions of far poorer accuracy.

There is one generalization of Eq. (9-25), which Schrödinger made in the very early days of quantum mechanics: the extension to a function involving the time. Schrödinger argued in the following way: In the theory of relativity, as we have already mentioned, there is a certain parallelism between the three coordinates x, y, z of space, and the time t. Often these are treated as the four components of a four-dimensional vector. When this is done, it then appears that the three components of momentum p_x, p_y, p_z are associated with a fourth quantity, the energy E. There is not a complete parallelism; if we use x, y, z, t, then it appears that we should use p_x, p_y, p_z, $-E$ as the four components of a momentum vector, the minus sign being associated with the fourth component. Schrödinger then asked why, if we transform p_x into an operator $-i\hbar\partial/\partial x$, and so on, we should not transform E into an operator $i\hbar\partial/\partial t$. If we were to do so, we should have a wave function, which we now shall call ψ, which would be a function of all the coordinates of the system and of the time.   In place of Eq. (9-25), we should have

$$H\psi = i\hbar \frac{\partial \psi}{\partial t} \tag{9-26}$$

Schrödinger examined the consequences of this equation, and they proved to be reasonable.   Therefore he postulated that this was the equation for the wave function involving the time.   It is the equation whose application to the motion of a wave packet we have already mentioned.

From Eq. (9-26), we can get back to Eq. (9-25) very easily in a case in which the system is in a stationary state.   For then we can assume that $\psi(q_1, \ldots, q_n, t) = u(q_1, \ldots, q_n) f(t)$, where $f(t)$ is a function of t to be determined.   If we substitute this formula in Eq. (9-26), the operator H operates only on u (since it involves the coordinates, but not the time), while the time derivative operates only on f.   We then have

$$(Hu)f(t) = u \left(i\hbar \frac{df}{dt} \right) \tag{9-27}$$

Let us divide both sides of Eq. (9-27) by $uf(t)$, obtaining

$$\frac{Hu}{u} = i\hbar \frac{1}{f} \frac{df}{dt} \tag{9-28}$$

Here we have a characteristic situation in the theory of differential equations: the quantity on the left side of Eq. (9-28) is a function of the coordinates alone, that on the right a function of the time alone. The equation must hold for all values of all coordinates, and at all values of the time; this is impossible unless each side is constant.   Let this constant be called E.   Then from the left side of Eq. (9-28), we find that $Hu = Eu$, or Schrödinger's equation in the form of Eq. (9-25), not involving the time.   From the right side, we have

$$i\hbar \frac{df}{dt} = Ef \tag{9-29}$$

whose solution is easily found to be

$$f = \text{constant} \exp - \frac{iEt}{\hbar} = \text{constant} \exp - \frac{2\pi iEt}{h}$$

That is, the time part indicates a sinusoidal oscillation (expressed in complex exponential form) with a frequency E/h. The wave function corresponding to a stationary state, then, has the form

$$\psi = u(q_1, \ldots, q_n) \exp - \frac{2\pi i E t}{h} \qquad (9\text{-}30)$$

A solution like Eq. (9-30) represents a single stationary state; but it can be shown that a sum, or linear combination, of solutions like that of Eq. (9-30), connected with different stationary states, gives a more general solution of Schrödinger's equation. That is, if u_m is the wave function, and E_m the energy, associated with the mth stationary state, we can set up a solution of the form

$$\psi = \sum (m) c_m u_m \exp - \frac{2\pi i E_m t}{h} \qquad (9\text{-}31)$$

where the c_m's are constants. It is such a solution that we must use in discussing wave packets and similar problems; those are cases in which we cannot say that the particles are in definite stationary states, but in a certain sense are having transitions from one stationary state to another.

The function of Eq. (9-31) is, in fact, well suited to show properties of transitions between stationary states. We can show this by setting up the quantity $\psi^*\psi$, the probability function. We can write the product of two single sums, like Eq. (9-31), in the form of a double sum. Thus, we can write $\psi^*\psi$ in the form

$$\psi^*\psi = \sum (m,n) c_m^* c_n u_m^* u_n \exp \frac{2\pi i (E_m - E_n)t}{h} \qquad (9\text{-}32)$$

Equation (9-32) contains terms of two sorts: first, terms for which $m = n$, which are independent of time; secondly, terms for which $m \neq n$, varying sinusoidally with the time with a frequency $(E_m - E_n)/h$. This frequency is just that given by Bohr's frequency condition for the radiation emitted on the transition between the mth and nth states; and it is in such a way that the frequency condition finds its way into wave mechanics.

The terms for $m = n$, Eq. (9-30), are assumed to be connected with stationary states, and those with $m \neq n$ with transitions between stationary states, and there is an elaborate theory worked out to interpret the meanings of the various terms. Part of this meaning comes when we find the average value of an operator F, a function of coordinates and momenta. We do this according to Eq. (9-22), with

u replaced by ψ. When we do so, we find that

$$(F)_{\text{av}} = \sum (m,n)c_m^* c_n F_{mn} \exp \frac{2\pi i(E_m - E_n)t}{h} \qquad (9\text{-}33)$$

where

$$F_{mn} = \int, \ldots, \int u_m^* F\left(q_1, \ldots, q_n, -i\hbar \frac{\partial}{\partial q_1}, \ldots, -i\hbar \frac{\partial}{\partial q_n}\right)$$

$$u_n \, dq_1, \ldots, dq_n \qquad (9\text{-}34)$$

The quantities F_{mn} are called matrix components of the operator F, those for which $m = n$ are called diagonal matrix components, and those for which $m \neq n$ are nondiagonal matrix components. We can see from Eq. (9-33) that the diagonal matrix components are associated with the terms independent of time or with the time average of the quantity F, while the nondiagonal matrix components come into the terms depending on time, and are associated with the various transitions between stationary states.

It is these matrix components which were used in the matrix mechanics, developed by Heisenberg and others just before the development of wave mechanics. There are very interesting algebraic relations between the matrix components of various quantities, which were discovered without the use of Eq. (9-34) connecting them with the wave function. One can, in fact, formulate a great deal of quantum mechanics in matrix form, and for some purposes this is more convenient than the formulation in terms of the Schrödinger wave function, but generally it is less convenient and less easy to understand physically.

There is one mathematical principle, closely allied with Schrödinger's equation, which is extremely useful in looking for approximate solutions of Schrödinger's equation. This is what is called the variation principle. Let us suppose we are looking for a solution of Eq. (9-25), $Hu = Eu$. Let us suppose that we do not have the correct wave function u, but have a function, containing some parameters, which we think may approximate the true function fairly well, for suitable values of the parameters. We seek a criterion for choosing these parameters so as to get the best possible approximation. Let us then form the average value of the energy $\int u^* Hu \, dv$ for this function. This is an extension of Eq. (9-23); the integration $\int dv$ symbolizes integration over all the coordinates of the system. The function u is assumed to be normalized. Then one can show that, if we are trying to approximate the ground state of the system, the integral $\int u^* Hu \, dv$ is always greater than the true energy E, but approaches it more closely, the more closely u approaches the true wave function.

We can then use this principle in the following way: We can vary the parameters in our approximate function u, and compute the integral as a function of these parameters. Then we can find those values of the parameters which make the energy integral a minimum. These values will give the best approximation to the true wave function; and the energy of the true solution of Schrödinger's equation will be lower than the energy integral, computed for the approximation function. It is interesting to note that, in the very accurate calculations of the wave functions of the hydrogen molecule and helium atom to which we have referred, this variation principle was used, and as the wave functions improved, the energies constantly went down, finally approaching the correct energy extremely closely for the best approximate functions.

Very often one approximates a wave function by a linear combination of a number of different functions. Then the variation principle allows us to find the coefficients of the linear combination which best approximates the true function. This method of combining solutions is very frequently met in chemical problems, where we can set up different functions, generally called unperturbed functions, each of which might be considered to give a plausible approximation to the ground state. By making a linear combination of these functions, we can get a better approximation. This method of combining functions is sometimes called by the name of resonance, and is a very characteristic process in the approximate solution of Schrödinger's equation.

In this chapter, we have tried to give a general idea of the nature of wave mechanics. It was a subject which developed with extraordinary speed. The time was ripe for it, it involved types of mathematics which were familiar to a great many mathematical physicists, and all the developments mentioned in this chapter were worked out within a year or two. Wave mechanics has so permeated physics, since its discovery in 1926, that one can hardly understand any of the subsequent developments in physics without having some idea of its methods. We have not tried to give anything more than a little familiarity with its concepts and its language, and the student will have to study much further than is possible in this book, before he really understands it. Nevertheless, with this very superficial sketch, it is possible to understand some of the most important consequences of wave mechanics. In the next chapter we shall go on to consider some of the interesting features and developments of wave mechanics as they concern application to problems in the structure of molecules and solids.

PROBLEMS

9-1. An electron moves with energies of 1 ev; 100 ev; 10,000 ev. Find the de Broglie wavelength in each case, and consider whether the wavelengths would be appropriate for use in electron diffraction experiments with crystals.

9-2. A hydrogen atom moves with the energy $\frac{3}{2}kT$ associated with $T = 300°K$. Find the de Broglie wavelength, and consider whether atoms of such energies would be expected to be diffracted by crystals.

9-3. Using the results of Sec. 9-2, write down the solution of Schrödinger's equation for a linear oscillator corresponding to the ground state $n = 0$. Substitute this solution in Schrödinger's equation, Eq. (9-5), and prove that it satisfies the equation.

9-4. Compute the solutions of Schrödinger's equation for the linear oscillator for $n = 0, 1, 2, 3$, from Eqs. (9-6) and (9-9), plot the functions, and show that they agree with Fig. 9-2.

9-5. The radial charge density in an atom is defined as the charge contained in a shell bounded by two spheres of radii r and $r + dr$, divided by dr. That is, it is proportional to $4\pi r^2$ times the square of the part of the wave function depending on r. Find the radius at which the radial charge density is a maximum for the $1s$, $2p$, $3d$ states of hydrogen. Show that these radii are the same as the radii of the corresponding circular orbits in Bohr's theory.

9-6. Substitute the wave function for the ground state of hydrogen into Schrödinger's equation for hydrogen, and prove by direct calculation that it is a solution of the equation.

9-7. Proceed as in Prob. 9-6 for the $2p$ state of $m = 0$, for hydrogen. If you wish to do this in rectangular coordinates, note that $r \cos \theta = z$.

9-8. A parallel beam of electrons of energy 100 ev passes through a slit of width 10^{-4} cm. Find the angle through which the diffracted beam will be spread. How far from the slit must we go in order that the beam should be spread by diffraction into an appreciably greater breadth than the width 10^{-4} cm of the slit?

9-9. One interesting, simple problem in wave mechanics is that of a particle in a potential well; that is, a region in which the potential is constant, but surrounded by walls at which the potential goes infinite. It can be shown that at such a potential barrier the wave function must go to zero, so that the wave function inside the well will satisfy Schrödinger's equation for a constant potential, but must go to zero on the walls. Consider a particle in a one-dimensional potential well extending from $x = 0$ to $x = L$. Find its wave functions and energy levels.

9-10. A three-dimensional potential well in the form of a cube extends from $x = 0$ to $x = L$, $y = 0$ to $y = L$, $z = 0$ to $z = L$. Show that an appropriate solution of Schrödinger's equation is

$$u = \sin \frac{n_1 \pi x}{L} \sin \frac{n_2 \pi y}{L} \sin \frac{n_3 \pi z}{L}$$

where n_1, n_2, n_3 are integers which serve as quantum numbers. Find the energy associated with the state of quantum numbers n_1, n_2, n_3.

CHAPTER 10

ATOMS, MOLECULES, AND SOLIDS

10-1. Introduction. With the formulation of Schrödinger's equation in 1926, a great new world was opened to the theoretical physicist. Here was a new branch of mathematical physics, one which showed every indication of explaining all the puzzling features of atomic structure which had been the main concern of the physicist for the preceding twenty-five years, but which at the same time gave promise of explaining all the properties of molecules and solids, of all the material objects which we see around us. The years from 1926 to about 1930 saw an almost bewildering number of striking applications of wave mechanics to problems in the structure of matter, and by 1930 we had at least a good beginning toward the theories of most aspects of the subject. Progress then began to slow down somewhat. This was only natural. The easy things were done first; and physicists then began to be increasingly aware of the fact that wave mechanics is really an exceedingly difficult branch of mathematical physics. In addition, the study of the nucleus began to take on new life, and more and more physicists went into that field, which we shall describe in the next chapter. The study of molecules and solids, though it continued through the 1930's, gradually declined in interest, and during the war it practically stopped.

Since the war, however, it has built up again more vigorously than ever. New attention is being focused on the mathematical problems, and the newly developed computing machines are proving capable of overcoming mathematical difficulties that had seemed nearly insuperable ten or fifteen years before. Furthermore, new experimental advances were turning practical attention more and more toward problems in the structure of solids. The use of semiconductors in electronics started in a large way in wartime radar development, and with the development of the transistor in the last few years, it has led to very important practical applications. Ferromagnetic materials, particularly the ferrites, are finding greatly increased applications. The study of the mechanical properties of solids, such as breaking strength and plasticity, has gone so far that it is proving an important

guide to practical metallurgy.   New experimental methods of studying
solids have become available: neutron diffraction, magnetic resonance,
and others.

All these things have turned the attention of the scientist to the
problems of molecules and solids more insistently than ever before, and
at the moment, the study of the solid state has become one of the two
most active fields of physics, nuclear physics being the other one.   In
this chapter we shall survey rather briefly this development of interest
in molecules and solids, from 1926 to the present.   We must understand at the outset that it is the added understanding of the structure
of matter given by the wave mechanics which has been at the bottom
of all this development.   Hence we shall base our discussion primarily
on the working out of those wave-mechanical ideas, and on those
aspects of the study of solids which grew out of them.

We have stated that discoveries in the application of wave mechanics
to molecules and solids came thick and fast in the years from 1926 to
1930.   They came so fast, in fact, that it was hard to sort them out,
and this to some extent has led to a confused view in the theory of
molecules and solids, which has persisted even to the present.   In an
effort to make the subject rather clearer, we shall separate our discussion into two parts: the one-electron theory of atoms, molecules,
and solids, and the effects of electron interactions.   The one-electron
picture is an extension of the sort of argument we used in Chap. 7: a
study of matter by replacing the many-electron problem by a one-
electron problem, in which a single electron moves in the field of all the
nuclei, and of smeared-out charge distributions representing the other
electrons.   The effects of electron interaction form an extension of our
discussion of Chap. 8, where we took up the structure of complex
atoms.   We found it desirable to separate our earlier discussion into
these two topics, for historical reasons as well as for clarity.   In our
present discussion of molecules and solids, as we have said, the two
aspects of the problem have grown up together; but we can understand
them better if we take them separately.

The one-electron treatment is, as we should expect, mathematically
simpler than the electron-interaction problem, for it treats merely the
motion of a single electron in a potential field, rather than a many-
electron problem.   We can well start our discussion with Hartree's
self-consistent field treatment of atoms, a direct outgrowth of the discussion of Chap. 7.   But then we can go on to problems of molecular
and solid-state structure which we have not been able to handle at all
so far.   In molecules, this method becomes that known as the method
of molecular orbitals, developed in the late 1920's by Hund in Germany,

by Mulliken in the United States, and by Lennard-Jones in England. This method showed itself capable of giving a great deal of qualitative information, and some quantitative results, on the structure of diatomic and polyatomic molecules. In solids, the corresponding treatment is that of energy bands, and the Fermi statistics. Many persons contributed to this treatment in the late 1920's and early 1930's: Bloch, Peierls, Bethe, and Sommerfeld, in Germany, Brillouin in France, Wilson in England, Wigner and Seitz in America, and many others. It is this theory which has been so successful in treating the properties of semiconductors, and hence has been so much in the forefront of recent technical advances.

The first steps in the electron-interaction problem, like those in the one-electron treatment, came immediately after the discovery of Schrödinger's equation. The first striking results were those of Heisenberg, in 1926, on the explanation of the singlets and triplets in the helium spectrum. We have pointed out in Chap. 8 how puzzling it was that the energy difference between these states was so large, even though they differed only in the orientation of the spins of the electrons. Heisenberg showed that a completely new effect, usually called exchange, appeared when these problems were handled by wave mechanics, which had not even been suspected in the older quantum theory, and which explained the observed separations very successfully. This started a line of research in which Hund, Wigner, and various others took part, trying to set up a theory of complex atomic spectra according to the wave mechanics, incorporating both the vector model of Chap. 8 and Heisenberg's new ideas. This research was carried to a conclusion by the author in 1929.

Another important step in the electron-interaction problem was the theory of the structure of the hydrogen molecule, given by Heitler and London in Germany in 1927. They set up an approximate treatment of this molecule in which the main attention was focused on the electron interaction, whereas in the method of molecular orbitals the main attention was focused on the one-electron behavior. Both methods had their successes. Unfortunately, a rivalry between these two methods developed, in the minds of many physicists and chemists, some being partisans of the one method, some of the other. It is really only since the war that this rivalry has died down, and that it has been realized that a treatment of molecular structure is so difficult mathematically that, even with all the facilities of modern digital computers, it is still almost impossible to get solutions of any molecular problems except the simplest ones which have more than qualitative correctness.

Still another important step in the electron-interaction problem was also taken by Heisenberg—his treatment of ferromagnetism in 1928. For a number of years, the experts in the study of magnetism had been greatly puzzled as to the physical reasons why the elementary magnets in such a material as iron lined up when it was magnetized. It had been established that it was the electron spins in neighboring atoms which formed these elementary magnets, but the energy differences between the states when they were lined up and when they were not proved to be far greater than could be explained by magnetic interaction forces. Heisenberg, in his 1928 paper, suggested that this problem might be similar to the problem of atomic multiplets, and that the same features of wave mechanics which resulted in the energy difference between singlets and triplets in helium might also result in the lining up of the spins in a ferromagnetic solid. This suggestion has been the start of a long series of studies of ferromagnetism, resulting in a universal conviction that Heisenberg's fundamental idea was correct. Here, unfortunately, as in the molecular problem, it is extremely difficult to get quantitative results out of the theory, on account of its great mathematical complication. But in both of these problems, progress is being made at present, with the new mathematical facilities of the digital computers.

We shall now go ahead and describe more in detail some of these results, both of the one-electron and the electron-interaction treatments of the properties of atoms, molecules, and solids. Then we shall close the chapter with a section indicating the present status of our understanding of the solid state.

10-2. The Self-consistent Field Method for Atoms. Hartree in 1928 proposed the method of the self-consistent field, for getting an approximate solution of problems in atomic structure. He assumed that the electrostatic effect of all electrons but one, on that remaining one, can be approximately replaced by the electrostatic effect resulting from their time-average charge density, as determined from their Schrödinger wave functions. This potential, plus that of the nucleus, will be approximately spherical; Hartree simplified by using its spherical average. He then solved Schrödinger's equation for this spherical problem, found the wave functions of the various quantum states in this problem, found the average charge densities connected with these various wave functions, which by the principles of Chap. 9 are proportional to the squares of the magnitudes of the wave functions, and demanded that these charge densities be the same ones he had started with. This was his condition of self-consistency. He found that in practice he could obtain such a self-consistent field by a method of successive approximations.   If he started with charge densities which were not quite right, went through the procedure we have sketched, and came out at the end with new wave functions and charge densities, the mathematics usually was such that the new ones were closer to the self-consistent values than the original ones, so that after a number of repetitions of this process the method converged, and finally the self-consistent condition was fulfilled, to a satisfactory degree of accuracy.

In carrying through the solution of the self-consistent problem, Hartree made essentially the same three postulates which we have described in Sec. 7-4: first, the postulate of self-consistency; secondly, the Pauli exclusion principle, limiting the allowed number of electrons in any shell; third, the postulate that the electrons fill the lowest available orbits.   Thus, this procedure is essentially simply a rephrasing of the arguments of Chap. 7, in wave-mechanical language.

Two things result from Hartree's calculation.   First, we have the energy levels of the various electrons in their central fields.   Hartree compared these with the observed energies required to remove the various electrons from the atom, as known from X-ray and optical data, and found that they agreed well; a comparison, for Rb^+, is shown in Table 10-1.   It was soon proved by the Dutch physicist Koopmans

TABLE 10-1. OBSERVED TERM VALUES FOR Rb^+, AS COMPARED WITH VALUES CALCULATED BY HARTREE'S METHOD (OBSERVED VALUES AS IN TABLE 7-1)

Electron	Energy observed, Rydbergs	Energy computed
$1s$	1,119.4	1,102.3
$2s$	152.0	144.2
$2p$	137.2	132.2
$3s$	23.7	21.28
$3p$	17.4	16.64
$3d$	8.3	8.40
$4s$	2.3	2.707
$4p$	1.46	1.586

that this agreement was to be expected theoretically.   We notice in particular that the order of the energy levels, as computed, agrees with the observed order, so that we should have been able to deduce directly from the calculation what were the lowest stationary states, and hence which states would be filled in the ground state of the atom.   In other words, a completely theoretical calculation of the energy levels of all the atoms became possible, including the question as to which states were occupied, so that the theory of the periodic table was made quantitative.

The discrepancies between the observed and computed energies in Table 10-1 are not a result either of experimental error or inaccuracy in computation, but rather a result of the fact that Hartree's method itself represents an approximation. The electrons do not really move in an averaged central field produced by the other electrons, but rather are constantly interacting with each other; and the discrepancies in Table 10-1 are a measure of the inaccuracy in the assumption of the

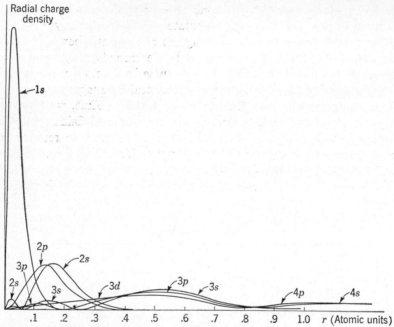

Fig. 10-1. Radial charge density for inner electrons of Rb, determined from self-consistent field.

self-consistent field. Some of these discrepancies are removed by the treatment of electron interaction which we shall sketch later, but even that treatment, as usually carried out, is only an approximation, still not leading to perfect agreement between theory and experiment. A really accurate solution of Schrödinger's equation is, as we have stated, still too much to hope for by any of the existing approximation methods, for any but the simplest problems.

The other thing which Hartree's calculations lead to, besides the energy, is a set of wave functions for the various electrons, and hence the charge density, and its subdivision into the various shells of electrons. A radial charge density distribution for Rb$^+$ is given in Fig.

10-1. We see the way in which the radii increase from one shell to another. The figures previously given in Table 7-2 represent the radii of maximum charge density in the various shells, as determined from calculations like those shown graphically in Fig. 10-1. These calculations form the best knowledge which we have for the charge densities inside the various atoms. We remember that X-ray diffraction can give information about these charge densities; but the X-ray measurements are not in general so accurate as the calculations, though they agree with them in most cases within the error of experiment.

This sketch of Hartree's calculations will show that they lead to results in good qualitative agreement with our knowledge of the structure of atoms, as determined by spectroscopy and other sources of information, and that the quantitative agreement, though not perfect, is good, considering the approximate nature of the method. Calculations by these methods have now been made for a variety of atoms, though not for nearly all of them.

10-3. The Method of Molecular Orbitals. It did not take long after the development of wave mechanics to extend it to the problem of molecular formation, a problem where the older quantum mechanics had been helpless. The first step was the calculation of the structure of the H_2^+ ion, consisting of a single electron moving in the field of two protons. Fortunately this problem is exactly soluble in wave mechanics, and Burrau and various others discussed its solution within a year or so after the discovery of Schrödinger's equation. The energy levels and wave functions of the problem proved to be extremely interesting, and to point the way to much more complicated molecular problems. The energy levels of the two lowest states, as a function of internuclear distance, are shown in Fig. 10-2. Here we see that the lowest energy level shows the character to be expected from our discussion of molecular spectra in Chap. 8. It has a minimum, indicating stable binding. The next level is a repulsive one; some of the higher levels, which we have not shown in Fig. 10-2, are attractive, some repulsive. The energy levels as calculated agree with those as observed from the band spectrum of H_2^+.

We may well ask, what are the features which lead to the binding of the two atoms into a molecule, in the lower level of Fig. 10-2? The answer becomes somewhat clearer when we look at the wave functions. In Fig. 10-3 we show the behavior of the wave functions for the two states shown in Fig. 10-2, along the line passing through the two nuclei. We see that the function for the lower, bound state of the molecule is symmetric in the mid-point between the nuclei, while that for the upper, repulsive state is antisymmetric.

We can now see two reasons why the symmetric wave function has a low energy, the antisymmetric function a high energy. First, the symmetric wave function will have a lower potential energy. In Fig. 10-4, we show the behavior of the potential energy of an electron, in the field of two hydrogen nuclei. The potential energy goes to minus infinity near each nucleus, rises to zero at infinite distance, but

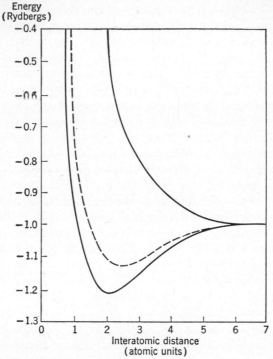

FIG. 10-2. Energies of lowest states of H_2^+, as function of interatomic distance. Dotted line indicates approximate calculation of energy of lowest state, by using linear combination of atomic orbitals.

is depressed midway between the nuclei on account of the attraction of the two nuclei. The symmetric wave function corresponds to having a large concentration of charge density in the region midway between the nuclei, where it is attracted by both nuclei; the potential energy is low, with a rather small concentration on the sides of each nucleus away from the other, where the potential energy is higher. In contrast, the antisymmetric function has its maximum charge concentration away from the region of low potential energy between the two atoms.

The second reason why the symmetric wave function has a lower energy is that it has a lower kinetic energy.   In a very general way, we see that the antisymmetric function of Fig. 10-3 looks like a sinusoidal wave with two half wavelengths, and hence with shorter wavelength than the symmetric function, which corresponds to one half wave. Thus, in the antisymmetric case, the electron has a larger momentum and larger kinetic energy.   For both reasons, then, the antisymmetric function has a higher energy than the symmetric one; and this is consistent with the fact that the antisymmetric function leads to repulsion, the symmetric one to attraction.   From this simple example, we see

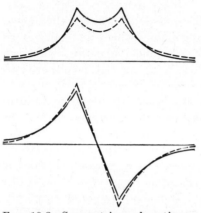

that an electron in a wave function shared between two atoms can lead to binding, while one in an antisymmetric type of wave function leads to repulsion; in later development, the wave functions of these types were called molecular orbitals, and the symmetric type was called a

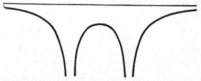

FIG. 10-3. Symmetric and antisymmetric wave functions of H_2^+ problem, along line passing through nuclei. Dotted lines, LCAO approximation.

FIG. 10-4. Potential energy in field of two hydrogen nuclei, along line of centers.

bonding orbital, the antisymmetric type an antibonding orbital.

As we have stated, this problem of H_2^+ was exactly soluble, but this unfortunately is not the case for any other molecular problem, or for any other case of two centers.   It was therefore recognized at once that it was highly desirable to have approximate methods for solving such problems, which could be applied in more complicated cases, and could be checked as to their accuracy by means of the known solution for H_2^+.   Almost immediately after the exact solution for H_2^+ was worked out, various workers set up an approximation which has been the foundation of much later work.   We notice from Fig. 10-4 that the potential near each nucleus is almost as if that nucleus were present alone.   We should expect, then, that the wave function around this nucleus would be much as if it were present alone.   We find, from Eq. (9-13), that the wave function for the $1s$ state of hydrogen is simply $\exp(-r/a_0)$.   We note that this is similar to the behavior of the wave function of H_2^+, as shown in Fig. 10-3, near the nuclei.   In Fig. 10-3, we have shown the value of the wave function along a line joining the two nuclei, and we note that as we go away from a nucleus in either direction, the distance from that nucleus is increasing.   The peaks in Fig. 10-3, at the nuclei, are similar to what we should have if the wave function fell off exponentially, like exp $(-r/a_0)$, going away from the nucleus in either direction.

The big difference between the atomic wave functions which we have just described and the molecular orbitals of Fig. 10-3 is that the former are concentrated around only one nucleus, while the latter have numerically equal values at the two nuclei, being either symmetric or antisymmetric functions with respect to the mid-point between the nuclei. It is possible to predict directly, by arguments which we shall not go into, that the real wave functions of a problem like this, with two identical potential wells as shown in Fig. 10-4, must all be either symmetric or antisymmetric, just as we have found.   It seems very natural, then, to try a wave function which consists of either the sum (for the symmetric case) or the difference (for the antisymmetric case) of the two atomic wave functions, as an approximation to the true function.   In Fig. 10-3, we have shown these sums and differences by dotted lines, and we see that they are qualitatively correct, though far from quantitatively accurate.

We can test these approximate wave functions by computing their energy, as described in Sec. 9-7.   We showed in that section that if we find the average energy, $\int u^*Hu \, dv$, for an incorrect wave function, the result will always lie higher than the true energy, but will approach it more closely the more accurate the wave function is.   Thus, we can use the average value of the energy as a test for the accuracy of an approximate wave function.   In Fig. 10-2 we have shown by a dotted line the average energy for this approximate wave function, for the symmetric state.   We see that it is not very close to the true energy, except in the limit of infinite internuclear distance, where it becomes exact; but still it is qualitatively correct.

The valuable feature of this method is that it can be extended to cases where an exact solution is impossible.   It is the method known as linear combination of atomic orbitals; the molecular orbital method using it is often abbreviated MO LCAO.   It has been used, both for a qualitative understanding of molecular orbitals and for more quantitative calculations, in a great variety of cases.   The quantitative results are not very good; the errors are always at least of the order of magnitude indicated in Fig. 10-2.   Nevertheless, in more complicated molecules any more accurate method becomes almost impossible to handle mathematically, so that we are glad to get results even of this rather poor accuracy. This LCAO method is the foundation not only of a great deal of molecular theory but also of Bloch's important approach to the study of energy bands in solids, which we shall take up in Sec. 10-4.

Now let us use our knowledge of molecular orbitals and their energy to go on to more complicated molecules than the H_2^+ ion, which we have been discussing. In that simple case, the single electron moved only in the field of the two nuclei, so that there was no electron-interaction problem to be considered. Once we go to a more complicated molecule, however, we have more than one electron, and we must use the method of the self-consistent field, unless we wish to treat the electron interactions in the more elaborate ways which we shall indicate later. A great deal of qualitative use has been made of the idea of the self-consistent field in molecular orbital calculations, though quantitative applications have been made only in the last few years. Let us first ask what we can expect qualitatively, for a simple diatomic molecule composed of two like atoms.

In such a symmetric diatomic molecule, each atom will have an identical charge distribution for its electrons. Then the potential energy will be qualitatively similar to that of Fig. 10-4, consisting of two identical potential wells. General principles, as we have mentioned, indicate in such a case that all wave functions must be either symmetric or antisymmetric. The charge distribution of either a symmetric or an antisymmetric wave function, being proportional to the square of the wave function, will be symmetric. Hence the total electronic charge distribution will be symmetric, and our assumption that the potential function is symmetric is a self-consistent assumption. We can then approximate the wave functions, or molecular orbitals, as linear combinations of atomic orbitals, and they will have qualitatively the form shown in Fig. 10-3, and energies qualitatively like those of Fig. 10-2.

Let us now consider the H_2 molecule, the next more complicated symmetric diatomic molecule after H_2^+. We have two electrons, and both of them can go into the symmetric, or bonding, orbital, one with each spin. It seems reasonable to hope that the model of the molecule, as set up in this way, using linear combinations of atomic orbitals as approximate molecular orbitals, will show bonding. The results of such a calculation are in qualitative agreement with observation for hydrogen, though the quantitative agreement is not very good. It is good enough, however, to show that we are on the right track in the calculation, and this furnishes a simple model of the covalent or homopolar chemical bond, the type of bond which one finds between two atoms which, like hydrogen, are identical or have equal valences.

We shall mention only a few further applications of molecular orbitals, and of their description of the covalent bond. For one thing, the method gives a very convincing explanation of the reason why the inert gases, and closed shells of ions, repel rather than attracting. Let us consider, as the simplest example, the interaction of two helium atoms. The energy levels of the molecular orbitals will be similar to those shown in Fig. 10-2, but we now have four electrons to be taken care of. Since we can accommodate only two electrons, one of each spin, in an orbital, we shall have two electrons in the bonding orbital of lower energy and two in the antibonding orbital of higher energy. The bonding and antibonding effects approximately cancel; more care ful calculation shows that the antibonding preponderates, resulting in a net repulsion. In other words, the atoms do not attract each other to form a molecule, and the repulsion is just what gives them their finite size. The calculated repulsion can be compared with that found from the kinetic theory of gases, from the equation of state, viscosity, and other properties, depending on the atomic dimensions, and the agreement proves to be very good.

Similar results apply for the other inert gases, and also for the closed shells of ions. For instance, in a molecule or crystal of NaCl, we suppose that the atoms are ionized, to form Na^+ and Cl^- ions, the first having just the same number and arrangement of electrons as in the neon atom, the second being like the argon atom. For the same sort of reason we have just sketched, these ions will repel each other at close enough distances. In contrast to the inert-gas atoms, however, they will attract each other on account of the Coulomb attraction of the oppositely charged ions, at larger distances. Hence we shall have a curve similar to that of Fig. 10-5, giving the energy of the two ions, as a function of internuclear distance, made up of a Coulomb attraction at large distances and a repulsion superposed on it at small distances. Here, then, we have the mechanism for the interatomic attraction and repulsion of ions, in contrast to the covalent binding which we have found in H_2.

The study of chemical binding, by the molecular orbital method, has proceeded far enough in the last few years so that we have a good qualitative idea of the various sorts of chemical compounds. In particular, the method has been applied to a great variety of organic compounds, and is giving a good general understanding of the nature of the chemical bonds met in those compounds, the difference between the aliphatic, or chain, compounds and the aromatic, or ring, compounds, and so on. This is not the place to go into such chemical details, but in the theory of chemical binding we find one illustration of the way in which our understanding of the wave mechanics of electrons has led to completely new concepts of the structure of matter.

10-4. Energy Bands in Solids and the Fermi Statistics. In Fig. 10-2, we have seen the way in which a single energy level of two isolated atoms, in the problem of H_2^+, becomes split into two levels as the atoms approach. The lower energy level corresponds to a bonding orbital, with charge distribution concentrated between the atoms,

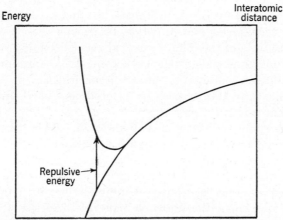

FIG. 10-5. Energy of Na^+ and Cl^- ions, as function of internuclear distance.

while the upper level corresponds to an antibonding orbital, with the electrons avoiding the mid-points between the atoms. This is merely the simplest case of a much more general problem, which was discussed in the early days of wave mechanics, and which led to profound advances in the theory of solids. Suppose, instead of two atoms, we had a chain of N atoms, equally spaced? Or, to go to three dimensions, suppose we had N atoms, arranged in a regular lattice such as we find in a crystal? This problem was considered by Bloch, Brillouin, Peierls, Bethe, and numerous other workers in the few years following 1926, and the general results were worked out in detail, though exact numerical calculations of the energy levels and wave functions are very difficult to carry through.

The result of all this work was that each energy level of the separated atoms becomes split, as the atoms approach, not into two but into N levels; the case of a diatomic molecule is the special case where $N = 2$. The lowest energy level is bonding, and the highest one antibonding, as in the case of the diatomic molecule, and as a matter of fact the energy separation between these extreme cases is about what it is in the diatomic molecule. But if N is very large, as it will be if it represents the number of atoms in a crystal, energy levels will be distributed between these two limits practically continuously. In other words, each energy level of an atom will for practical purposes broaden into a continuous band, called an energy band.

Several different methods were used for arriving at these results. Perhaps the most straightforward was that used by Bloch. It was essentially an extension of the MO LCAO method which we have just been discussing for molecules. We can easily describe the type of wave function used by Bloch. Suppose we first set up a plane wave, of arbitrary wavelength and direction, traversing the crystal. Let us find the amplitude of this plane wave, at any particular atom. Then Bloch used this amplitude as the coefficient of the appropriate atomic orbital, in a linear combination of atomic orbitals.

We can illustrate this process by a one-dimensional problem. Let us assume that we have atoms at $x = 0, a, 2a, \ldots$ Let the wave be expressed in exponential form, as $\exp(2\pi i x/\lambda)$. Then, the coefficients of the atomic orbitals located on the atoms at $0, a, 2a, \ldots$, according to Bloch, are to be given by the values $1, \exp(2\pi i a/\lambda), \exp(4\pi i a/\lambda)$, $\ldots$ We note that if the wavelength is infinite, these coefficients will all be equal; that is, this wave function has an analogy to the symmetric function in the diatomic molecule. If the wavelength is given by the relation that a, the distance between molecules, is a half wavelength, the successive coefficients will be $1, \exp(\pi i), \exp(2\pi i)$, $\ldots$, or $1, -1, +1 \ldots$ In this case, in other words, the coefficients of the atomic functions on successive atoms are equal in magnitude, but have opposite sign, as in the antisymmetric function with the diatomic molecule.

Between these two limiting cases, it is not hard to prove in the case of a finite crystal with N atoms that there are just N possible values of wavelength, leading to the N states predicted by the energy-band theory, whose energies all lie closely spaced between the energy values appropriate for the symmetric and antisymmetric states of the diatomic molecule. It is by use of arguments of this general type that one is led to the existence of energy bands. Furthermore, we see that each wave function has a certain resemblance to a plane wave, and as a matter of fact this resemblance to a plane wave, or to the wave function of a free electron, is very far-reaching, and of great use in the application of this theory to electrical conductivity.

In Fig. 10-2, we note that the energies of symmetric and antisymmetric states for a diatomic molecule coincide at infinite internuclear distance, and begin to spread apart as the atoms approach.   One can, as a matter of fact, show that the spreading begins to be appreciable when the atomic wave functions on the two atoms overlap significantly. We may expect that the same sort of thing should happen in a crystal. We imagine the crystal to remain always geometrically similar to itself, but to have a lattice spacing which can vary, all the way from infinity down to finite values.

In Fig. 10-6, we show the energy levels of the sodium crystal, computed by one of the approximate methods for solving Schrödinger's equation for a crystal lattice.   It is plain how the various atomic energy levels $2p$, $3s$, etc., broaden into bands as the atoms approach.   As in the molecule, a given level proves to start broadening, as the atoms come closer, when the corresponding atomic orbitals begin to overlap appreciably.   A consequence of this dependence of the broadening on the overlapping of the atomic orbitals is that the levels of higher principal quantum number, which are

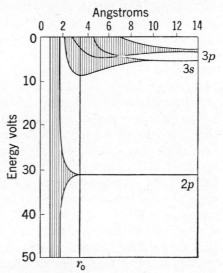

FIG. 10-6. Energy bands of metallic sodium as function of internuclear distance.

connected with atomic orbitals which spread out far from the nucleus, will broaden at larger interatomic distances than those of smaller principal quantum number.

We must now consider how the electrons fill up these bands.   Each band can hold just as many electrons per atom as the corresponding atomic levels which were split to form the band.   Thus, in sodium, the bands arising from the $1s$, $2s$, and $2p$ atomic levels will just accommodate the K and L electrons of sodium.   Furthermore, at the actual internuclear distance in the crystal, they will not be appreciably split; the X-ray levels, in other words, will be just about as sharp in the metal as in the isolated atom.   On the other hand, the sodium atom has one electron in the $3s$ state, and correspondingly there will be one electron per atom in the band arising from this state, which is broadened considerably.   This band, however, could accommodate two electrons per atom, one of each spin.   Consequently it will be only half filled, the electrons going into the lower half of the band.   Just as in the molecular case, these lower energy levels correspond to wave functions of a bonding type, which explains in a qualitative way the binding energy of the sodium crystal. In fact, a more careful treatment along these lines, taking account of the electron interaction, gives a good quantitative value for the cohesive energy of sodium, the energy required to break it up into its atoms. It is clear, then, that the type of binding in a metal like sodium is not completely different in its general nature from covalent binding.

The fact that the 3s band in metallic sodium is only half filled leads to the very important consequence that this material is an electrical conductor. The physicists who first worked out the band structure of the energy levels in solids, particularly A. H. Wilson, an English physicist, showed in the early 1930's that an entirely filled band could not carry any current, when placed in an external electric field, but that a partly filled band could carry current, much as an assembly of free electrons would. In other words, the distinction between an insulator and a conductor is that in an insulator we have certain filled bands, then an energy gap above them, and empty bands above the gap; whereas in a conductor, the topmost band containing electrons is only partly filled. It is obvious from this that sodium will be a conductor; and studies similar to this, carried out for other metals, show that they should be conductors too, as of course they are known to be.

One can carry these ideas of conductivity further, and discuss many properties of metals on the basis of energy-band theory. If a band is only partly filled, the electrons can be shown to act much like free electrons, and Sommerfeld and his collaborators carried out a very significant discussion, soon after 1926, on the behavior of a simplified model of a metal in which the electrons were really free, in the sense that they moved in a field-free space, but in which they obeyed the wave mechanics. Much of this theory can be taken over with only small change to the actual case where the electrons move in a periodic potential.

One of the interesting features of the theory relates to the mechanism of electrical resistance. In the simple electron theory of Lorentz and Drude, resistance was ascribed to the existence of a mean free path for electrons, limited by collisions between the electrons and the atoms. In wave mechanics, it was shown that a free electron would not be scattered by the lattice, unless it happened to have the correct wavelength and direction for Bragg reflection; otherwise, the wave representing the electron would proceed undisturbed through the crystal. Hence a perfect crystal would have no electrical resistance. On the other hand, the waves would be scattered by irregularities in the lattice, as light is scattered by imperfections in glass or other transparent material. The irregularities which scatter the electron waves in a crystal are ordinarily of two sorts: impurity atoms and thermal agitation. The scattering by thermal agitation proves to be proportional to the absolute temperature, leading to an understanding of the empirical law that the resistance of a metal is approximately proportional to the absolute temperature. The scattering by impurity atoms leads to a small added resistance, independent of temperature, called the residual resistance. This is observed in actual metals.

Wave mechanics was thus successful in explaining the conductivity of metals. It led also to an explanation of the observed fact that the electrons in a metal have a negligible specific heat, whereas the

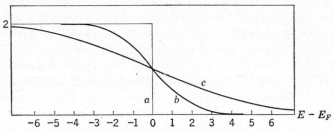

FIG. 10-7. Fermi distribution function, as function of $E - E_F$, for several temperatures. Curve a, $kT = 0$; b, $kT = 1$; c, $kT = 2.5$.

Lorentz-Drude theory would have indicated that they should act like an ordinary gas, and have a heat capacity of $\frac{3}{2}k$ per electron. The explanation comes from the Fermi-Dirac statistics, a treatment of the statistical behavior of independently moving particles subject to the exclusion principle. Fermi and Dirac discussed this problem in the very early days of wave mechanics, and derived what is called the Fermi distribution function. This function tells us the average number of electrons, of both spins, which will be found in an energy level of energy E, at a temperature T, in thermal equilibrium. The function is

$$f(E) = \frac{2}{\exp\left[(E - E_F)/kT\right] + 1} \qquad (10\text{-}1)$$

where E_F is a constant called the Fermi energy, k is Boltzmann's constant. This function $f(E)$ is shown in Fig. 10-7.

We see from Fig. 10-7 that the Fermi function is equal to two for E much less than E_F, and equal to zero for E much greater than E_F. That is, the lower states will be nearly filled, the upper ones nearly empty, and the Fermi energy forms a dividing line between these two types of levels. At the absolute zero of temperature, the Fermi function falls infinitely rapidly from the value 2 when $E < E_F$ to 0 when $E > E_F$, so that the Fermi energy indicates the top of the filled levels. It is to be fixed by the condition that the filled levels hold just enough electrons to equal those known to be present. This same condition applies in general, and in a metal one finds that to a first approximation the Fermi energy is independent of temperature.

One now sees that, as the temperature is raised from the absolute zero, a few electrons will be removed from the states slightly below the Fermi level, and will be raised to levels slightly above it. One finds that the average increase of energy of each of these electrons is of the same order of magnitude as the thermal energy $\frac{3}{2}kT$ of a free electron according to classical statistics; but the number of electrons raised is proportional to the temperature, in contrast to classical statistics, where all the electrons increase their energy. Hence it comes about that the electronic specific heat, instead of being constant as in classical theory, is proportional to the temperature, and is much less than the classical value. This is in agreement with observation. As a matter of fact, though this electronic specific heat is very small, particularly at low temperatures, nevertheless it is just at low temperatures that it is possible to observe it, for there it is proportional to T, while the specific heat of lattice vibrations, given by Debye's theory, is proportional to T^3, and hence gets much smaller at low temperatures. The observed electronic specific heats in this low-temperature range prove experimentally to be proportional to T, and the absolute magnitudes agree well with the theoretical values.

One can draw other interesting conclusions about properties of metals, and by contrast about properties of insulators. For one thing, one can conclude that metals are opaque at all frequencies, while insulators will be transparent from long wavelengths down to a definite limit, beyond which they will absorb light. The reason is simple. Immediately above the occupied energy levels in a metal, one has unoccupied levels; hence transitions are possible with absorption of photons as small as one pleases, or with arbitrarily low frequencies. On the other hand, in an insulator, any photon which is absorbed must raise an electron from the lower, occupied band to the upper, empty band, and hence must have an $h\nu$ at least equal to the gap width. The opacity of a metal can be easily described in terms of the Lorentz-Drude theory, which leads to formulas for the optical constants, at infrared wavelengths, derivable from the conductivity. These formulas are verified by experiment; but in the visible part of the spectrum, the simple formulas break down, and the band structure must be taken into account to give a good account of the optical properties. The transparency of an insulator, predicted by the theory, is also verified experimentally. One observes transparency through the visible part of the spectrum, but strong absorption starting in the ultraviolet.

Certain materials, called semiconductors, have properties intermediate between metals and insulators. Like insulators, they have certain lower bands filled, then a gap, and have the upper bands empty. The only difference between them and insulators is that the gap is narrower. Silicon and germanium are examples of such materials, and have become famous in the last few years on account of the practical applications of their semiconducting properties in the development of the transistor, a device having many of the properties of a vacuum tube.

The narrowness of the gap has several effects. In the first place, it is narrow enough so that the $h\nu$ connected with it lies in the infrared. Thus these materials are transparent in the far infrared, but are opaque in the visible, since any visible wavelength of light can raise electrons from the lower to the upper band. Secondly, the gap is narrow enough so that thermal agitation can raise electrons from the lower to the upper band, at ordinary temperatures, and this can be shown to result in conductivity. The Fermi energy E_F lies within the energy gap. Hence the only reason why we have any empty states or holes in the lower band, or electrons in the upper band, is that the tail of the Fermi function extends out to some distance from E_F. Thus, in the upper band, we are interested in $f(E)$ for an energy large compared to E_F. In Eq. (10-1), we see that under these circumstances the exponential becomes very large, and unity can be neglected compared with it, so that we can rewrite $f(E)$ as

$$f(E) \sim 2 \exp - \frac{(E - E_F)}{kT} \tag{10-2}$$

similar to the Maxwell-Boltzmann distribution law of classical statistics. Obviously the greater the gap width, or the lower the temperature, the smaller will be the exponential, or the fewer the number of electrons in the upper band. Hence, it is only with a relatively narrow gap that we get such electronic excitation; and as a rough rule of thumb, we can say that those materials in which the gap is narrow enough so that they are opaque will have appreciable electronic excitation at ordinary temperatures, while those which are transparent will not.

One can now examine the electrical conductivity of such a substance with electronic excitation, and one finds that it will carry current. The electrons in the upper band, which is ordinarily called the conduction band in such materials, will conduct electricity just as well as a similar number of electrons in a metal or other substance. In addition, the missing electrons in the lower band, which is called the valence band, will leave behind them empty energy levels, generally called holes, which can be shown to act much like positive carriers of charge, contributing also to the current. We shall then get a conductivity proportional to the number of electrons and holes, or involving the function given in Eq. (10-2). This leads to a conductivity increasing greatly with increasing temperature, and this is characteristic of semiconductors. From Eq. (10-2), it is clear that the logarithm of the conductivity should be proportional to $1/T$, or a plot of the logarithm of conductivity as a function of $1/T$ should be a straight line. Such experimental plots show good agreement with the theory. Furthermore, the gap width can be found from the slope of the curve of the logarithm of the conductivity vs. $1/T$, and also from the limit of optical absorption for the material in question. In general, these two determinations are found to agree well.

The type of semiconductor we have just been discussing is called an intrinsic semiconductor. More often in practice one uses a semiconductor containing some impurity atoms, which greatly modify its behavior. One may have a few impurity atoms, replacing atoms of the semiconductor in the lattice, whose atomic number is, for example, one unit greater than the atomic number of the atoms in the semiconductor. Each such impurity atom must then have an extra electron to make it electrically neutral. Under ordinary circumstances these extra electrons become detached from the impurity atom, and wander freely in the conduction band, furnishing conduction electrons whose number is independent of temperature, and hence leading to a conductivity independent of temperature. Such a semiconductor is called an n-type semiconductor, since it furnishes electrons, or negatively charged carriers of charge, to the conduction band. Other conductors have impurity atoms whose atomic number is one unit less than the semiconductor atoms. Each impurity atom diminishes the number of electrons in the crystal by one, leading to a hole in the valence band. Since this hole can be shown to act like a positive charge carrier, such a semiconductor is called a p-type semiconductor.

As we have mentioned earlier, semiconductors have important practical applications for electronic purposes. For instance, a junction between a sample of n-type and a sample of p-type semiconductors has rectifying properties: if a voltage is applied across the junction, the current is much greater if the voltage is applied in one direction than in the opposite direction. In this, the junction resembles a vacuum-tube diode. And by making suitable arrangements, the junction can also be made to resemble a triode, and one gets a transistor.   We shall not try to go further into these practical applications of semiconductors.

We have tried in this section to give an idea of the reasons why the energy levels of solids are split into energy bands, and the way in which the properties of the various sorts of solids, metals, insulators, and semiconductors depend on whether these bands are filled or not, and the size of the energy gaps adjacent to filled bands.   The subject has been carried a good deal further than we have indicated, in a number of directions.   For one thing, improved mathematical methods have made possible fairly accurate calculations of the energy bands, though really good calculations have so far been made in only a few cases. For another thing, calculations have been made for crystals of various types, to see whether the bands are really arranged in such a way that the theory would lead to a correct prediction as to whether the substance should be a metal, semiconductor, or insulator.   This brings the theory of energy bands into close relation with chemical bonds, and the indications are that the theory can predict correctly the type of substance.

10-5. Electron Interaction in Atoms.   In the preceding sections, we have been treating the one-electron approximation to the many-electron problem, assuming that each electron moved in the averaged field of the nuclei and all the other electrons.   This is only an approximation, however, and efforts were made immediately after the development of Schrödinger's equation to take more accurate account of electron interactions, rather than merely assuming, as in the one-electron approximation, that they affect each other only in an averaged way.   As far as atoms are concerned, these efforts were directed toward incorporating the theory of atomic multiplets into wave mechanics.   The first and decisive step in this direction was taken by Heisenberg, who discussed the spectrum of the helium atom in 1926, immediately after the discovery of Schrödinger's equation.   Further steps were taken by Dirac and Pauli, by Wigner and several others, including the author, in the years between 1926 and 1929, and the theory was largely completed by 1930.   The result of this work was to verify the general theory of complex spectra which we have described in Chap. 8, but in addition to give an explanation of the energy differences between multiplets arising from different orientations of electron spins, which were hard to understand without wave mechanics.   We can understand the situation from the simple case of helium, as well as from more complicated examples.

Suppose we have a helium atom in a configuration with one $1s$ and one $2s$ electron.   We know from the discussion of Chap. 8 that we shall have a singlet and a triplet, ^1S and ^3S, the first arising if the spins of the two electrons are antiparallel, the second if the spins are parallel. Furthermore, an empirical rule of Hund tells us that the triplet will lie lower; and observation shows that the energy difference is much greater than can be explained by magnetic interaction between the magnetic moments of the two spinning electrons. In the older quantum theory, we were left with a great puzzle: where does this energy difference come from?

Heisenberg approached this problem by considering Schrödinger's equation, in the form of Eq. (9-25), $Hu = Eu$, where H is the operator constructed from the energy. In the helium atom, with its two electrons, both the energy operator and the wave function u must depend on the coordinates of both electrons. Let us symbolize these coordinates by x_1 and x_2, as a matter of fact, the points which we are going to bring out would hold if each electron moved only in one dimension rather than three, so that we can think of these x's as representing the positions of the electrons along the x axis. The energy will be the sum of the kinetic energies of both electrons, their potential energy in the field of the nucleus, and the repulsive electrostatic energy arising from their interaction with each other. The kinetic energy of the first, plus its potential energy in the field of the nucleus, may be written in the operator form

$$f_1 = -\frac{\hbar^2}{2m}\frac{\partial^2}{\partial x_1^2} + V(x_1) \qquad (10\text{-}3)$$

The kinetic energy of the second, plus its potential energy, will be a similar expression f_2. The repulsive interaction energy will be g_{12}, a quantity which by Coulomb's law is proportional to $1/r_{12}$, where r_{12} is the distance between the two electrons. We now notice that f_1 depends only on the coordinate of the first electron, f_2 only of the second, while g_{12} depends on both. Our Schrödinger equation then is

$$(f_1 + f_2 + g_{12})u = Eu \qquad (10\text{-}4)$$

The case of the self-consistent field, without electron interaction, is that in which the term g_{12} is missing, and the potential V is modified to represent the potential of the nucleus and the averaged potential of the other electron. In this case, Eq. (10-4) reduces to $(f_1 + f_2)u = Eu$. In such a case, we can solve a one-electron problem, for one electron alone, as

$$f_1 u_1(x_1) = E_1 u_1(x_1) \qquad (10\text{-}5)$$

That is, we have set up Schrödinger's equation for a single electron, moving in the field of the nucleus and the averaged charge distribution of the other electron, and have indicated its solution, with the energy value E_1. Similarly we can set up a solution $u_2(x_2)$ for the second electron, with an energy E_2. This may be a different solution, though the differential equation it satisfies is just like Eq. (10-5), except for the energy E. Specifically, for the case of the helium atom we are considering, u_1 might correspond to the $1s$ state, u_2 to the $2s$ state, since we assume we have one electron in each state, and the quantities E_1 and E_2 might be the appropriate energies.

We can now show that the product $u_1(x_1)u_2(x_2)$ furnishes a solution of the Schrödinger equation

$$(f_1 + f_2)u = Eu \qquad (10\text{-}6)$$

which we are trying to satisfy. For we have $f_1u_1u_2 = E_1u_1u_2$, when we consider Eqs. (10-3) and (10-5), and similarly $f_2u_1u_2 = E_2u_1u_2$. Hence $(f_1 + f_2)u_1u_2 = (E_1 + E_2)u_1u_2$, so that the product u_1u_2 satisfies Eq. (10-6), with the energy $E_1 + E_2$. In other words, if two particles move independently of each other, the product of their one-electron wave functions is a solution of Schrödinger's equation for the problem of the motion of the two particles. This carries a very natural consequence. If we square the magnitude of the wave function, and multiply by $dx_1\, dx_2$, to get the probability that the first particle be found in the range dx_1 of the variable x_1, and the second be found in dx_2, the result is $|u_1(x_1)|^2\, |u_2(x_2)|^2\, dx_1\, dx_2$, which is the product of the probability that the first electron be found in dx_1, and the probability that the second be found in dx_2. This is what we should expect for particles moving independently of each other: the probability of finding the first particle in dx_1 is independent of where the second particle is located, and vice versa. We have not, then, any correlation between the motion of the two particles, in this approximation.

Heisenberg proceeded along these lines, but pointed out that another equally valid wave function, corresponding to the same energy, would be $u_2(x_1)u_1(x_2)$, corresponding to the case where the second electron was in the $1s$ state, the first in the $2s$. Since the electrons are identical, one of these solutions is as good as the other. Then he considered the actual Schrödinger equation, Eq. (10-4), with its interaction term g_{12}. He asked if either of the functions $u_1(x_1)u_2(x_2)$ or $u_2(x_1)u_1(x_2)$, or linear combinations of them, would form good approximations to solutions of this actual equation. The answer to which he came was very direct: the best approximations to solutions which we can form out of linear combinations of these functions are the sum and difference

$$u = u_1(x_1)u_2(x_2) \pm u_2(x_1)u_1(x_2) \qquad (10\text{-}7)$$

The first of these is said to be symmetric in interchange of x_1 and x_2, since it is unchanged when we make this interchange; the second, which changes sign when we make the interchange, is said to be anti-symmetric. This symmetry or antisymmetry of the solutions is not very different, in its fundamentals, from the symmetry or antisymmetry of the wave functions in the problem of the symmetric diatomic molecule, which we have considered in Sec. 10-3.

Heisenberg calculated the average energy of the helium atom in the state with one $1s$, one $2s$ electron, for the symmetric and antisymmetric wave functions. He found an energy difference between the two cases, the energy involving a term

$$\pm \int\int u_1^*(x_1)u_2^*(x_2)g_{12}u_2(x_1)u_1(x_2)\ dx_1\ dx_2 \qquad (10\text{-}8)$$

One can prove that the integral of Eq. (10-8) is always positive. Heisenberg now postulated that the symmetric wave function of Eq. (10-7) represented the singlet term, the antisymmetric wave function the triplet. The energy difference between them then came from the integral of Eq. (10-8), a quantity called an exchange integral, since the order of the wave functions preceding and following g_{12} is exchanged. This energy difference comes from a Coulomb repulsion, or is a large electrostatic term, which can be calculated from approximate values of the u's. It proves to be of the order of magnitude observed for the separation between singlet and triplet. Furthermore, Heisenberg's postulate is such as to give the lower energy for the triplet, obeying Hund's rule, which had been derived from experiment.

This hypothesis of Heisenberg had one immediate consequence, which agreed with the development of Chap. 8. Suppose that, instead of taking a case of two electrons in different states, as in the case of $1s$ and $2s$ which we have been discussing, we have both electrons in the same state, for instance, in $1s$. Then the functions u_1 and u_2 are identical with each other. In this case, in Eq. (10-7), the antisymmetric function, with the minus sign, is zero. In other words, one cannot set up an antisymmetric function if both electrons are in the same state. But this fits in precisely with the results of Sec. 8-3. There we found that two nonequivalent s electrons lead to a singlet and triplet, but that the triplet is forbidden by the exclusion principle if the two electrons are equivalent. According to Heisenberg's hypothesis, this is a very straightforward result: the wave function for the triplet state is antisymmetric in the coordinates of the electrons, and no such state can be set up in the case of equivalent electrons.

This treatment which Heisenberg gave for the two-electron problem was very simple, but somewhat arbitrary, in that he had to postulate the relation between the symmetry or antisymmetry of the wave function and the multiplicity of the state. In the next three years, as a result of a great deal of work on the part of a number of workers, a generalization for the n-electron case was worked out, which was perfectly straightforward, and at the same time showed a close analogy to the treatment of complex spectrum theory which we have given in Chap. 8. In the general case, it was found that combinations of wave functions, showing symmetry properties something like those of Eq. (10-7), but much more complicated, had to be used. The net result of this work was to set up a theory which combined the behavior of the electron spin and the effect of the exclusion principle, leading to expressions for the energies of the various multiplets which involved exchange integrals similar to that of Eq. (10-8).

Though this theory was complicated, the essential physical features were simple, and we can explain them in qualitative language, using the two-electron example. We remember, in Eq. (10-7), that if two electrons have the same spin, we are to use the antisymmetric wave function, corresponding to the $-$ sign in the equation. This wave function, which is $u_1(x_1)u_2(x_2) - u_2(x_1)u_1(x_2)$, then has a very interesting property: the function vanishes if $x_1 = x_2$, and by continuity it becomes small if x_1 and x_2 are nearly equal. In other words, when we remember the statistical meaning of the wave function, we see that this means that the probability of finding two electrons, of the same spin, close to each other, is small, and the probability of finding them at the same point of space is zero. That is, the symmetry property of the wave function has introduced a type of correlation between the motion of the electrons, which automatically keeps electrons of the same spin apart from each other. It has not introduced any such effect if the two electrons have opposite spin.

It is this effect, which is often called the exchange effect (on account of its close relation to the exchange integral of Eq. (10-8)), which is responsible for the large energy difference between singlets and triplets, which was so puzzling in the older quantum theory. Electrons of the same spin avoid each other more than electrons of opposite spin. But there is a positive repulsive term in the potential energy, coming from the repulsive interaction of electrons. If the electrons have the same spin, and are hence kept apart by the antisymmetric nature of the wave function, this positive repulsion will be less effective than if they have the opposite spin, and can get closer to each other. In other words, a positive term in the energy will be missing if they have the same spin, but will be present if they have the opposite spin; or the state with the same spin will lie lower than that with opposite spin.

But it is the triplet in which the electrons have the same spin, the singlet where they have opposite spin. Hence the triplet lies lower than the singlet, or Hund's rule. One sees, then, that this rule has a very fundamental physical explanation; but that the explanation, resulting from the rather surprising requirement that the wave function be antisymmetric, certainly has no analogy whatever in classical physics, but is rather a very typical result of the wave mechanics.

The method of treating complex spectra, which we have sketched in this section, is a very decided improvement on the simple one-electron method. It gives a description of spectrum theory which is qualitatively correct, and quantitatively agrees fairly well with experiment; the exchange integrals computed from atomic orbitals determined by the self-consistent field method are of the right order of magnitude. Nevertheless it is far from perfect. The main reason for this was found by comparing the solution for the helium atom found in this way with the very accurate calculation made by Hylleraas in the early days of wave mechanics, which we have already described.

The calculation of Hylleraas was for the ground state of the atom, where the electrons have opposite spin, and are both in the $1s$ state. Thus there is no question of antisymmetry, and the wave function, as given by our present methods, is merely $u_1(x_1)u_1(x_2)$, as far as the function of coordinates is concerned, where u_1 represents the $1s$ wave function. This wave function, in other words, does not depend on the relative positions of the two electrons. But Hylleraas's much more accurate wave function did depend on the relative position of the electrons: it decreased as the electrons approached each other. This is only natural, for they repel each other, and naturally they keep out of each other's way on account of this Coulomb repulsion, which is not taken into account in detail in the one-electron calculation. In other words, electrons of the opposite spin stay out of each other's way to some extent on account of electrostatic repulsion. This is not nearly so complete an avoidance of each other as we find with electrons of the same spin, arising from antisymmetry; but still it has to be reckoned with, and it results in a very appreciable reduction in the energy of the atom.

This effect, by which electrons of the opposite spin avoid each other, is usually called the correlation effect. Clearly it will diminish the calculated singlet-triplet separation: the energy of the triplet state is depressed considerably by exchange, since the electrons avoid each other on account of antisymmetry, but the energy of the singlet will be depressed somewhat by correlation, bringing the two states closer together if we are looking at a state such as that where one electron is in the $1s$ state, the other in the $2s$, and the triplet lies lower.   Calculations of correlation should be included if we wish a really good quantitative result from Schrödinger's equation; but it is hard to calculate it quantitatively, and few calculations take it accurately into account.

10-6. The Heitler-London Method for Molecules.   In Sec. 10-1, we stated that Heitler and London considered the structure of the hydrogen molecule, in 1927, putting major emphasis on the electron interaction.   Their calculation, in fact, takes rather good account of the correlation effect which we have just been discussing, and gives a rather good representation of the molecule for this reason.   We can describe their calculation in language very much like that used by Heisenberg for discussing the singlets and triplets in helium.   Let u_1 be an atomic orbital around one hydrogen atom, u_2 an atomic orbital around the other.   If we assume that one electron is located in each of these atomic orbitals, we should have a function of the form of $u_1(x_1)u_2(x_2)$ representing the system.   But here, just as in helium, an equally good function is $u_2(x_1)u_1(x_2)$.   And as in helium, it can be shown that the best functions made up as linear combination of these have the form given in Eq. (10-7).   Furthermore, the whole discussion of the effect of the spin goes through as for helium, and we find that the symmetric function of coordinates corresponds to the singlet, the antisymmetric to the triplet.

We can go further and calculate the average energy of each of these states.   When Heitler and London did this, they found that the exchange integral giving the singlet-triplet separation was more complicated than that given in Eq. (10-8), and proved to have the opposite sign.   The net result was that the singlet state lay below the triplet, rather than above.   When they calculated the energies of these two states as a function of internuclear distance, the result looked qualitatively like the curves of Fig. 10-2.   The lower, attractive curve represented the singlet state, while the upper, repulsive curve represented the triplet.   The singlet gave a decidedly good representation of the observed ground state of the molecule.

The Heitler-London calculation is particularly interesting from the point of view of its comparison with the molecular orbital method, and of its possible generalization to more complicated molecules.   The Heitler-London wave function leads to a rather small probability that the two electrons, in the singlet state, should be found close to each other.   For instance, if the two atoms are far apart, the function $u_1(x_1)u_2(x_2)$ is appreciably different from zero only if electron 1 is located near atom 1, electron 2 near atom 2, which means that the electrons are not close together.   The molecular orbital wave function for the ground state, however, gives a large probability of finding the electrons close together. If both electrons are located in the bonding molecular orbital, one with each spin, each electron independently will spend half the time on each atom. There is then a chance of 1/4 that both electrons will be on atom 1, 1/4 that both will be on atom 2, and 1/2 that one will be on one atom, the other on the other atom. In other words, there is a 50 per cent chance of finding the electrons on the same atom, or close together, which is absent in the Heitler-London wave function. As a consequence of this fact, the molecular orbital energy lies much higher than the Heitler-London value, and consequently represents a much poorer approximation, particularly at large internuclear distance. At smaller distances the difference is not nearly so marked.

We see, then, that the Heitler-London wave function takes account of correlation rather effectively, keeping the electrons of opposite spin out of each other's way, while the molecular orbital function does not. This would seem to suggest that the Heitler-London method was superior in general to the molecular orbital method. Unfortunately, it has proved rather difficult to generalize the Heitler-London method to more complicated molecules. Formulas have been set up for doing so, but they have been so complicated that very few mathematically rigorous calculations have been made with them. The molecular orbital method has proved far more tractable, both qualitatively and quantitatively, for treating complicated cases.

Nevertheless, the molecular orbital method suffers from its lack of an adequate way of handling correlation. There has been a continuous stream of papers, ever since Heitler and London's original work, based on their methods, and it cannot be doubted that an eventual treatment of molecular problems, which we may hope will improve some of the shortcomings of the molecular orbital calculation, will incorporate a treatment of electron correlation, either by methods like those of Heitler and London or by substitutes. This is a field of research where active work is still going on. We know the sort of result we wish to achieve from the approximate solutions of Schrödinger's equation, but the difficulties of the many-electron problem are still so great that we are far from answers of really satisfactory accuracy, and at the same time of manageable simplicity.

10-7. The Nature of Ferromagnetism. We have taken up two cases of electron interaction: the problem of atomic multiplets, where we get nowhere without considering these interactions, and the problem of molecular structure, where they lead to more accurate results, but where the one-electron molecular orbital method has still led to valuable results. Now we turn to the third important application of these ideas, made soon after the discovery of Schrödinger's equation— the problem of ferromagnetism. We have already mentioned that Heisenberg's paper on this subject in 1928 really laid the foundation for the theory. This is a problem where the results of wave mechanics, relating to the antisymmetry of the wave function, and the exchange and correlation effects, really are of complete importance. Without wave mechanics, we should have nothing resembling ferromagnetism.

It has, of course, been known for a very long time that the metals iron, cobalt, and nickel, and a good many compounds of these metals and some others, are ferromagnetic. That is, they have permanent magnetic moments. Such materials are found to consist of small domains, of microscopic size, each domain being magnetized to saturation; the processes of magnetization, hysteresis, and so on with which we are familiar arise from the interactions of the domains. For a good many years it was a great puzzle as to why the magnetic moments were lined up in a single domain; what was the nature of the forces aligning them? Good evidence indicated that the elementary magnets were the electron spins of the electrons. One then finds experimentally, in these cases, that the state of the crystal in which the spins are lined up has a lower energy than that in which they are in opposite or random directions.

It had been found years ago that the energies of interaction between these elementary magnets were many times greater than could be expected if they were merely acting on each other by magnetic forces. Heisenberg suggested, on the basis of his explanation of the energy difference between singlet and triplets in helium, that the same sort of explanation might hold for ferromagnetism. In other words, he suggested essentially that ferromagnetic materials were showing applications of Hund's rule, the states of maximum multiplicity lying lowest.

The detailed methods which Heisenberg used to work out this suggestion were rather different from the energy-band theory. Since then, however, ferromagnetism has been worked out in the language of the energy-band theory, and we have a fairly good understanding of it and of the materials which show the phenomenon. The basic question which we have to answer is simple: Suppose we have some electrons partly filling a band; under what circumstances will the lowest energy of the system come if the electrons all have parallel spin, as in a ferromagnetic state, rather than if half of them have their spins oriented in one direction, half in the other, as in a nonmagnetized state? If we start with the nonmagnetized state, in which the electrons are located in the lowest possible energy levels, each of these containing an electron of each spin, and magnetize the crystal, turning all spins parallel, we shall increase the one-electron energy of the sample.   The reason is that if all spins are parallel, say with positive spin, we can have only one electron in each energy level on account of the exclusion principle. Hence we must take electrons which originally had a negative spin, and lay in the lower part of the band, and must raise them to the upper part of the band, with positive spin.   As far as this term is concerned, clearly the nonmagnetized state will lie lower, and this energy difference will be greater, the broader the energy band.

There is another effect coming in, however, also arising from the exclusion principle.   We remember from our discussion of multiplets and Hund's rule that electrons of parallel spin keep out of each other's way better than those of opposite spin, and hence have smaller Coulomb repulsive terms in the energy, or lie at lower energy.   This effect tends to make the magnetized state lie lower.   The question as to whether the material is really ferromagnetic or not depends on which of these effects is greater.   A large Fermi energy, or a broad energy band, will tend to make ferromagnetism impossible.   The indications are that in a vast majority of cases the actual energy bands are too wide to permit ferromagnetism.   On the other hand, the $3d$ bands of the elements iron, cobalt, and nickel, which are only partly filled in those elements, prove to be among the narrowest of the partly occupied bands to be found in any metals.   It is reasonable, then, that these should be the substances to show ferromagnetism, and such arguments are at the basis of the energy-band explanation of ferromagnetism.

10-8. The Present Status of Solid-state Physics.   We have spent most of this chapter in describing the application of various parts of wave mechanics to the study of the electronic wave functions and energies in molecules and solids.   These are the really new ideas which have come into molecular and solid-state theory in the last twenty-five years.   However, they are far from exhausting the topics which are interesting solid-state physicists at present, and in this concluding section we shall describe some of those other interests.

In the first place, the experimental methods of X-ray, electron, and neutron diffraction have added immeasurably to our understanding of the nature of solids, and of the binding between atoms.   We have given a description of the methods of X-ray diffraction in Chap. 6, and have mentioned electron diffraction in Chap. 9.   Neutron diffraction, the third of the trio, became possible only with the development of the nuclear reactor during the Second World War.   The beams of neutrons emerging from the reactor are intense enough to use like

beams of X rays or electrons. In accordance with the general principles of wave mechanics, neutrons have wavelike properties, just as any
particles do. They are uncharged particles with approximately the
mass of the proton, and with a magnetic moment and spin. They are
scattered by direct interaction with atomic nuclei, on account of the
nuclear forces which we shall describe later. They are also scattered
by magnetic fields, on account of possessing magnetic moments. They
can thus be used to determine directly the nuclear positions in crystals,
whereas the X rays determine the electron clouds; and also the neutrons
can give information about the distribution of magnetic moments
within the individual atoms.

By use of these diffraction methods, we now possess very complete
information about the atomic arrange-
ments in a great many crystals, and
about their electronic charge distributions. The information which we
get in this way supplements the find-
ings of the chemists in a remarkable
way; in fact, diffraction has come to
be one of the very important techniques of the chemist in studying different types of substances. This is
not the place to go into any long discussion of chemistry, or the nature of
chemical compounds, but our ideas

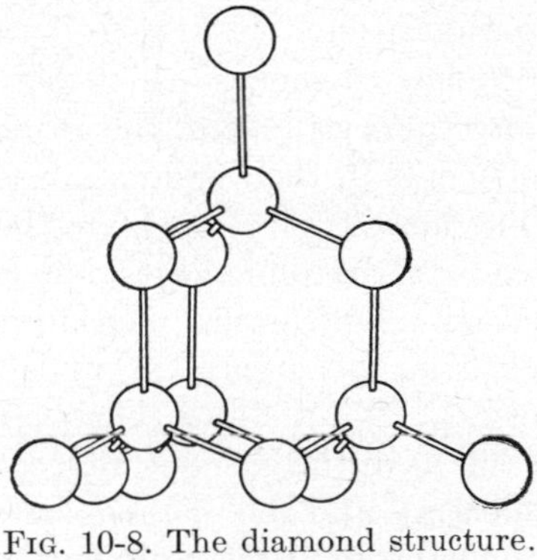

FIG. 10-8. The diamond structure.

will be a little clearer if we give a short summary of various types of
solids and their chemical structures.

Most of the elements are metals; and most of the metals crystallize
in one of a few rather simple crystal types, called the body-centered
cubic, face-centered cubic, and hexagonal closest packing, which may
be pictured as various ways of stacking spheres rather closely together.
It is these cases in which we find that the energy-band theory indicates
partly filled bands, and typical metallic behavior. Some of the elements crystallize in rather different crystal forms, showing definite
indications of covalent binding. Thus, carbon, silicon, and germanium
crystallize in what is called the diamond structure, in which each atom
is surrounded by four neighbors in a tetrahedral arrangement, as is
shown in Fig. 10-8. The reader familiar with chemistry will realize
that this is the typical way in which carbon appears in the chain compounds, surrounded by four neighbors in this same arrangement.

When the energy bands of these substances are investigated, it is
found that there are just enough electrons to fill certain bands, leaving

a gap above.   This gap is quite wide for diamond; hence it is an insulator.   For silicon and germanium, it is narrower, and these are two of
the best-known semiconductors.   This situation, where the electrons
just fill certain bands, leaving a gap above, is characteristic of substances held together by covalent binding.   They tend to be insulators
or semiconductors, and to have atomic arrangements in which bonds
come off from a given atom in a few definite directions, rather than
having the type of close packing characteristic of the typical metals.
There are a few of the elements which are intermediate between these
types.   Bismuth, for instance, which is known to have many peculiar
physical properties, has one energy band almost filled, another one
with a few electrons in it, and a peculiar crystal structure; these
features of its energy-band structure seem to explain its physical
peculiarities.

These elements which we have mentioned show no indication of
molecular structure; the atoms are not grouped into molecules.   Some
elements in their solid state, however, show the presence of molecules.
The most typical ones are the solid forms of those elements which we
know as diatomic gases under ordinary circumstances: H_2, O_2, N_2, and
so on.   Diffraction measurements show that the diatomic molecules
exist in the crystal as well: the atoms are arranged in pairs in the
crystal, the distance between the atoms in a pair being roughly the
same as in the gaseous molecule (where it can be determined from band
spectra), and the distance between molecules being considerably larger
than the molecular dimensions.   The interpretation here is that the
forces between the atoms in a single molecule are covalent bonds, of
the type which we have met in our discussion of diatomic molecules;
while the intermolecular forces are of a much weaker type, called Van
der Waals attractions, resulting from electrostatic effects, and also
present in the gas, where they lead to the deviations from the perfect-
gas law which are sometimes described by an equation of state called
Van der Waals' equation.

When we consider crystals of alloys and chemical compounds, we
find the same types of binding as with elements, as well as some others.
The alloys have the same types of structures as the metals, and the
same type of interatomic forces.   Much work has been done on the
electronic band structure of alloys, and its relation to their stability.
A great many chemical compounds are held together by covalent
bonds, and as with the elements, some of these show molecular structure, some do not.   These in general are insulators or semiconductors,
as with the elements.   One great class of crystals held into molecules
by covalent bonds comprises the organic compounds,

But in addition to these types of binding, we have also the ionic crystals, held by electrostatic attractions between oppositely charged ions. The forces encountered here are of the same type which we have seen in Sec. 10-3, where we considered such a molecule as NaCl, formed from the Na+ and Cl− ion, held together by electrostatic attraction, and kept from collapsing by the repulsions between the closed electronic shells found in the ions. The structures of such crystals do not show the existence of molecules; the NaCl molecule can exist in the gaseous form, but not in the solid. Rather we have regular arrangements of the positive and negative ions, as in the familiar case of NaCl, shown in Fig. 10-9.

We could go on almost indefinitely discussing the types of crystals, but this is enough to indicate the main types of interatomic forces

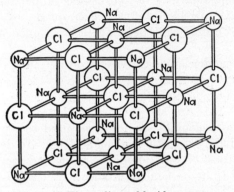

FIG. 10-9. The sodium chloride structure.

encountered in solids: covalent binding, and the related metallic binding; ionic binding; Van der Waals attraction. Once we understand these forces, we can begin to think of the mechanical and elastic properties of solids. Some of the earliest work along these lines was carried out by Born and his collaborators, in the period from about 1910 on, treating ionic crystals, largely of the type of NaCl. They assumed that the forces between ions consisted of the electrostatic attractions or repulsions, and in addition a repulsion setting in at small distances, increasing very rapidly as the distance decreased; they assumed generally that this repulsion could be represented by a term proportional to r^{-n}, where r was the distance between ions, n a larger integer of the order of magnitude of 9. We now know, on the basis of wave mechanics, that this repulsion is that arising between closed shells from the preponderance of the antibonding effect over the bonding effect, but Born and his collaborators had to postulate this term empirically.

Born and his group were then able to find theoretical relations, which could be checked experimentally, between such quantities as the compressibility of the crystal, its lattice spacing, and its heat of vaporization. They were able to go further, and to discuss the elastic vibrations of the crystal, and their relations to the thermal energy. By extension of these ideas, a rather complete theory of the dynamics of ionic crystals was set up. A number of empirical parameters, of course, had to be used in such a theory; but recently, by use of wave-mechanical methods, Löwdin in Sweden has been able to make quantitative calculations of the properties of these same crystals, without use of empirical parameters, and has found very good agreement with experiment. In other words, the wave mechanics has shown itself capable of explaining the properties of ionic crystals in a quantitative way. Similar investigations of the elastic properties of metals, on the basis of wave mechanics, have been made by Wigner, Seitz, Bardeen, and a number of others, again with good agreement with experiment.

These theoretical discussions have led to the feeling that interatomic forces are rather well understood. But these ideas were applied, in the early 1930's, to a problem in which they seemed to give completely wrong answers. This was the problem of the mechanical strength of crystals. One can calculate the force required to separate a perfect crystal into two halves, cutting it along a plane. In doing this, all the bonds between atoms on one side of the plane and atoms on the other side are assumed to be broken simultaneously. When such a calculation is made, the theoretical breaking strength so computed proves to be of the order of magnitude of a thousand times the actually observed breaking strength. This discrepancy astonished the solid-state physicists when it was discovered, and led to a whole field of research on the deformation of crystals which has become increasingly active as time has gone on.

The first suggestion as to the explanation of the observed breaking strength was made in 1934, by Orowan and Taylor. They proposed that an actual crystal is not perfect, but instead contains many little imperfections, slightly resembling cracks, which they called dislocations. When a crystal breaks, they showed that the stress would tend to be concentrated around such a dislocation, so that in the process of breaking, it would not be necessary to break all the bonds at once, but only those in the neighborhood of such a dislocation. The situation was a little like that found when one tears a piece of paper or cellophane; once a tear starts, it is much easier to continue the tear than to start it. Their hypotheses were much more precise than this qualitative and descriptive discussion would indicate; an elaborate theory of possible types of dislocations has grown up, and there is now very good experimental evidence that they actually exist, and are instrumental in determining the mechanical properties of solids and the behavior of such phenomena as plasticity and brittle fracture.

A corollary of these theories was the fact that real crystals are not perfect, but rather have various sorts of imperfections in them. Experimental evidence for this had been found experimentally, by X-ray diffraction methods, in the very earliest work with X rays: X-ray lines were broadened, as if different small parts of a crystal were oriented in slightly different directions, scattering the X rays, according to Bragg's law, slightly differently. Since then, X-ray methods have proved very valuable in investigating the distortions of solids produced by such things as cold work.

Experiments of quite a different sort led to the conviction that there were other sorts of imperfections in crystals. These were experiments on the optical properties of alkali halide crystals, performed over a long period by Pohl and his coworkers in Germany, and since then in many other places. Such crystals can be easily blackened, by exposure to X rays, or in many other ways. Careful investigation showed that these properties were not characteristic of the perfect crystal, but resulted rather from the existence of minute holes in the crystal, each formed by the absence of a single atom. Such a missing atom site can often attract an electron, and the blackening is a result of the absorption involved in raising this trapped electron to an excited energy level. In other optical experiments, notably on phosphorescence, impurity atoms were found to play a vital role. In the familiar phosphors which are used, for instance, in television screens, it is the excitation of electrons attached to impurity atoms which are substituted for the normal atoms of the lattice which produces the phosphorescent light. Still other examples of the effect of impurity atoms are found in the case of semiconductors, where we have mentioned in Sec. 10-4 that the presence of impurity atoms is of the greatest importance in the semiconducting properties.

These are just a few of the many cases in which the attention of the solid-state physicist, particularly in the last few years, has been focused on problems of lattice imperfections and impurities. Many of the most important practical properties of solids are found to be what is called structure-sensitive, that is, dependent on the presence of minute amounts of impurities. These structure-sensitive properties are coming to be better understood; and at the same time, improved chemical technique is making it possible to get materials of increased purity, so that one can actually know what impurity atoms one has present in any given experiment. The study of imperfections in crystals, and their manifold effects, is occupying the solid-state physicists at present much more than the study of perfect crystals. And such study promises practical results of the greatest importance, as well as interesting contributions to theory; for as we find that many of the ordinary properties of solids really depend on the impurities and imperfections present in the crystal, and as we learn to control these impurities and imperfections, we discover how to produce solids with new and desirable properties.

In this section we have illustrated a few of the many types of solids, and some of their properties. The whole field of chemistry, of metallurgy, of crystallography, really is embraced in the study of such substances, not to speak of a great deal of biochemistry and the structure of living material. The whole outlook of these sciences has been revolutionized by the two concepts provided by modern physics: the use of X-ray diffraction to locate the atoms, and of the theory of electronic energy levels to understand the mechanical, chemical, and electrical and optical properties of the substances. The proper study of these problems would demand a complete volume, and we have merely tried to suggest some of the results of such a study. As we have emphasized before, we are no longer looking in these studies for the fundamental theoretical laws of the behavior of solids. We rather are seeking to apply principles of wave mechanics, already understood in a general way, to the almost infinite variety of behavior found in nature. As time goes on, we may be sure that continued progress will be made in the understanding of all sorts of matter, inorganic, organic, and living. The answers to all these questions must follow from the postulates of wave mechanics, the great theoretical generalizations which were developed during the years of the present century, culminating in the 1920's and 1930's.

PROBLEMS

10-1. In a NaCl molecule, we may assume that the Na^+ and Cl^- ions have an attractive term in the energy arising from electrostatic attraction equal to $-e^2/4\pi\epsilon_0 r$, where r is the internuclear distance. Assume that the repulsive term in the energy arising from the interaction of the inert-gas shells can be written as a/r^n, where a and n are constants. Take this energy as a function of internuclear distance, and find where the minimum energy comes, hence finding the position of equilibrium of the atoms, in terms of the unknown constants a and n. Calculate also the dissociation energy of the molecule, in terms of a and n.

10-2. As an approximation, set n in Prob. 10-1 equal to 9. Find a value of a

which will lead to the observed internuclear distance of 2.73 A for the NaCl molecule. Compute the dissociation energy, in electron-volts.

10-3. Using the method of Probs. 10-1 and 10-2, compute the second derivative of the potential energy of the NaCl molecule, with respect to r, at the equilibrium distance. Use this information to compute the vibrational frequency of the molecule, proceeding as follows: When the two atoms vibrate, their center of mass will remain fixed. You can use the second derivative of the potential energy, found above, to get the restoring force pulling either of the two atoms back to its equilibrium position, when it is displaced. Knowing this restoring force, and the mass, you can calculate the vibrational frequency from the properties of simple harmonic motion.

10-4. An analytic formula which is found to represent rather well the energy of a diatomic molecule as a function of internuclear distance was given by Morse, and is usually called a Morse curve. It is

$$E = D[e^{-2a(r-r_0)} - 2e^{-a(r-r_0)}]$$

where D, a, and r_0 are constants. Show that D is the energy of dissociation, r_0 the equilibrium internuclear distance. Find the vibration frequency in terms of these constants, assuming that the two atoms in the molecule are alike. Find also the moment of inertia for rotation about an axis passing through the midpoint of the line joining the nuclei, perpendicular to that line.

10-5. For the molecule Na_2, the equilibrium distance is 3.07 A, the energy of dissociation is 0.75 ev, and the constant a in the Morse curve is 0.84 reciprocal angstroms. Find the vibrational frequency, and the moment of inertia.

10-6. From the results of Prob. 10-5, and using the result of Prob. 8-8, find the spacing of the vibrational and rotational levels of the Na_2 molecule in its ground electronic state. If the spacing of vibrational levels were just what you have found, how many such levels would there be, at energies below that required to dissociate the molecule?

10-7. Suppose a given semiconductor has a gap width of 1 ev, and that the Fermi level is located in the middle of the gap. What number of electrons, on the average, will be found in an energy level at the bottom of the conduction band, at $T = 300°K$?

10-8. For the semiconductor described in Prob. 10-7, find the slope of the curve of the logarithm of conductivity plotted as a function of $1/T$, and plot such a curve. (You will not be able to find the height of the curve, but you can determine its slope.)

10-9. An insulator has an optical absorption which occurs for all wavelengths shorter than 1,800 A. Find the width of the forbidden gap for this insulator, in electron-volts.

10-10. For an insulator described in Prob. 10-9, find the number of electrons to be found in an energy band at the bottom of the conduction band, at $T = 300°K$. Compare this with the value found in Prob. 10-7 for a semiconductor. If you assume that the conductivity is proportional to the number of electrons in the conduction band, find the ratio of the conductivity of the insulator to that of the semiconductor.

CHAPTER 11

NUCLEAR PHYSICS AND HIGH-ENERGY PARTICLES

11-1. Introduction. The complacency with which we ended the preceding chapter does not apply in any sense in the field of nuclear and high energy physics. Here we are still deeply immersed in the discovery of fundamental laws, the inductive process which had culminated in the extranuclear field with the discovery of Schrödinger's equation in 1926. We are still fitting together the pieces of the puzzle. And our treatment of these things must necessarily be different in spirit from anything which has gone on so far in this volume. In the earlier chapters, we were, it is true, trying to recapture the spirit of those who were putting together the puzzle of wave mechanics, to describe the reasoning which led them to their conclusions. But we cannot really recapture the spirit completely, for we now know the answer. We know which were the successful attempts to solve the puzzle, which the unsuccessful ones. And an author would be less than human, in such a discussion, if he did not devote himself to those attempts which worked, and leave out those which led up blind alleys and were given up.

In nuclear physics, on the contrary, we are still in the middle of the puzzle; we are now, in 1955, in much the same relative position where wave mechanics was, perhaps, in 1920. We have consolidated many branches of the subject, and feel that we understand them. But so long as we have no general success, nothing comparable to Schrödinger's equation, we cannot be sure that even the things which seem surest about our present knowledge may not prove in the end to be wrong. We cannot, then, proceed with any such systematic assurance as we have been able to do in the earlier part of our work. We shall tell of the attempts which have been made to understand the nucleus, the types of experiments and theories which are being worked on now with this aim in view. But we cannot predict which points of view are likely to succeed in the end. We can only say that at present, in spite of intense efforts, we still are far from the goal of complete understanding. But we can, on the other hand, indicate a conviction that rapid and striking progress is being made, and a very strong hope that there will be eventual success, as complete as we have had in the discovery of Schrödinger's equation in the field of extranuclear atomic physics.

In Chap. 4, we have carried our discussion of nuclear physics as far as was required to understand the nuclear atom. Further striking progress started, however, in 1919, long before the other developments which we have been taking up in the preceding chapters, and we now go back to that period to resume the study of the development of nuclear physics. Before 1919, natural radioactivity was well known; we knew that atoms of certain heavy elements could give off radiation of three different sorts, transmuting themselves into other elements, and emitting alpha particles, or helium nuclei; beta particles, or electrons; and gamma rays, or electromagnetic radiation of very short wavelength. But no way was known experimentally of influencing the radioactive decay; it occurred spontaneously, and the experimenter could do nothing about it.

Then, in 1919, Rutherford succeeded in producing the disintegration of an atom artificially. He had been measuring the ranges of alpha particles in various gases. It is a characteristic of the passage of heavy particles through gases that they produce a trail of ions as they plough through the atoms of the gas, and this ionization becomes stronger as the heavy particles slow down and stop. The reason for this is that the slow particles stay longer in the neighborhood of each atom, and have a greater chance of ionizing it. Finally the heavy particles are brought to rest, after traversing a quite definite distance, which can be accurately measured. When Rutherford tried measuring the range of alpha particles in nitrogen, he observed a phenomenon quite different from that found with any other gas. The ionization practically stopped a given distance from the source, and he interpreted this distance as the range. But a small amount of ionization persisted to much greater distances. This indicated the presence of a very few particles of much greater range. Careful study convinced Rutherford that these particles were protons. There was nowhere that they could have come from, except the nitrogen atoms themselves. Rutherford, then, was led to the conclusion that by bombardment with an alpha particle the nitrogen atom had been broken up, and a proton had been shot off. Thus started a whole new era in nuclear physics, the study of artificial disintegration of nuclei.

Other disintegrations were discovered, following this one, and naturally it was interesting to find what sort of particles were shot off. In Rutherford's disintegration of nitrogen, it had been a proton. But a real surprise came in 1932, when Chadwick was able to prove that in the disintegration of beryllium by alpha particles a particle of an entirely new type was shot off, having a mass approximately the same as a proton, but no charge. This was named the neutron; and it proved to be of the utmost importance in nuclear structure. In fact, it proved to be one of the fundamental building blocks in making up nuclei. It was known, from the atomic weights and atomic numbers of the elements, that the atomic weights of almost all elements were equal to twice the atomic number, or more. Before the discovery of the neutron, it was supposed that the nuclei were made of protons and electrons, that the number of protons indicated the atomic weight (that is, the mass), and that the atomic number (the net charge) was the number of protons minus the number of electrons. Chadwick's discovery of the neutron, however, suggested that an alternative possibility was that the nucleus contained no electrons, but just protons and neutrons; that the number of protons equaled the atomic number, and the number of protons and neutrons combined equaled the atomic weight, or mass number. This latter view has proved to be correct.

Chadwick's discovery of the neutron proved to be closely linked with another discovery of the same period, the discovery of the positron. Dirac, in 1928, produced a remarkable theory of the structure of the electron. He tried to set up a theory of the electron which satisfied the principles of relativity, and was automatically led to a theory which predicted the electron spin, just as it had earlier been postulated by Uhlenbeck and Goudsmit. His theory went further, however: it predicted the existence of a positive electron, or positron, having essentially the same properties as the electron, but positive charge. Furthermore, he predicted that the electron and positron could collide with each other, and mutually annihilate each other, their energy being converted into gamma radiation. Conversely, gamma radiation of the suitable energy could materialize itself, and produce a positron-electron pair. This process of production of pairs could occur only in the presence of an intense electric field, such as is produced by a nucleus; in free space, certain conditions of conservation of momentum could not be satisfied.

These predictions soon proved to be experimentally verified, by the cosmic-ray experiments of Anderson, the American physicist, in 1932. Anderson found evidence, in cloud-chamber photographs of cosmic-ray events, for the pair production which Dirac had predicted. This was a very striking example of the prediction of a new particle, before its experimental discovery. The properties of the positron, as they have been extensively investigated since 1932, have entirely verified Dirac's theory.

Another new particle was postulated soon after this: the neutrino, which was predicted by Pauli. It was a very elusive particle: its most conspicuous characteristic is that it hardly interacts at all with any type of matter, and therefore is practically impossible to observe, and all attempts to get direct experimental evidence of its existence have so far failed. However, it is quite necessary to assume that it really exists, for reasons which we can easily sketch. These reasons concern radioactive beta emission, and have a close relation to the existence of neutrons and of positrons.

In beta decay, one can measure the energies of the emitted beta particles, by suitable deflection experiments in magnetic fields. It is found that beta particles come off, in any given case, with a continuous distribution of velocities, all the way from very slow ones up to a definite maximum value. Yet there is excellent evidence that the atoms which were decaying all had the same energy, and furthermore the atoms into which they were transformed all had the same energy. How can we reconcile definite initial and final energy levels, with an indefinite amount of energy emitted by the beta particle? The only simple assumption, consistent with conservation of energy, is that there is another, invisible particle, which is emitted at the same time as the beta particle, and which carries off the rest of the energy. That is, we should assume that the sum of the energies of the beta particle and the invisible particle, which we call the neutrino, was always the same, but that the energy was divided in an arbitrary manner between the two.

This postulate would lead to one direct consequence. The maximum energy which the beta particle could carry off would be the difference between the initial and final energies of the nuclei. It would carry off this total energy, in the special case when the neutrino did not have any energy. This would explain the fixed upper limit for the beta-particle energy. It would also predict that this end point for the beta-decay energy should represent the energy difference between the initial and final energy levels. This hypothesis has been verified experimentally in many cases, by study of the energy levels, as we shall describe later.

Another reason why the neutrino has to be postulated relates to angular momentum. We shall show later that the angular momentum of a nucleus can be determined, by various experimental methods. One can then find the angular momentum of the initial and final nucleus in a case of beta disintegration. We know that the electron has an angular momentum of $\frac{1}{2}\hbar$. Therefore, if a vector rule of addition applies to nuclear angular momenta, we should expect that if the initial nucleus had, for instance, an angular momentum of zero, the final nucleus would have to have an angular momentum of $\frac{1}{2}\hbar$, or of this value plus an integral multiple of $\hbar$, just as adding an electron to the outer part of the atom changes the angular momentum from an integral multiple of $\hbar$ (as in an inert gas) to a half-integral value (as in an alkali metal). This was not observed to be the case, however. The nuclei before and after a beta disintegration either both have integral or both have half-integral angular momenta. This is not consistent with the conservation of angular momenta, unless we postulate that the neutrino carries away angular momentum, as well as energy. It must be assumed that it, like the electron, has an angular momentum of $\frac{1}{2}\hbar$, so that the two can compensate each other, and lead to the observed fact that there is no change from integral to half-integral angular momenta in a beta disintegration, or vice versa.

Though the neutrino is very elusive, this proves to be what we should expect. According to Pauli, as we have said, the neutrino must have no charge (because the beta particle takes care of the conservation of charge), it has negligible rest mass (because the maximum energy of the beta particle accounts for all the energy, or mass, difference between the initial and final state), but can have kinetic energy (to make up the conservation of energy), and has an angular momentum of $\frac{1}{2}\hbar$. In spite of its apparently elusive properties, it is generally agreed that it exists, and one can even make an estimate of its probability of collision with an atom. It is always possible to estimate the probability of an inverse process from that of a direct one, and the inverse of the emission of a neutrino and a beta particle by the atom is the capture of the same two particles by an atom. One can find how likely the capture of the neutrino is, in the presence of an electron, and one finds that it is so small that the neutrinos would pass through ordinary matter without appreciable interference.

Now we come to the relation between the electron, positron, and neutrino, and the question of the neutron. In a beta disintegration, a beta particle and a neutrino are shot off from the nucleus, and of course the charge on the nucleus increases by one unit, though its mass is approximately unchanged. It came to be considered, in the early 1930's, that this did not mean that an electron and a neutrino were originally present in the structure of the nucleus, and were ejected simultaneously. Instead, it was assumed that the nucleus consisted only of protons and neutrons, as we have mentioned, and that the beta particle and the neutrino were created in the process of beta decay.

This is pictured as something very much like the way in which a photon is created in the process of the emission of electromagnetic radiation. To take care of the conservation of charge, it is assumed that, at the same time, one of the neutrons inside the nucleus is transformed into a proton.

Heisenberg, about 1932, proposed that we regard this situation rather more literally, and think of the neutron and the proton as merely two different states of the same sort of particle, which we now call a nucleon.   These two states have different charges; and one transforms a neutron into a proton by emission of an electron and a neutrino. It then seems natural, by symmetry, that another process might well occur, in which a proton would be transformed into a neutron, by emission of a positron and a neutrino.   If this were the case, we could have transitions back and forth between the proton and the neutron, as often as we pleased.   Heisenberg suggested an analogy between the fact that the nucleon can exist in two states, that of the proton and the neutron, and the fact that an electron spin can exist in two states, pointing up and pointing down with respect to a fixed axis.   As a result of this analogy, a quantity originally called the isotopic spin, now sometimes called the isobaric spin, has been introduced, a sort of quantum number, which has one value for a neutron, another for a proton.   Rather elaborate theories of nuclear force have been based on this isotopic spin.

We have just seen how theory suggested the possibility of the emission of positrons as well as electrons in nuclear disintegrations.   This hypothesis was very soon verified, by the discovery of artificial radioactivity, by M. and Mme. Curie-Joliot, the son-in-law and daughter of Mme. Curie, in 1934.   They found that, when certain elements were bombarded by alpha particles, they became radioactive; instead of instantly disintegrating, as in the cases that had been discussed earlier, they decayed after a finite lifetime, as in any radioactive decay.   This started a long study of artificial radioactivity, carried out by bombarding all sorts of elements with various particles, to see what happened to them.   And the interesting thing was that the commonest types of disintegration found in these cases of induced radioactivity were the emission of beta particles or of positrons.   Here, then, was direct evidence of the way in which neutrons and protons could transform into each other.

For studying artificial radioactivity and nuclear transmutations, the invention of various accelerators for charged particles proved to be extremely valuable. Cockcroft and Walton in England, Van de Graaff and Lawrence in America, invented in the late 1920's and early

1930's various types of devices for accelerating positive ions—deuterons (or nuclei of the hydrogen isotope of mass 2, which had been discovered by Urey shortly before), or protons—to energies of millions of electron-volts. These particles could be used to produce disintegrations, as well as the alpha particles provided by radioactive processes. By use of these projectiles, a tremendous number of artificially radioactive isotopes of practically all the known elements were found to exist, and their properties were measured.

Not only were these transformations observed, but also very valuable studies of the energies involved were made. The energies of the impinging particles in a nuclear collision could be measured; so also could the energies of the ejected particles after the collision, for example, by deflecting them in a magnetic field. One could then apply the law of the conservation of energy, and deduce the energy difference between the initial and final nuclei. The first result of this sort of study was to show that the nuclei fitted in with the fundamental laws of quantum mechanics. They had definite energy levels. Furthermore, when they emitted gamma rays, the frequency of the gamma ray was related to the difference of energy levels by the quantum relation that the energy difference equaled $h\nu$. At least to this extent, we were on familiar ground in dealing with nuclear properties. By now, the techniques of measuring nuclear energy levels have so improved that we are able to get elaborate and accurate energy-level diagrams, which are gradually becoming almost comparable in complexity with the energy levels of the outer electronic structure of the atoms. One cannot doubt that eventually these energy-level diagrams will be as valuable in understanding nuclear structure as atomic spectroscopy has been in atomic structure. But we are still in the early days of such a development.

There has been one extremely important verification of the general correctness of this picture of nuclear energies. We have mentioned the mass spectrograph of Aston, which determined nuclear masses. This instrument was gradually refined, by the work of Aston himself, and of the Americans Dempster, Bainbridge, Nier, and others until it became so precise that one could not only be sure that the masses of all isotopes were very approximately integral but could measure the deviations from the integral values with great accuracy. One could then apply the conservation of mass in the case of a nuclear transmutation: did the sum of the masses of the initial particles equal the sum of the masses of the final particles? The experimental answer was that it did not. But this was not unexpected. We remember that according to Einstein's theory of relativity an amount of energy E is equivalent to a mass m, by the relation $E = mc^2$, where c is the velocity of light.   We expect, then, that in a reaction in which energy is given off the sum of the masses of all particles will decrease accordingly.   And when this was taken into account, conservation held precisely: the kinetic energy, and energy emitted in gamma rays, had to be taken into account.   Mass-spectrum data, then, provided independent verifications of the energies determined directly, and the two determinations proved to check each other within experimental error.

We now have, then, a very good general idea of nuclear energies. We can give a general suggestion of the sort of results obtained.   In the first place, the elements of intermediate atomic weight are the most stable.   That is, if light elements, in particular hydrogen, were to be combined to make somewhat heavier elements, energy would be given off; but also if the heaviest elements were to be broken up into elements of intermediate atomic weight, energy would be given off.   It was suggested in 1939 by Bethe that a process of fusion of hydrogen, by several steps, into helium, was the reaction responsible for the energy given off by the sun and stars, and this hypothesis is generally accepted.   It was also regarded as likely that the reason why the heaviest elements were radioactive was that their energy could be decreased by breaking up, and it was surmised that these elements might be broken up in more violent ways by bombardment with neutrons.   Charged particles, like alpha particles or protons, are repelled so strongly by the heavy nuclei that they cannot get close enough to cause disintegration. Neutrons, however, would not be repelled, and Hahn, Strassmann, and Lise Meitner, in Germany, in 1939, showed that uranium on bombardment with neutrons underwent fission, breaking up into two fragments of roughly equal size (though one fragment is considerably larger than half, the other smaller).

These results, of course, were the ones which have since led to the development of atomic energy, and the fission and fusion, or thermonuclear, bombs.   The fundamental processes used in them were known by 1940.   We can see this clearly, for instance, from a remarkably prophetic paragraph written by Sir William C. Dampier, in the third edition of his "A History of Science."†   He wrote in 1941:

Some of the energy changes in these forced transformations are even greater than those in natural radioactive disintegrations.   For instance, a deuteron of energy 21,000 volts will transform an atom of lithium with an emission of energy of 22.5 million volts.   There is, therefore, a large gain of energy, and at

† W. C. Dampier, "A History of Science," 3d ed., pp. 509–510, Cambridge University Press, London, 1942.   Quoted by permission of Cambridge University Press.

first sight it looks as though we had at command a limitless source of atomic energy. But only about one deuteron in 10^8 is effective, so that on balance, more energy has to be supplied than is emitted, and, in the case of neutrons, the neutrons themselves can only be obtained by very inefficient processes. In 1937 Lord Rutherford pronounced that "the outlook for gaining useful energy from the atoms by artificial processes of transformation does not look promising." On this one can only remark that before now in the history of applied science prospects of even less promise have confounded the prophets. Indeed, in 1939 Hahn and Meitner found that, when an atom of uranium was struck by a neutron, its nucleus divided into two main parts, accompanied by two, three, or four other neutrons. At first sight, this seems to be the cumulative process sought, but it is only the lighter isotope which dissociates to any useful extent, and it is present only in small quantities. Similar processes occur with thorium. The separation of isotopes is being actively pursued in many laboratories; but the difficulties are great, and the doubt remains whether, if they were overcome, it would be safe to put the destructive powers of atomic energy into the hands of man.

The reader of the newspapers in 1955 will realize that the reactions mentioned by Dampier in 1941 seem to be among those which have proved most powerful in the development of atomic and thermonuclear bombs.

The study of nuclear energy levels has not only led to practical applications on an immense scale; it has also begun to give definite ideas regarding the laws which must govern the structure of the nucleus. Other properties besides the energy values have been extremely valuable in this study. These properties are mainly two: first, the angular momentum and magnetic moment of nuclei; second, the types of nuclear transformations. Several experimental methods have been developed for studying angular momenta and magnetic moments, and by careful interpretation of the results of these experiments, ideas about nuclear structure are being built up which are rapidly approaching the completeness of the pictures of atomic structure on the basis of the vector model which we had in the early 1920's. The study of transformations likewise has been of the greatest importance; when bombarded with various types of particles, many different sorts of nuclear changes can occur, with emission of different sorts of particles.

Originating from many of these facts, ideas regarding the nature of nuclear forces have been rapidly developing in the last few years; but they are still far from completeness. One of the most important of these ideas ties nuclear structure in with another field, that of cosmic rays. These rays, as we shall see, consist of high-energy particles shot into the earth's atmosphere from outer space, from an unknown origin.

In passing through the atmosphere, they collide with atoms, producing countless nuclear processes, of the sort which would be produced in the laboratory if we had powerful enough accelerators. By studying them, the experts on cosmic rays have been able to discover many of the facts of nuclear physics. In particular, they have found new types of particles, called mesons, of mass intermediate between that of the electron and the proton, of a variety of masses and properties. These particles have been particularly interesting to the theorists, for the existence of particles of this general sort had been predicted, before their discovery, by the Japanese physicist Yukawa, as a result of a theory of nuclear forces which he was working out. The study of mesons, though it has been going on for a number of years, is still in a very preliminary stage. New results are coming in from the experiments in bewildering number. Here we stand right in the middle of those new discoveries which we hope will fit eventually into a pattern, but whose interpretation we can hardly guess at present.

With this sketch of the development of nuclear and high-energy physics, we get some small impression of the complication and fascination of the field. We shall now go on to a more detailed study of some of the topics we have mentioned, starting with the theory of the positron.

11-2. The Positron. We have already mentioned the positron, and the fact that it was predicted theoretically before it was found experimentally. Dirac, in 1928, had set up a theory of the electron spin. In the first days of quantum mechanics, there had been attempts to set up a relativistic form of the theory, which would hold when the velocities of the particles were comparable with the velocity of light; but this had not been easy. Part of the difficulty can be illustrated by the fact that the energy of a particle, in the theory of relativity, is given by the formula

$$H = (m_0^2 c^4 + p^2 c^2)^{1/2} + V \tag{11-1}$$

where m_0 is the rest mass of the particle (that is, the mass at low velocity), c is the velocity of light, p the momentum, and V the potential energy. One can expand the square root, for small momenta, in a power series, starting with the terms

$$H = m_0 c^2 + \frac{p^2}{2m_0} + \cdots + V \tag{11-2}$$

in which the term $m_0 c^2$ represents the energy equivalent of the mass of the particle, as demanded by the principle of relativity, the next term is the ordinary kinetic energy, the omitted terms represent the relativity correction, and the final term is the potential energy.

This seems perfectly straightforward, until one looks a little more closely at Eq. (11-1), and realizes that the relativistic principles really demand that there be a $\pm$ sign in front of the radical. In other words, there is no logical way of escaping from the possibility of having a particle of apparently negative rest mass (for if we change the sign of the radical, we see from Eq. (11-2) that this is equivalent to taking a negative m_0). When one converted the energy into an operator, and set up a Schrödinger equation from it, the solutions corresponding to negative masses could not be avoided.

Dirac studied this problem very seriously, and his results involved too much mathematical complexity for us to describe them. We can, however, give his conclusions, which were very striking. In the first place, he found that to give a rigorous treatment he had to introduce new mathematical quantities, somewhat like vectors or tensors, called spinors, and these involved peculiar features in the behavior of the electron which could be given a very simple interpretation: they led to the electron spin. Dirac showed, in other words, that the spinning electron was a consequence of the theory of relativity: he was not able to set up a logically consistent theory of the electron, combining Schrödinger methods with the relativity theory, unless the electron had a spin. Furthermore, the values of the angular momentum, and the magnetic moment, which had already been derived for the electron spin from study of complex spectra, proved to be predicted uniquely by the theory. This prediction of the properties of the spinning electron was a great triumph of the Dirac theory, and convinced everyone of its essential correctness.

The second conclusion related to the peculiar business of solutions of the Schrödinger equation with negative masses. Dirac's spinor treatment did not remove this situation: there appeared to be every reason to think that solutions of the Schrödinger equation existed, not only for all positive kinetic energies (that is, for all energies equal to or greater than m_0c^2, in a field-free space where the potential energy is zero), but also for energies less than or equal to $-m_0c^2$. It was as if the possible energy levels filled up a lower band, then left a gap of $2m_0c^2$, then an upper band, as shown in Fig. 11-1. Why, we ask, do we not observe these lower levels? Why does an electron not fall down from one of the positive levels to one of the negative ones, and radiate energy in the process?

This question was investigated. In the first place, the amount of energy which would be radiated could be computed. The gap width was $2m_0c^2$; when converted into the units of electron-volts, this amounts to about 1 Mev (1 million electron-volts), and a photon of this size would correspond to a gamma ray, which could easily be observed. In the second place, the probability of the transition could be computed, by using the theory of radiation, and it was shown to be so probable that all the electrons in the universe would have had transitions to these states of negative mass in an exceedingly small fraction of a second after they were first created.

Why did they not have this transition? Dirac made a simple suggestion: he assumed that all these lower energy levels were filled, and since electrons satisfy the Pauli exclusion principle, there was no possibility of having an electron fall into one of the levels. This disposed of the difficulty; but at the same time it introduced a fascinating possibility. Why could not a photon of an energy something greater than 1 Mev be absorbed by apparently empty space, and raise an electron from one of the negative levels to a positive level? It could be shown that this could not really happen in empty space, for it would be impossible to satisfy simul-

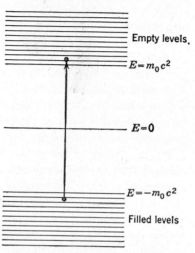

FIG. 11-1. Empty levels of positive energy, filled levels of negative energy, in Dirac's theory of the electron. Arrow indicates transition leading to positron-electron pair production.

taneously the laws of conservation of energy and momentum without having some other particle to remove the excess momentum. But if a photon hit, for instance, a nucleus, which would act as a third particle, why could not an electron, and a hole in the lower energy band, be simultaneously created?

Dirac asked how this hole would act; and it was easy to show that it would behave, under the action of an external electric field, and in fact in all respects, like an electron of positive charge, but ordinary electronic mass. It was not immediately obvious how to interpret such a particle, since such a thing had never been observed. It did not seem like a proton, or other known nuclear particle. As we have mentioned, however, the situation dramatically changed, in 1932, when Anderson, the American expert in cosmic rays, discovered in the cloud chamber that positive particles of the electronic mass, now called positrons, really existed. Here was a remarkable case of a theoretical prediction of a particle, before it had ever been seen; and here was the beginning of a really new era in interpreting the theory of elementary particles.

If a positron represented really a state of negative energy which was not occupied by an electron, then it should be possible for an electron to fall down into it, and emit radiation of energy $2m_0c^2$, or about 1 Mev, as we have just mentioned. To satisfy conservation of momentum as well as energy, one can show that two photons must be emitted, each of energy m_0c^2, or about $\frac{1}{2}$ Mev, in opposite directions. The net result of this process would be the annihilation of a positron-electron pair, with conversion of its energy into radiation. As a matter of fact, just such annihilation radiation is observed when positrons strike ordinary matter, in which they can collide with electrons. Here again we have a verification of the interpretation of the positron as a hole in the otherwise filled energy levels of negative energy.

The discovery of the positron was the first interesting development connected with the structure of the electron, after the discovery of wave mechanics. The second concerned the beta disintegrations, the neutrino, and the relation between beta and positron disintegrations, which we have discussed in Sec. 11-1. We are then ready to go ahead with a more detailed study of nuclear reactions and energies; but first we shall go into the experimental side of the question, considering the particle accelerators, which were being produced at the same time, and which provided many of the fast particles which were used to produce artificial transmutations and induced radioactivity.

11-3. Particle Accelerators. Nuclear transformations are not always produced by accelerators; but those accelerators form the most manageable experimental tool of the nuclear physicist, and their development, from the late 1920's until the present, has been an important feature in nuclear physics. For purposes of preliminary orientation, we should state that the energies of particles necessary to investigate nuclear energy levels run from a few kilovolts up to a few million electron-volts. On the other hand, the energies required to produce artificial mesons run from hundreds of millions up to billions of electron-volts. Accelerators for the lower energy range have been available for a good many years; those for the higher energy range only for the last few years.

The first type of accelerator was that devised in England in the 1920's by Cockcroft and Walton. It was a fairly conventional application of familiar electrical engineering principles, operating with transformers and condensers, and was able to get to an energy approaching 1 million electron-volts. A good many nuclear transmutations can be carried out with protons and deuterons accelerated to such energies, so that the Cockcroft-Walton accelerator has proved to be a useful device, and is still in use in many places.

In the late 1920's in America, Van de Graaff devised an electrostatic generator capable of going to energies, in the most recent models, of

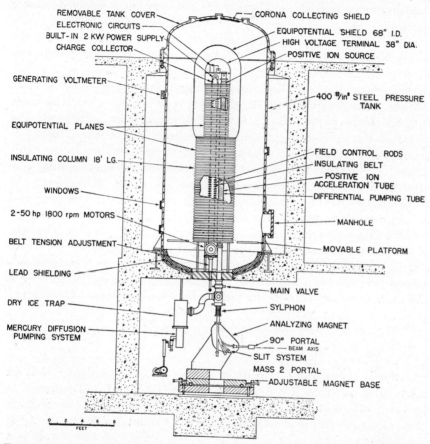

FIG. 11-2. Van de Graaff generator at Massachusetts Institute of Technology. The belt carries charge to the high-voltage terminal at the top of the column. (*Courtesy of W. W. Buechner.*)

the order of magnitude of 8 million electron-volts, just the most useful range for investigating nuclear energy levels. This generator operates mechanically, by means of an insulating belt which carries electricity by convection to a high-voltage terminal. A drawing of an accelerator of this type is shown in Fig. 11-2. The particularly valuable feature of the Van de Graaff generator is that its voltage is easily regulated and extremely constant. Thus it can serve as a source of particles of definite and precise energy, a very valuable thing in studying the energies of nuclear interactions. By bombarding nuclei with deuterons, for instance, of known energy, one can then observe the ejected particles, usually protons, measure their energies precisely by deflecting them in magnetic fields, and in this way get very finely resolved nuclear spectra.

Quite a different type of accelerator was the cyclotron, invented about 1930 by Lawrence. This machine has two main features. First, a magnet is used to bend the paths of the particles into circular paths. Secondly, the accelerating voltage, instead of being a direct voltage, is alternating, but the particles travel in bunches, and when they reach the part of the path where they are to be accelerated, the phase of the accelerating field is always such as to speed them up, though in between these times the field is reversed in phase. This allows acceleration by means of relatively low voltages, acting time after time as the particles pass the accelerating part of the path.

To understand this machine, which is typical of most of the later accelerators, we must first consider very simply the dynamics of a particle of mass m, charge e, in a transverse magnetic field. The field B will exert a force transverse to the motion, of magnitude evB, where v is the velocity of the particle, if we use mks units. By Newton's second law, this must equal the centripetal force, or mv^2/r, where r is the radius of curvature of the path. By equating these, we find

$$evB = \frac{mv^2}{r} \qquad \frac{v}{r} = \omega = \left(\frac{e}{m}\right) B \qquad (11\text{-}3)$$

where ω is the angular velocity of rotation of the particle. It is an interesting fact that this frequency, called the cyclotron frequency, is just twice the so-called Larmor frequency, the frequency of precession of an electron orbit in a magnetic field, as encountered in the theory of the Zeeman effect. The most conspicuous feature of a cyclotron is a large magnet, capable of producing a magnetic field of the order of magnitude of 15,000 gauss. In such a magnetic field, the cyclotron frequency is of a convenient magnitude to be generated by conventional electrical engineering methods.

Between the magnetic poles, one has a structure similar to that snown in Fig. 11-3, called dees, on account of their resemblance in shape to the letter D. As a particle rotates inside one of the dees, it is practically in a field-free space, since they are made of metal and operate like Faraday cages. However, one applies a difference of potential between the two dees, alternating with the angular frequency ω.   Thus when a particle crosses the region between the two dees, it feels an electric field, which can be accelerating or retarding according to the phase of the alternating field.   If a particle crosses this region in an accelerating phase, then it will pass around a semicircle, and by the time it crosses the corresponding region on the other side of the dees, the phase of the field will have changed, and it will again be accelerated.   In this way it receives one accelerating impulse after another, it is speeded up, and by Eq. (11-3) the radius of its orbit

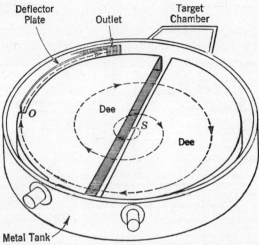

Fig. 11-3. Cyclotron structure.   The positive ions emitted from the source S (not shown on the diagram) are accelerated each time they pass from one dee to the other.   They leave the left dee at opening O, and are pulled out of their circular path by the negatively charged deflector plate so that they hit the target.   (*Courtesy of O. Oldenberg.*)

increases as the velocity or kinetic energy increases.   Starting at the center of the dees, it finally will find its way to the circumference, where arrangements are made to eject the beam.

In this way, many cyclotrons have been built operating with deuterons of 15 to 20 Mev, or corresponding energies for other types of particles.   These cyclotrons formed the main tool for study of nuclear disintegrations in the 1930's.   It was then thought that a natural limit was set to the energy which could be obtained in this way, by the relativistic change of mass with velocity.   As a particle is accelerated too much, its mass m will begin to increase, and by Eq. (11-3) the cyclotron frequency will decrease.   The particle will no longer be in step with the field, and acceleration will cease.

This difficulty was overcome, soon after the Second World War, by the invention of the synchrocyclotron, which used some of the principles of the synchrotron, an electron accelerator invented toward the end of the war independently by McMillan in America and Veksler in Russia. In the synchrocyclotron, one uses a pulse of protons or other particles, starting out together from the center of the cyclotron. As they move outward on their spiral paths, one then gradually decreases the frequency applied to the dees, to keep in step with the decreasing

FIG. 11-4. Large synchrocyclotron at the University of California. (*Courtesy of E. O. Lawrence and O. Oldenberg.*)

cyclotron frequency. Such machines have been built to accelerate particles to the order of three or four hundred million electron-volts, a high enough energy to produce some types of mesons. A large synchrocyclotron is shown in Fig. 11-4.

There is no reason why a synchrocyclotron should not be built to reach as high energies as desired, except cost: the magnet becomes impossibly expensive. To avoid this difficulty, the possibility was next investigated of making an accelerator in which the radius of the orbit would remain fixed, so that the magnet could be of a ring-shaped or annular form, involving much less material than in the cyclotron. From Eq. (11-3), we see that we can impose the condition that r remain constant, provided we are willing to have both the cyclotron frequency and the magnetic field vary as functions of time, while a pulse of particles is being accelerated. The synchrotron, a machine for accelerating electrons, which we have already mentioned, had been built shortly before, using a fixed radius. Electrons reach practically the velocity of light at energies of the order of a million electron-volts, and the synchrotrons were designed for a constant velocity c (the velocity of light) for the particles. If r is also kept constant, we see from Eq. (11-3) that ω is constant, while the magnetic field B must be

FIG. 11-5. The Brookhaven cosmotron. (*Courtesy of Brookhaven National Laboratory and O. Oldenberg.*)

built up proportionally to the mass of the electron which increases with its kinetic energy according to Einstein's relation. Synchrotrons have been built accelerating electrons to several hundred million electron-volts, where their masses are hundreds of times the rest mass.

By combining the variation of frequency and magnetic field, then, so that Eq. (11-3) is continually satisfied with constant r, one can build a machine accelerating positive particles to any desired energy, in an annular path. Such a machine is a proton synchrotron, of which the two largest, at the time of writing, are the Brookhaven cosmotron, operating at about 2.75 billion electron-volts, and the Berkeley bevatron planned for about 6 bev. The Brookhaven accelerator is shown in Fig. 11-5. The difficulty in going still higher is that it becomes increasingly hard to focus the ion beams into their circular paths, as the paths get longer.   However, a new principle of focusing, called the strong-focusing method, has recently been discovered, and by use of that, proton synchrotrons intended to produce particles of about 25 bev are now being designed.

The accelerators which we have mentioned are not the only ones which are in use, though they are perhaps the most important ones. One additional type is the betatron, an electron accelerator devised by Kerst before the war.   This, like the synchrotron, accelerates electrons in a circular path, but builds up their energy from low values, and hence must use an increasing magnetic field to keep them in the same orbit.   Instead of accelerating them by an alternating voltage, as in the cyclotron or synchrotron, their acceleration is produced by electromagnetic induction.   There is a magnetic flux through their orbit, which builds up as the magnetic field increases, and produces enough electromotive force to give them their required acceleration.   Betatrons accelerating electrons to about 300 Mev have been built.

Still another type is the linear accelerator, which has been built for both electrons and protons.   This, as the name indicates, is a linear machine, not using a magnet to bend the paths into a circle.   The particles are accelerated by passing through a series of sets of electrodes, which, like the cyclotron dees, are fed with alternating voltages, so phased that the voltage accelerates the particles when a bunch of particles is passing through, though the voltage would be in the opposite phase a half cycle later, when there are no particles going through. This machine, like the cyclotron and synchrotron and most of the other accelerators, has the virtue that it can operate with an alternating voltage, of relatively modest magnitude, rather than requiring a very high direct voltage, as in the Van de Graaff generator.

As we have stated, the main use of the low-energy accelerator, such as the Van de Graaff generator or the older type of cyclotron, is to investigate nuclear energy levels.   The scale of energies found in nuclei is such that these machines produce particles of just about the right energy.   Similarly, the use of the high-energy accelerators is to investigate mesons, and the type of phenomenon which can otherwise be observed only in cosmic rays.   The reason why the accelerators are so much more convenient than the older methods of investigation, by the use of naturally ejected radioactive particles for nuclear energy levels and cosmic rays for mesons, is that one has a controlled and collimated beam, of high intensity, rather than having to wait for chance particles to come along.

The experiments carried out with these accelerators generally consist of bombarding atoms of various types with the particles shot out from the accelerator. When an atomic collision occurs, various particles are ejected: perhaps the original particle is elastically scattered, perhaps it enters the nucleus and other disintegration products are shot out. The measurements made are generally those of the energies of the ejected particles, their nature (charge, mass, etc.), the direction of ejection, and the cross section for the collision (that is, the effective area within which the particle must hit the target atom to produce the collision). Elaborate techniques, involving counters, cloud chambers, measurement of tracks of particles in the emulsions on photographic plates, combined with magnetic fields to deflect the particles, have been worked out, so that extremely complicated measurements can be made. By using these techniques, most of the experimental information of modern nuclear physics has been acquired.

11-4. Nuclear Reactions and Nuclear Energies. When a fast particle, such as a proton, deuteron, alpha particle, or neutron, strikes a nucleus, several things can happen. The particle can be elastically scattered. But also the impinging particle can stick to the nucleus, become embedded in it, and then, in a time too short to observe, the resulting compound nucleus can eject some other particle. There are some indications that in this process the compound nucleus has time to come to a sort of equilibrium state before it breaks up. This evidence is of the following sort: sometimes there are two ways in which a compound nucleus can be formed. One can start with two different initial nuclei, bombard with two different types of particles, but in such a way that the final compound nucleus in each case has the same number of neutrons and of protons. In such cases, there are fairly good indications that the disintegration is identical for the compound nucleus, no matter in which of the two ways it was formed.

This compound nucleus, having been formed by shooting a fast particle into a previously stable nucleus, is highly excited and unstable. As we have stated, it will proceed to undergo a transmutation, in which particles of various sorts are shot off, such as protons or neutrons, leaving an entirely different nucleus behind. This nucleus will very often be left in an excited state, and by measuring the energies of the ejected particles, one can determine the energy levels of the various nuclei. The resulting nucleus is very likely to have transitions from one of its excited energy levels to another with emission of electromagnetic radiation, just as an atom can, the short-wave radiation in this case being called gamma rays. By observing these gamma rays, energy-level diagrams for the nuclei have been worked out, with levels differing by hundreds of thousands or millions of electron-volts. There are many cross checks which can be given for the nuclear energy levels, by interrelating the gamma-ray frequencies and the energies of the ejected particles.

We shall mention later that theories are being worked out according to which the various energy levels can be described in much the same language as the energy levels of complex atoms. There are various quantum numbers, some of them associated with angular momenta, and there are selection principles governing the transitions between them. The study of these energy levels and transitions is proving as useful in understanding nuclear structure and nuclear forces as was the study of complex spectra in the theory of atoms. So far, however, we have not got nearly so far with the nuclear theory as with atomic theory.

Some types of nuclei, when they have fallen to their ground state with emission of gamma rays, are found to be completely stable. These are the nuclei found in nature, the stable isotopes. Often there may be several isotopes with the same atomic number, but different atomic weights (that is, with the present interpretation, with the same number of protons, but different numbers of neutrons). These isotopes have practically identical chemical properties, and the chemical element occurring in nature is a mixture of them. This mixture was probably set up when the earth was molten and the materials in it were well stirred, so that we find the same proportion of isotopes in a sample of the same material, no matter where it is found on the earth.

Many of the nuclear species produced by transmutations, however, are radioactive. Their disintegration times vary all the way from millions of years to small fractions of seconds. The long disintegration times can, of course, be measured by observing in the laboratory what fraction of the atoms of a material disintegrate per second; if this is a very small fraction, it can still be observed, since individual disintegrations can be observed by means of counters, but the half-life so determined may be extremely long. The artificially radioactive materials can disintegrate by emission of various types of particles, usually electrons or positrons.

Then there are the naturally radioactive substances. These occur in nature, only because they, or the parent substances which led to them, disintegrate so slowly, or have such long half-lives (the length of time required for half the atoms to disintegrate), that we still have a good fraction of the materials which existed when the earth was formed, some billions of years ago. For instance, uranium disintegrates very slowly, so that it occurs in nature; though some of its disintegration products, such as radium, disintegrate rapidly, and the only reason why we have them is that they are being produced all the time.   In the naturally radioactive materials, it happens that the only types of particles they shoot out are alpha particles and electrons, or beta particles.

It is worthwhile for the reader to know the notation used to describe nuclear species and nuclear transmutations.   The symbol of a nucleus must indicate both its atomic number and mass number or atomic weight.   The chemical symbol, of course, indicates the atomic number, but sometimes it is convenient to indicate this explicitly as well, and this is done if desired by a subscript to the left of the chemical symbol. The mass number is given as a superscript to the right of the symbol. Thus, for instance, the isotope of boron with mass 11 is denoted by $_5B^{11}$.   Very often one leaves off the subscript indicating the atomic number, and would write this as B^{11}.

If one bombards a nucleus of B^{11} with a deuteron, which is usually denoted by d, though it could be written more explicitly as $_1H^2$, there would be an instantaneous formation of a compound nucleus $_6C^{13}$, but this does not last long enough, in the very excited state in which it is formed, to be observed directly.   Instead, it immediately breaks up. It can emit a proton, leaving $_5B^{12}$, or can emit a neutron, leaving $_6C^{12}$. We could indicate these reactions in a very explicit way, including the compound nucleus in parentheses, by the equations

$$_5B^{11} + _1H^2 \rightarrow (_6C^{13}) \begin{cases} _5B^{12} + _1H^1 \\ _6C^{12} + _0n^1 \end{cases} \qquad (11\text{-}4)$$

Ordinarily, however, a much more condensed notation is used.   The compound nucleus is omitted, the deuteron, proton, and neutron are symbolized by d, p, and n, and the reactions would be written

$$B^{11}(d,p)B^{12} \text{ or } B^{11}(d,n)C^{12} \qquad (11\text{-}5)$$

respectively, where the symbol (d,p) indicates that a deuteron is shot in, and a proton comes off.   In the case illustrated above, the isotope C^{12} is stable, so that if it is formed, nothing more happens.   However, the B^{12} is a beta emitter, disintegrating with a half-life of about 0.022 sec into a beta particle and C^{12}.   If we wished to write an equation for this reaction, we should write

$$_5B^{12} \rightarrow _6C^{12} + \beta^- \qquad (11\text{-}6)$$

By such studies of disintegrations, one has found very large numbers of nuclear species, both stable and unstable, and knows their proper-

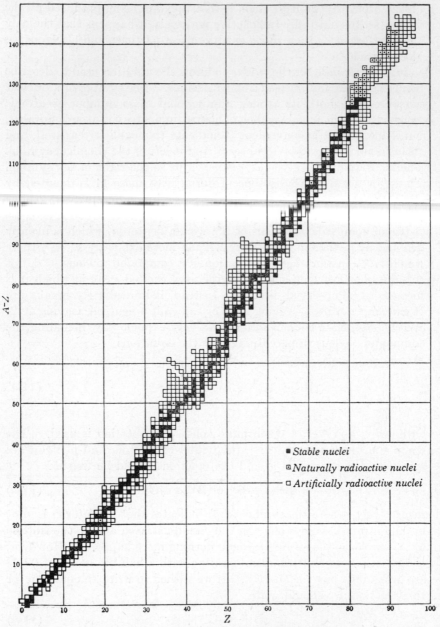

FIG. 11-6. Chart of known nuclei. (*From F. Bitter, "Nuclear Physics,"* 1950, *Addison-Wesley Publishing Company, Inc., Cambridge, Mass.*)

ties. It is extremely interesting to give some simple results concerning these nuclei. In the first place, in Fig. 11-6, we show the known nuclear species, the atomic number or the number of protons being plotted as abscissa, the number of neutrons as ordinate. Stable nuclei are shown black, radioactive ones unshaded. One gains the impression from this curve that the line of stable nuclei must indicate a minimum of energy of nuclei, regarded as a function of the two parameters, the number of protons and number of neutrons. If we depart in either direction from this minimum, the nuclei are unstable; that is, they can lose energy by disintegrating toward the line of stable nuclei.

This tells us at once the type of disintegrations to be expected in the various parts of the diagram. Those isotopes which have too many neutrons, or too few protons, to lie in the stable region will disintegrate with emission of beta particles, which remove negative charge, hence increase the positive charge, changing neutrons into protons, and bring the nucleus closer to the stable region. On the contrary, those isotopes with too few neutrons, or too many protons, will emit positrons, changing protons into neutrons and pushing them in the desired direction. These predictions are borne out by fact; in every case, the observed disintegrations are in the direction to bring a nucleus toward the stable region. Furthermore, nuclei which are far from the stable region tend to disintegrate much more rapidly, or have shorter half-lives, than those closer to the stable region.

It is clear from this discussion that if we plot nuclear energy as a function of the two variables used in Fig. 11-6, there will be a deep minimum along the line of the stable nuclei, like a deep valley with rapidly rising sides. This is the case. But it is interesting furthermore to look at the way in which the energy of the stable nuclei varies with atomic number; that is, to investigate the height of the floor of the valley, as we go from one end to the other. We find in the first place that the binding energy, the energy of the nucleus when referred to the separated protons and neutrons as a zero of energy, is approximately proportional to the atomic weight, or in other words the energy per nuclear particle (or per nucleon, as nuclear particles are called) is approximately constant. Hence the most convenient way to plot the binding energy is to give this energy per nucleon, as a function of atomic weight. Such a curve, called a binding-energy curve, is given in Fig. 11-7.

There are two main features to be observed from this curve. First is the general form: the very light elements, and the very heavy ones, are less tightly bound than the intermediate ones. It is this fact that leads to the possibility of developing atomic energy by fusion (combination of two light elements into a heavier one) or by fission (splitting of a very heavy element into two smaller fragments). We shall discuss the applications of this possibility in Sec. 11-8. The other feature is the existence of peaks noticeable particularly among the lighter elements. Thus, we find that the alpha particle $_2He^4$, composed of two protons and two neutrons, and the oxygen atom $_8O^{16}$, composed of eight protons and eight neutrons, have a particularly large binding

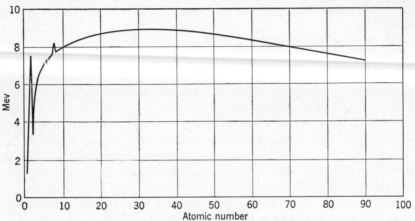

FIG. 11-7. Binding energy per nucleon, as a function of atomic number. The two peaks at low atomic number are for $_2He^4$ and $_8O^{16}$.

energy, showing that these nuclei are particularly stable. More careful study shows that particularly stable nuclei are found when either the number of protons or neutrons equals one of a certain set of integers, found empirically, and often called "magic numbers," equal to 2, 8, 20, 50, 82, and 126. These numbers give a clue to the arrangement of nuclear particles in shells, something like the shells of electrons which lead to the periodic system of the elements, and we shall come back to them in Sec. 11-10.

11-5. Examples of Nuclear Reactions. In the preceding section we have been discussing in a qualitative way the nature of nuclear reactions and energy levels. Now let us become more specific, and ask precisely how such reactions are studied and how the energies are determined. We shall use many examples which we have already mentioned in a descriptive way.

The first thing which we must understand is the relation between nuclear energies and atomic weights. We have already seen that Einstein's relation, that a mass m is equivalent to an energy E by the equation $E = mc^2$, is the key to this situation, but we wish to get the numerical way to apply this. Let us find how much energy, in million electron-volts, is equivalent to the mass of an atom of unit atomic weight. The energy can be written as eV, where e is the charge on the electron, V the equivalent voltage. For the mass m, we wish the mass of an atom of unit atomic weight, and can make use of Avogadro's number N_0. This gives the number of atoms in a gram-atom. But a gram-atom of atoms of unit atomic weight would weigh just 1 g, so that the mass of an atom of unit atomic weight is $1/N_0$ g. We shall make our calculation in mks units, for then the answer will come out directly in volts. We then take for c the quantity 3.00×10^8 m/sec, for e the quantity 1.602×10^{-19} coulomb, for the mass $(1/N_0) \times 10^{-3}$ kg, where $N_0 = 6.025 \times 10^{23}$ per gram. Then we have

$$V = \frac{c^2}{e(10^3 N_0)} = \frac{(3.00 \times 10^8)^2}{(1.602 \times 10^{-19} \times 6.025 \times 10^{26})}$$
$$= 931 \text{ Mev} \tag{11-7}$$

This figure, that an atom with atomic weight of unity is equivalent to 931 Mev, serves as a conversion factor between mass and energy, just as the mechanical equivalent of heat serves as a conversion factor between energy and heat.

Let us now use this conversion factor for a few obvious calculations regarding binding energies. For instance, the mass of a hydrogen atom is 1.00814 atomic mass units (often abbreviated amu). The mass of a neutron is 1.00898. The mass of a helium atom is 4.00387. (These values, and others, are given in Appendix 2.) We then ask, how much energy would be liberated if two hydrogen atoms and two neutrons combined to form a helium atom? It is true that we do not know a direct reaction to make this happen, but the question is interesting, nevertheless. The mass of the particles going into the reaction is $2(1.00814) + 2(1.00898) = 4.03424$ amu. This is greater than the mass of the helium atom by the amount

$$4.03424 - 4.00387 = 0.03037 \text{ amu}$$

Using our conversion factor, this corresponds to

$$931 \times 0.03037 = 28.28 \text{ Mev}$$

We see, then, the large amount of energy which would be liberated in this reaction, if it could be brought about.

To orient us on magnitudes, let us compare such energies as these with chemical energies. When two hydrogen atoms combine chemi-

cally to form a hydrogen molecule, they liberate about 4.72 ev; this is
the dissociation energy, as derived from band spectra or chemical data.
We have just seen that the same two atoms, plus two neutrons, uniting
to form a helium atom by union of their nuclei, would liberate 28.28
Mev, or about six million times as much energy. This is about the
order of magnitude of the ratio generally found between energies
released in nuclear reactions, and in similar chemical reactions.

The energy of 28.28 Mev released when two hydrogen atoms and
two neutrons combine to form one helium atom is what we have already
discussed as the binding energy. In Fig. 11-7, we showed binding
energies per nucleon. In the case of helium, with four nucleons, we
should get the binding energy per nucleon by dividing the energy of
28.28 by 4, so that it is 7.07 Mev. When we carry out a corresponding
calculation for the elements near helium in the periodic table, we get
considerably smaller values, for we have already mentioned that
helium is unusually tightly bound. On the other hand, when we do
it for an element near the center of the periodic table, where the curve
of Fig. 11-7 is near its maximum, we get a value of approximately
8.5 Mev per nucleon. For the heaviest elements, we have approximately 7.6 Mev per nucleon.

From these figures we can find approximately the amount of energy
released when a heavy atom undergoes fission. If a uranium atom of
atomic weight 235 undergoes fission, and its fission fragments fall in
the part of the periodic table where the binding energy is approximately 8.5 Mev per nucleon, we see that the energy given off will be
the difference between 8.5 and 7.6, multiplied by the atomic weight,
or the number of nucleons. That is, it will be of the order of magnitude
of $0.9 \times 235 = 211$ Mev. This is the order of magnitude of the
observed energy given off in a fission, much greater than is given off in
any ordinary radioactive disintegration.

As a contrast to these very large energies, let us consider a very
small one. The mass of the deuteron is 2.01474 amu. We may ask
how much energy will be given off, if it is formed from a hydrogen atom
and a neutron. Their masses add to $1.00814 + 1.00898 = 2.01712$, so
that the energy given off is $2.01712 - 2.01474 = 0.00238$ amu,
equivalent to 2.22 Mev. This can be checked by direct observation.
Deuterons can be produced by bombarding hydrogen with neutrons of
very low energy, according to the reaction $H^1(n,\gamma)H^2$, where (n,γ)
symbolizes that a neutron is shot in, and a gamma ray emitted. In a
careful experiment of this sort, the frequency of the emitted gamma
rays was measured, converted to energy units, and was found to be
2.230 Mev.

We note from the calculation we have just made that the deuteron is stable, in the sense that energy must be put into it to dissociate it into a hydrogen atom and a neutron. On the other hand, the neutron itself is not stable: it can dissociate into a proton and an electron, essentially a beta disintegration, with decrease of energy. The energy released is $1.00898 - 1.00814$, equivalent to 0.78 Mev. This radio-activity of the neutron has been observed experimentally, the half-life being of the order of magnitude of a half hour.

Now let us consider some more complicated cases of reactions, and their uses to determine nuclear energies. As an illustration, we shall take an experiment in which a boron target was bombarded with deuterons of a fixed energy, from a Van de Graaff generator. The boron target contained both B^{10} and B^{11}, the two stable isotopes of boron, so that reactions of both of these had to be taken into account; though a subsidiary experiment, with a target consisting almost entirely of B^{10}, made it possible to separate the effects of the two isotopes. The deuterons then produced the reactions $B^{10}(d,p)B^{11}$ and $B^{11}(d,p)B^{12}$. The energies of the emerging protons were measured, and in this way the energies of the B^{11} and B^{12} nuclei resulting from the disintegrations were computed. To make possible a detailed discussion, let us first consider just how the disintegration process takes place.

In the experiment, a boron atom, originally at rest, is bombarded by a fast deuteron. After the collision, a proton is ejected, and the resulting boron atom has an atomic weight greater by one unit, since it has retained a neutron in the encounter. In this process, momentum must be conserved, and this means that part of the kinetic energy is transferred to the boron atom, which recoils. The geometry of the experiment is arranged so that only protons coming off in directions exactly 90° to the direction of the incident deuteron are observed. We can measure the velocity of this ejected proton, for in the experiment it is bent through a semicircle by an electromagnet, and the momentum, or velocity, of the proton can be found from the magnetic field and the radius of curvature of its path. From the final velocity of the proton, and the known initial velocity of the deuteron, we can solve for the final velocity of the boron atom resulting from the transmutation. Hence we can find the final kinetic energy of all particles, and since we know the initial kinetic energy, we can find the increase in kinetic energy, or the energy liberated in the reaction. This energy liberated is called the Q of the reaction; and from it, we can calculate the difference between the initial and final masses of the particles, and check with values of this difference obtained from known atomic masses.

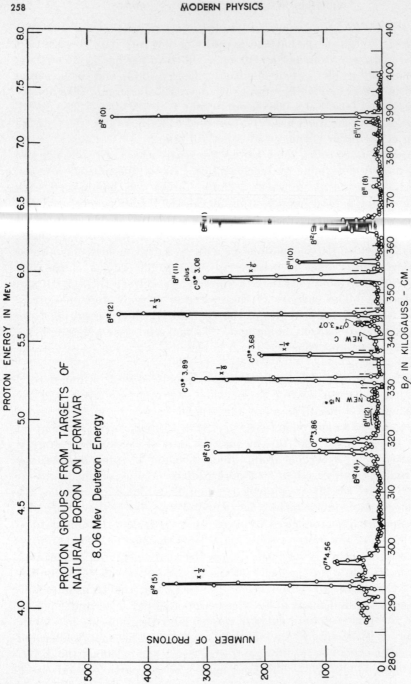

FIG. 11-8. Proton groups from targets of natural boron, bombarded by deuterons of energy 8.06 Mev. The peak which should be labeled B¹¹(9) is incorrectly labeled B¹²(9). (*Courtesy of M. M. Elkind and W.W. Buechner.*)

In a typical experiment of this sort, the result which was obtained is shown in Fig. 11-8. Here the proton yield is plotted, as a function of the magnetic field in the analyzing magnet, which in turn determines the proton energy. In a moment we shall calculate the relation between these two quantities, but first we look at the general results of Fig. 11-8. We see a great many groups of emitted protons, each of very sharply determined energy. Most of these come from the reactions resulting in either B^{11} or B^{12}, and they are so labeled; though a few come from oxygen and other impurities. As we have mentioned, the B^{11} and B^{12} peaks were distinguished from each other by another experiment using the enriched isotope B^{10} on the target, in which case only the B^{11} peaks appeared. Let us fix our attention particularly on those peaks marked B^{12}. The one of highest energy, marked $B^{12}(0)$, coming at about 7.25 Mev, is thought to come from a process in which the B^{12} atom is left in its ground state, after the reaction $B^{11}(d,p)B^{12}$. But we have a series of other peaks, marked $B^{12}(1)$, $B^{12}(2)$, etc., corresponding to lower proton energies. In these cases, it is thought that the B^{12} atom is left in an excited state after the reaction, and the difference in energies tells us how high these excited states lie. The sharpness of the peaks in Fig. 11-8 shows that we can determine the energy levels very exactly.

The peaks arising from B^{11} are labeled with larger numbers, such as $B^{11}(7)$, $B^{11}(8)$, etc. This is because the Q's of the reactions $B^{10}(d,p)B^{11}$ are much higher than for $B^{11}(d,p)B^{12}$. Hence the protons come out with much greater energy, and those arising from the ground state of B^{11}, and the first six excited states, come at energies too high to observe in this particular experiment; they have been determined in other experiments. Hence the peak marked $B^{11}(7)$ is thought to come from the seventh excited state in the B^{11} atom.

It will be observed from this preliminary view of the experimental results that in such a case as this we are faced, not with a single reaction, but with a variety of reactions, for the final atom can be found in many different energy levels. Each of these reactions will have its own Q, and our first problem is to see how these are determined from the experimental data. Let us first look into the question of the relation between the scale at the bottom of Fig. 11-8, labeled $B\rho$ in kilogauss-centimeters, and the upper scale, labeled proton energy in million electron-volts. In the actual experiment, the protons are bent around a semicircle of very accurately known radius, in a magnetic field whose magnetic induction B can be varied. From earlier work we know that the momentum, and hence the velocity, of a particle in such a magnetic field is proportional to the product $B\rho$, where ρ is the radius of the circle.   The measurement consists of observing the number of protons coming through the apparatus in a fixed time interval, for each magnetic field, and Fig. 11-8 is a plot of the results of this experiment.

Let us remind ourselves of the theory of the deflection of particles in a magnetic field.   The transverse force on a particle of charge e, traveling with velocity v in a magnetic field B, is equal to evB, in mks units.   This equals mv^2/ρ, where v^2/ρ is the centripetal acceleration. Hence we have $B\rho = mv/e$.   But the kinetic energy of the particle, using classical mechanics (which is nearly accurate enough for this problem, though the relativistic corrections are just appreciable, and relativistic mechanics was actually used in the discussion of this particular case), is of course $mv^2/2$.   Hence we can write this in terms of $B\rho$, obtaining

$$\frac{1}{2} mv^2 = \frac{1}{2}\left(\frac{e^2}{m}\right)(B\rho)^2 \tag{11-8}$$

We wish to convert this into electron-volts, so we set it equal to eV, and find that

$$V = \frac{1}{2}\left(\frac{e}{m}\right)(B\rho)^2 \tag{11-9}$$

Let us now find the numerical value of the coefficient to use, if V is to be in million electron-volts, and $B\rho$ is in the units used in Fig. 11-8, namely, kilogauss-centimeters.   We shall do this, as usual, by going to mks units, in which V will come out directly in volts.   In these units, we are to use $e = 1.602 \times 10^{-19}$ coulomb, and m, the mass of the proton, is 1.672×10^{-27} kg.   We are to put B in webers per square meter (1 weber/sq m = 10 kilogauss), and ρ in meters.   Hence, if $B\rho$ equals 1 kilogauss-cm, it is $(10^{-1}$ weber/sq m$) \times (10^{-2}$ m$)$, or is 10^{-3} mks units.   Hence we have

$$V = \tfrac{1}{2}\frac{1.602 \times 10^{-19}}{1.672 \times 10^{-27}} \times 10^{-6}(B\rho)^2$$
$$= 47.9(B\rho)^2 \text{ ev} \tag{11-10}$$

where $B\rho$ is in kilogauss-centimeters.   As an illustration of this, we consider the peak marked $B^{12}(0)$ in Fig. 11-8, which comes for $B\rho = 389$. Substituting in Eq. (11-10), we find $V = 7.248$ Mev.

Next let us ask how to find the Q value from such an observation. The incident deuterons in the experiment of Fig. 11-8 are stated to have an energy of 8.06 Mev, and this would lead us at first sight to think, since the proton comes off with only 7.25 Mev, that the Q was negative, and energy was not given out in the reaction. This is not the case, however; we shall find that the recoiling boron atom has enough energy so that there is a positive Q. To find this recoil energy, we have to use very elementary principles of mechanics.

In Fig. 11-9 we show a diagram of momentum vectors for the problem. We show the momentum $m_d v_d$ for the incident deuteron, the momentum $m_p v_p$ of the emerging proton, emerging exactly at right angles to the deuteron's velocity, by the arrangement of the experiment, and the momentum $m_b v_b$ of the recoil boron nucleus. We note that the mass m_b of the boron refers to the final mass of this atom after the transmutation. By the law of conservation of momentum, the vector sum of the momenta of the proton and the recoil boron nucleus after the collision must equal the momentum of the deuteron before collision, since the original boron nucleus was at rest. We see, then, that one component of the momentum of the boron equals the initial momentum of the deuteron, while the other equals (in magnitude) the final momentum of the proton.

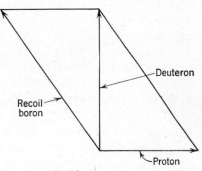

FIG. 11-9. Incident momentum of deuteron and final momenta of proton and recoil boron, in reaction $_5\mathrm{B}^{11}(d,p)_5\mathrm{B}^{12}$ described in the text.

We can then at once find the kinetic energy of the boron recoil atom. Its two components of velocity are $m_d v_d/m_b$ and $m_p v_p/m_b$, so that its kinetic energy is

$$E_b = \frac{1}{2}\,m_p v_p^2 \frac{m_p}{m_b} + \frac{1}{2}\,m_d v_d^2 \frac{m_d}{m_b} \qquad (11\text{-}11)$$

The Q of the reaction is then the sum of the proton and boron energies, minus the deuteron energy, or

$$Q = \frac{1}{2}\,m_p v_p^2 \left(1 + \frac{m_p}{m_b}\right) - \frac{1}{2}\,m_d v_d^2 \left(1 - \frac{m_d}{m_b}\right) \qquad (11\text{-}12)$$

For this part of the problem, it is accurate enough to use whole numbers for the masses, so that we set $m_p = 1$, $m_d = 2$, $m_b = 12$. If we then insert 9.06 Mev for $\frac{1}{2}m_d v_d^2$, the energy of the incident deuteron, and 7.25 Mev for $\frac{1}{2}m_p v_p^2$, the energy of the recoil proton, we find that the energy of the recoil boron nucleus is 1.95 Mev, and the Q is 1.14 Mev. In other words, this amount of kinetic energy is released in the reaction.

We should now be able to compare this release of kinetic energy with the difference of masses before and after the reaction. This is a case, however, where this cannot be done directly, for B^{12} is a radioactive nucleus, whose mass cannot be found by the methods of mass spectroscopy, which are used to find the masses of the stable nuclei. Let us then use the experiment to find the mass of B^{12}, and see if a check on this value is not possible from some other experiment. We should find that the sum of the masses of the incident deuteron and the original B^{11} nucleus should equal the sum of the masses of the emerging proton, the final B^{12} nucleus, and the mass equivalent of the energy Q released as kinetic energy. That is, we should have the mass B^{12} equal to the masses of $B^{11} + d - p - Q$, writing it symbolically. Now the mass of B^{11}, which is a stable isotope, is known fairly accurately, from mass spectrum data, to be about 11.01279 amu. As before, the masses of d and p are 2.01474 and 1.00814, respectively, and the mass equivalent of the Q of 1.14 Mev is 0.00122 amu. Hence we find that the mass of the B^{12} atom is $11.01279 + 2.01474 - 1.00814 - 0.00122 = 12.01817$.

As we have mentioned, this mass of B^{12} is not known directly from mass spectroscopy. However, there is a way to check it, for it disintegrates by beta emission into C^{12}. The maximum energy of the beta particles is known to be 13.43 Mev, and the mass of C^{12}, which is the common stable isotope of carbon, is known by mass spectrum data to be 12.00380 amu. Hence we should conclude that the mass of B^{12} should equal that of C^{12}, plus the mass equivalent of the energy 13.43 Mev of the beta particles. This mass equivalent is 0.01443 amu. Hence we should conclude that the mass of B^{12} should be 12.01823, in satisfactory agreement with the value determined by the entirely different experiment which we have been discussing.

There are two points which are worth mentioning, in connection with this result. In the first place, it would not have been obvious that the beta emission of B^{12} to yield C^{12} should have resulted in C^{12} in its ground state; it might have led to an excited state of C^{12}, which would later have decayed to the ground state by gamma emission. Or it could have started at an excited state of B^{12}. The good agreement of the two determinations of the B^{12} mass, however, indicates that this was not the case, and that the beta emission is from the ground state of B^{12} to the ground state of C^{12}. Incidentally, the rather large energy of the emitted beta particle is a result of the unusual stability of C^{12}, which we have already mentioned, as compared with less stable nuclei like B^{12}.

The other point worth mentioning is that we have tacitly disregarded the masses of electrons, in these calculations. This was justified, but requires a little thought, for the mass equivalent of an electron is by no means negligible, but is in fact 0.00055 amu, so that our agreement would have been completely lost if we had disregarded it incorrectly. All the atomic masses which we have used have been for neutral atoms; even for the deuteron and proton, we have really used the masses of the neutral deuterium and hydrogen atoms, containing an electron each. However, in each equation, examination will show that the number of electrons on both sides of the equation has balanced, so that we were justified in doing this. Thus, in the reaction $B^{11}(d,p)B^{12}$, the boron atom before and after the reaction contains the five electrons required to make it electrically neutral, and the deuteron and proton are charged, and do not contain electrons. But it is only the difference of deuteron and proton masses which entered, and this is the same as the difference between the masses of the neutral deuterium and hydrogen atoms. Again, in the beta disintegration of B^{12} to give C^{12}, there is a balance of electrons. This is not quite so obvious, for as we have emphasized, an electron is created in the process of beta disintegration. But this is just compensated by the fact that the C^{12} atom which appears only has the five electrons present originally in the B^{12} surrounding the nucleus. In other words, the C^{12} atom, suddenly created out of the B^{12} atom, is really created as a singly charged positive ion, lacking an outer electron. Thus here again there is a balance, the mass of the created beta particle compensating for the missing electron in the C^{12} positive ion. This suggests, however, that we have to be very careful about the electrons, as well as the nuclei, in making energy calculations of this sort.

In addition to the energies of the ground states of the various nuclei, the experiment we are describing leads to the energies of various excited states of the B^{12} nucleus. In some ways, the excited states of the B^{11} nucleus, which are also determined from the experiment, are a little more interesting, and we shall describe them. From Fig. 11-8, one can calculate the energies of the seventh and higher excited states of B^{11}, and the lower states are found from other experiments. From the known masses, using methods similar to those which we have already described in detail, we can find the energy of the ground state of B^{11}, and hence the excitation energies. When such a calculation is made, we find energy levels as shown in Fig. 11-10. This figure also shows levels for C^{11}, adjusted to have the ground states agree. These levels are determined by entirely different experiments, and the reason for comparing them will be mentioned in a moment. The interesting feature of the B^{11} set of energy levels is that a gamma-ray spectrum has been observed, leading to gamma rays coming from the transitions indicated in Fig. 11-10.   The gamma rays were observed as a result of an entirely different experiment, in which Li⁷ was bombarded with alpha particles, according to the reaction $Li^7(\alpha,\gamma)B^{11}$.   The bombardment results in having the alpha particle stick to the Li⁷ nucleus, forming the B¹¹ nucleus in an excited state, which then falls to a lower state with emission of a gamma ray.   Many of the transitions between

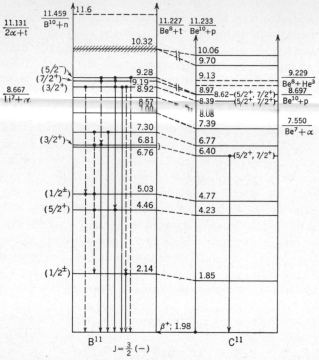

FIG. 11-10. Energy levels of mirror nuclei, B¹¹ and C¹¹.   *(Courtesy of M. M. Elkind and W. W. Buechner.)*

levels in Fig. 11-10 were observed as emitted gamma rays, and the energy differences so observed checked those found from the $B^{10}(d,p)B^{11}$ reaction.   This is an example of the sort of cross checks which are often found in nuclear-energy-level work.

The reason why it is interesting to compare the levels of B¹¹ and C¹¹, as is done in Fig. 11-10, is that they are what are called mirror nuclei. The nucleus of B¹¹ consists of five protons and six neutrons, while that of C¹¹ has five neutrons and six protons.   In other words, if we should change neutrons into protons, and vice versa, we should change one into the other.   Now some of the theories of nuclear structure suggest that, as far as nuclear forces are concerned, neutrons and protons act very much alike (except for the electrostatic forces met with protons), and that changing neutrons into protons, and vice versa, should make very little difference in the forces and energy levels.   We see from Fig. 11-10 that in fact there is a remarkable parallelism between the energy levels in these two cases, and this is one of the experimental checks of this hypothesis about mirror nuclei.

We have gone into great detail in describing these boron reactions, simply so that the reader will have an understanding of the sort of methods which are used experimentally in finding energy levels, and in checking them.   Some of the earliest examples of such checks came

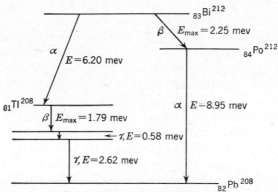

Fig. 11-11. Two methods by which $_{83}Bi^{212}$ disintegrates into $_{82}Pb^{208}$, showing consistency of energy determinations for the two methods.   Differences of height of energy levels show Q's of corresponding transformations.

in the radioactive disintegrations, which were worked on before the artificial transmutations were practicable.   A well-known example is shown in Fig. 11-11, in which we show the two alternative ways by which $_{83}Bi^{212}$ decays into $_{82}Pb^{208}$, in the thorium series of radioactive elements.   On the left, we see $_{83}Bi^{212}$ disintegrating with emission of an alpha particle to $_{81}Tl^{208}$.   The energy released in this reaction is about 6 Mev, so that $_{81}Tl^{208}$ is indicated on an energy level 6 Mev below $_{83}Bi^{212}$.   The $_{81}Tl^{208}$ in turn has a beta disintegration to an excited state of $_{82}Pb^{208}$, and this is followed by two successive gamma transitions, between excited states of $_{82}Pb^{208}$, ending up with the ground state of that atom.   On the other hand, $_{83}Bi^{212}$ can also disintegrate with emission of a beta particle to $_{84}Po^{212}$, which then has an alpha disintegration to $_{82}Pb^{208}$.   The final result is the same in either case, so that the sum of the energies given out in either case must be the same. This is verified experimentally, as shown in Fig. 11-11, and permits us to indicate the various atoms on an energy-level diagram, in which the energy differences in each case are the Q's of the reactions.

11-6. Further Examples of Nuclear Reactions. We have now indicated enough about these reactions so that the reader should have no trouble understanding further cases. Let us next describe a few well-known reactions, interesting for historical or other reasons. First, there is Rutherford's first observation of artificial disintegration, from the reaction which we now write $_7N^{14}(\alpha,p)_8O^{17}$. Then there is Chadwick's reaction which first led to the recognition of neutrons, $_4Be^9(\alpha,n)_6C^{12}$. This reaction still is useful as a neutron source. Among the early artificial radioactive transformations observed by the Joliot-Curies is the positron emission of $_{15}P^{30}$, which is produced by the reaction $_{13}Al^{27}(\alpha,n)_{15}P^{30}$, and which decays by positron emission to $_{14}Si^{30}$. We notice that these early reactions were produced by alpha-particle bombardment; for alpha particles from radioactive disintegrations were the only available particles in the earliest days.

Once the particle accelerators were available, transmutations were produced by other particles. In their first work in 1930, Cockcroft and Walton bombarded lithium with protons and deuterons, and observed the interesting reactions $_3Li^7(p,\alpha)_2He^4$ and $_3Li^6(d,\alpha)_2He^4$, in each of which a lithium atom is bombarded by a particle which supplies the necessary ingredients to form two alpha particles, and splits into these two alphas. Most accelerator work uses protons or deuterons, and the (d,p) reactions which we have described at length are typical of reactions produced in this way.

Once neutrons had been produced, initially by Chadwick's reaction $_4Be^9(\alpha,n)_6C^{12}$, they were used as projectiles in a very great number of nuclear reactions. There is one point regarding the disintegration of a nucleus by a charged particle like a proton, deuteron, or alpha particle, which we have not stressed so far, but shall take up in more detail later. There is a strong electrostatic repulsion between this charged particle and the nucleus. Hence, with a heavy atom, we cannot give the projectile enough kinetic energy to penetrate into the nucleus. Thus the reactions produced by the charged particles are ordinarily caused in fairly light atoms. On the other hand, there is no such repulsion for a neutron, and it can penetrate even the heaviest nucleus with ease. Hence there is a far wider field for neutron reactions than for those produced by charged particles. Fermi started studying such neutron reactions about 1934, and many others have continued the work since, first using neutrons from the $Be^9(\alpha,n)C^{12}$ reaction, and now more recently with the neutrons from the nuclear reactor. These studies have disclosed a variety of types of reactions, which are so important that we shall devote a special section to them.

As a final example of reactions not caused by neutrons, we shall describe Bethe's hypothetical set of reactions believed to produce the energy of the sun. This set of reactions is called the carbon cycle, for it requires the presence of carbon atoms, so to speak as a catalyst. That is, the carbon atoms are required in the reaction, but are not used up by it. The reason why we must have a cycle of this sort is that the net result of the process is to produce alpha particles out of protons, and there is no direct process for doing this. Bethe studied all known reactions involving other elements which might lead to the same result in an indirect way, and concluded that this carbon cycle was by far the most likely one to be actually taking place in the sun and stars.

One starts with an atom of $_6C^{12}$, and bombards it with a proton, resulting in the reaction $_6C^{12}(p,\gamma)_7N^{13}$. The $_7N^{13}$ produced in the transmutation is a positron emitter, with a half-life of 10 min, decaying to $_6C^{13}$ plus a positron. This atom can again capture a proton, by the reaction $_6C^{13}(p,\gamma)_7N^{14}$. The nitrogen so formed is the stable isotope of nitrogen, and again can capture a proton by the reaction $_7N^{14}(p,\gamma)_8O^{15}$. This isotope of oxygen is also a positron emitter, with a half-life of 2 min, decaying to $_7N^{15}$ and a positron. Finally $_7N^{15}$ can capture a proton, and this time, instead of merely emitting a gamma ray, it emits an alpha particle, according to the reaction $_7N^{15}(p,\alpha)_6C^{12}$. Thus the carbon atom is recreated, and the net result is the production of an alpha particle, out of four protons (with emission of two positrons, to balance the charge), and with a large production of energy. All these individual reactions are known in the laboratory. We must realize that on a laboratory scale, with the use of cyclotrons and other accelerators, we can produce particles of just as much energy as those met in the stars or the hydrogen bomb, so that these processes, which produce such vast and uncontrollable energy when carried out on a large scale, are susceptible of very precise experimental investigation.

Bethe's set of reactions was not one which could be set into action spontaneously, on account of the fact that some of the reactions involved required the particles to have a large amount of energy, corresponding to a temperature of millions of degrees. For this reason, any fusion reaction must start by having the materials heated to some such temperature, and this is the function of the fission bomb which has been used to set off a fusion reaction in the thermonuclear, or hydrogen, bombs with which we have become familiar. The situation is not essentially different from that of lighting a fire. A fuel which starts to burn by itself is not very useful. In most cases, we must have a match or other device to heat the fuel to a temperature at which it can start to react. The fission bomb is the match which has been used to ignite the fusion reaction.

As far as one can gather from the literature, the reactions used in fusion reactions so far are not the same ones concerned in the energy of the stars, and they do not proceed by direct use of hydrogen. They might use instead deuterium, $_1H^2$, or tritium, $_1H^3$, the isotopes of hydrogen containing one proton, and one or two neutrons, respectively. Clearly two deuterons, or deuterium nuclei, have just the right constitution to combine to give an alpha particle, $_2He^4$; similarly a tritium nucleus and a proton have the right constitution. One presumes that these are the constituents of some of the fusion explosions which have been produced. One gathers also that another type of fusion has been used: perhaps that of a lithium nucleus and a proton to produce two alpha particles, according to the reaction $_3Li^7(p,\alpha)_2He^4$. Since lithium is a common element, while deuterium and particularly tritium are hard to get, this appears to be a more practical reaction. It is interesting that it is similar to the one mentioned in 1941 in the rather prophetic paragraph which we have quoted from Dampier.

These fusion reactions, which proceed at such high temperatures in such a catastrophic way, cannot be controlled for the production of energy for peaceful purposes in any way which has yet been suggested. Rash statements are made that such control will never be possible. It seems rather sounder to take the view, as expressed in the paragraph mentioned earlier, that "before now in the history of applied science prospects of even less promise have confounded the prophets." Surely it is not absurd to suspect that an interpolation is possible between the large-scale operation of such a reaction on an explosive and catastrophic scale and the laboratory experiment in which it was first explored in a microscopic and peaceful way. Temperatures of hundreds of millions of degrees frighten an engineer accustomed only to thinking in conventional terms; the corresponding energies of millions of electron-volts do not frighten the physicist, who deals with such particles every day in his work.

11-7. Neutron Reactions and Nuclear Fission. In the preceding section, where we were studying mainly the reactions produced by charged particles, we stated that neutron reactions were much commoner than the others, since neutrons can penetrate even the heaviest nuclei with ease, whereas charged particles of moderate energy are repelled by heavy nuclei and cannot penetrate them to cause nuclear reactions. Furthermore, a great deal of study of neutron reactions has been carried out, on account of their practical importance in the nuclear reactor. In nuclear technology, it is vital to know the reactions undergone by any element which is introduced into the reactor, since as we shall see it is ordinarily important not to have neutrons captured, and this can happen in most types of neutron reactions.

One of the commonest types of neutron reactions is neutron radiative capture, with emission of a gamma ray. For example, one has the reaction $_{13}Al^{27}(n,\gamma)_{13}Al^{28}$. In any such case, the resulting nucleus tends to have an excess of neutrons, which it can overcome by a beta emission, which changes a neutron into a proton. Thus, for instance, $_{13}Al^{28}$ decays by beta emission into $_{14}Si^{28}$, which is stable. It is also possible, however, for an alpha particle or a proton to be immediately shot out of the nucleus, producing a transmutation by a reaction (n,α) or (n,p). Thus, for instance, the result of bombarding aluminum with neutrons can also lead to the reactions $_{13}Al^{27}(n,\alpha)_{11}Na^{24}$, or $_{13}Al^{27}(n,p)_{12}Mg^{27}$. Often these products are radioactive. Thus $_{11}Na^{24}$ is a beta emitter, decaying to $_{12}Mg^{24}$, and $_{12}Mg^{27}$ is also a beta emitter, decaying to $_{13}Al^{27}$, the original nucleus with which we started.

A very important physical quantity concerning these neutron reactions, as in fact any other nuclear reaction, is the so-called cross section. We have mentioned this before, but remind the reader of its meaning. Let us assume that a beam of neutrons strikes a thin target. A certain number of these neutrons will cause reactions, while the rest (ordinarily the greater part) will pass through. We can assign to each of the atoms a hypothetical cross section σ, such that the number of neutrons causing reactions is just equal to the number that would fall on these cross-sectional areas of all the atoms. That is, if there are N_a atoms in unit area of the target, if the number of neutrons falling on unit area of the target per unit time is I, and the number reacting in unit time is C, the ratio of the sum of all cross sections, to the unit area of the target, is $N_a\sigma$. We set this equal to the ratio C/I. That is, we have

$$\sigma = \frac{C}{IN_a} \qquad (11\text{-}13)$$

For this definition to hold, the target must be thin enough so that C/I is small compared with unity. If this is not the case, one atom, so to speak, will be in the shadow of another, and errors will be made.

If we have a thicker target, we can find how the number of neutrons falls off as we go through the sample, on account of their removal from the beam by reacting. Let N be the number of atoms per unit volume of the material. Consider a slab of the target, of unit area, perpendicular to the beam, and of infinitesimal thickness dx. Let this target be located at a distance x along the x axis, along which the beam is passing. Let $I(x)$ be the beam intensity at distance x; that is, the number of

neutrons crossing unit area per unit time.   Then in the slab of thickness dx, in which there are $N\,dx$ atoms, with total cross section $N\sigma\,dx$,
the number of neutrons having reactions will be $IN\sigma\,dx$.   This is the
decrease in I in the distance dx, or is $-dI$.   Hence we can set up the
differential equations

$$dI = -IN\sigma\,dx \qquad d\ln I = -N\sigma\,dx \qquad (11\text{-}14)$$

whose solution is

$$I = I_0 \exp(-N\sigma x) \qquad (11\text{-}15)$$

where I_0 is the initial intensity at $x = 0$.   In other words, the intensity
falls off exponentially with the distance.   In the case of such an exponential decrease of intensity, we define the mean free path as the distance in which the intensity falls to $1/e$ of its initial value.   Here the
mean free path equals $1/N\sigma$.

In work with neutrons, it is often of interest to know how many
atoms will have had neutron reactions during a given irradiation.   Let
there be n neutrons per unit volume in the beam, and let them be moving with a velocity v.   Then the intensity I, or the number crossing
unit area per second, will be nv.   If they fall on a unit volume of target,
containing N atoms, they will cause $nvN\sigma$ reactions per unit time.
Hence, in time t, we have

$$\text{Number of atoms reacting} = nvtN\sigma \qquad (11\text{-}16)$$

The cross sections for various types of nuclear reactions are usually
found to be of the order of magnitude of 10^{-22} to 10^{-26} sq cm.   We shall
see in Sec. 11-10 that the actual physical cross section of a nucleus is of
the order of magnitude of 10^{-24} sq cm.   We are not to think of the cross
sections for the various types of reactions as actually representing
physical areas such that if the neutrons strike those areas they react,
and otherwise they do not.   There will, in fact, ordinarily be a probability of reacting in a collision, which decreases rather rapidly as the
distance of closest approach of the neutron to the nucleus increases.
The cross section represents merely a sort of average probability of
reacting, having the same dimensions as an area.

The unit of cross section in common use is 10^{-24} sq cm, and is called
the barn.   The explanation usually given for the use of this term is one
illustrating the light-heartedness of physicists even in the midst of
serious circumstances.   It is said that, in the atomic-bomb project at
Los Alamos during the war, the scientists were often dealing with cross
sections small compared with 10^{-24} sq cm, so that a cross section equal

to 10^{-24} sq cm seemed to them "as big as the side of a barn." Hence the name; and this nickname, with its semihumorous origin, has now stuck, and become official.

The cross sections of various neutron processes depend strongly on the neutron energies. In connection with this, we should point out that the range of energies of neutrons experimentally available is very great. The nuclear reactor is the most prolific source of neutrons, and it furnishes neutrons of what are called thermal velocities: velocities equal to those of a gas at thermal equilibrium around room temperature. These are velocities of the order of magnitude of 10^5 cm/sec,

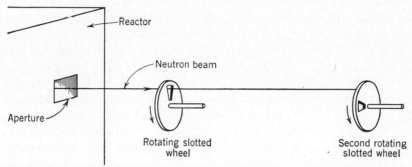

FIG. 11-12. Diagram to illustrate principle of neutron time-of-flight experiment. Neutrons emerging from aperture in reactor strike first rotating slotted wheel. Those striking it at a suitable time can get through the slot in the wheel. If they are traveling with the desired velocity, they will arrive at the second rotating slotted wheel after it has rotated far enough so that they can pass through its slot too. If they were traveling with the wrong speed, they would not be able to pass through the second slot, and would be stopped. The procedure actually used differs a great deal from that illustrated in details, but not in principle.

slow enough so that they can be determined by so-called time-of-flight experiments. In these experiments, the neutrons are allowed to pass through a shutter, equivalent in principle to a rotating slotted disk, as shown in Fig. 11-12. The neutrons then travel a relatively short distance, perhaps of the order of 20 ft, and pass through another such shutter. If the second shutter is arranged to open a definite time after the first, only those neutrons will pass through which have traveled the intervening distance in the fixed time interval, or which have a definite velocity.

Thermal neutrons can also be diffracted by a crystal, just as X rays can. If one calculates their de Broglie wavelengths, one finds that they are of the order of magnitude of an angstrom unit. Thus their wavelengths are right for crystal diffraction. They can be scattered elastically by nuclei, as we shall describe presently, and the corresponding scattered de Broglie wavelets can interfere, just as X rays do, to give diffracted beams satisfying the Bragg law. This allows the use of a crystal as a neutron monochromator. That is, we can let a beam of neutrons of a variety of energies fall on a crystal, arranged so that only those of a particular energy, and wavelength, will be scattered at the Bragg angle. This beam scattered at the Bragg angle will then consist of so-called monochromatic neutrons; that is, neutrons all of the same de Broglie wavelength, or all of the same energy. This then gives an alternative method, in addition to the time-of-flight method, for getting slow neutrons of definite energies, to use for experiments on the determination of nuclear cross sections as a function of neutron energy. At the same time, as mentioned in Sec. 10-8, neutron diffraction can be very useful, as X-ray diffraction is, for studying crystals.

In addition to thermal neutrons, the reactor is also capable of giving beams of neutrons of higher energies, way up to the energies of the order of 1 Mev at which they are produced in the fission reaction. These fast neutrons are also available from other sources: for instance, from such transmutations as the reaction $_4Be^9(\alpha,n)_6C^{12}$ originally used by Chadwick. They are also available from so-called photodisintegration reactions, (γ,n) reactions, in which gamma rays, produced for instance, as short X-ray *Bremsstrahlung* by electrons from a synchrotron or linear accelerator falling on a target, disintegrate an atom, emitting a neutron. An electron linear accelerator, for instance, is a very strong source of neutrons.

With this great range of neutron energies available, cross-section measurements have been made for most elements as a function of neutron energy. In many cases a fairly smooth variation with energy is found, with a tendency for the cross section to increase as the neutron energy decreases, often so that σ is proportional to $1/v$, where v is the neutron velocity. This behavior has a simple theoretical explanation. The length of time which a neutron stays within a given distance of a nucleus which it is bombarding is inversely proportional to the neutron velocity. The slow-velocity neutrons then have longer time to act on the nucleus, and this makes it plausible that they should have a greater chance of reacting.

In other cases, however, the cross sections for neutron reactions show very striking peaks. Such a peak is shown in a very well-known example, the reaction $_{92}U^{238}(n,\gamma)_{92}U^{239}$, a radiative capture, in Fig. 11-13. This peak, as we shall see in the next section, is of importance in the technology of the nuclear reactor. At the same time it is of theoretical interest, for it corresponds to a so-called nuclear resonance. If the neutron were to be incorporated into the nucleus, there would be an energy level for this particular energy; and one can show that a very large cross section is to be expected at just this energy.

We have been speaking so far in this section about the conventional types of nuclear reactions—the radiative capture process symbolized by (n,γ), and the processes in which a charged particle is given off, as (n,α) and (n,p). Next, we consider the fission processes, which are of an entirely different type. We have already stated that these processes were discovered in 1939, by Hahn, Strassmann, Meitner, and various collaborators, but it is interesting to see just the way the discovery came about. Hahn and Strassmann were bombarding uranium with neutrons, and had observed that an element which chemically resembled an alkaline earth—that is, Ca, Sr, Ba, or Ra—was given off. Since all preceding nuclear reactions had produced elements whose atomic numbers were only slightly different from the element being bombarded, the natural assumption was that this element was Ra. This proved not to be the case, however. The chemical evidence pointed to its being Ba, and this was verified when it was found that it was radioactive, with the half-life which was already well known for the isotope $_{56}Ba^{139}$. Here, then, was evidence of an entirely new type of process, in which the nucleus was really broken up into fragments of about the same size, split in two, as it were. Meitner and Frisch pointed out that the energy relations were right for such a process. We

have already pointed out that simple calculations of energy suggest that if a uranium atom were to break apart into fragments of the same size, something like 200 Mev of energy would be released, and this fitted in with observations of the extremely heavy ionization produced by the particles resulting from the uranium reaction. It was clear that the atom had really broken up, and the name fission was suggested for

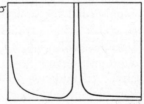

Neutron energy

FIG. 11-13. Radiative capture cross section of U^{238}, as a function of neutron energy (schematic). The cross section at low energy varies approximately as $1/v$. At the resonance, the cross section rises to several thousand barns.

it. It also was soon shown, by use of partially separated isotopes, that it was the rare isotope of uranium, $_{92}U^{235}$, rather than the plentiful isotope $_{92}U^{238}$, which was undergoing fission.

This discovery naturally started a great succession of experiments to discover what elements were capable of fission. Two other isotopes, in addition to $_{92}U^{235}$, were found to show fission, but they did not occur in nature, as $_{92}U^{235}$ does, but instead must be produced by nuclear reaction. In the first place, the common isotope of uranium, $_{92}U^{238}$, by radiative capture of a neutron, is converted into the isotope $_{92}U^{239}$, which decays by beta emission into a previously unknown element of atomic number 93, which was named neptunium; thus we have $_{92}U^{239} \rightarrow {}_{93}Np^{239}$ + beta. The neptunium has a half-life of only 2.3 days, and decays by another beta emission to an element of atomic number 94, which was named plutonium: $_{93}Np^{239} \rightarrow {}_{94}Pu^{239}$ + beta. It is interesting to ask why these elements were so named: uranium had been named for Uranus, the most distant planet at one time. But many years ago the planet Neptune was discovered outside the orbit of Uranus, and later Pluto was discovered outside Uranus. This very neatly provided names for the elements 93 and 94, but did not carry on for the elements 95 to 100, which have now all been discovered, and have had to be named in more conventional ways.

Plutonium is an alpha emitter of long half-life, about 24,100 years, decaying according to the reaction $_{94}Pu^{239} \rightarrow {}_{92}U^{235}$ plus α, back to the original uranium. But it is also found to be fissionable by slow neutrons, just as $_{92}U^{235}$ is. Thus arises the possibility of converting the common, nonfissionable isotope of uranium $_{92}U^{238}$ into the fissionable isotope $_{94}Pu^{239}$; and this possibility has been at the basis of much of the work on nuclear energy, since there is not enough $_{92}U^{235}$ in nature to provide a very extensive source of energy. Another similar reaction starts with thorium, which is also fairly common in nature. When $_{90}Th^{232}$ is bombarded by slow neutrons, it is converted by radiative capture into $_{90}Th^{233}$, which transforms by two successive beta emissions into $_{92}U^{233}$, which is also fissionable by slow neutrons. On account of the fair abundance of thorium, this may well be a very useful reaction in the future. In addition to these nuclei which are fissionable by slow neutrons, a number of the heavy isotopes are fissionable by fast neutrons, of energies in the millions of electron-volts.

11-8. The Nuclear Reactor. No reader of the press in these days can fail to know the general characteristics of the nuclear reactor, and its uses. It forms one of the most important and interesting applications of nuclear physics, and we shall now consider the details of its operation. It arose from a very natural thought. In the fission of $_{92}U^{235}$ a very large amount of energy is released: the order of magnitude of 200 Mev, as we have seen. Can we not somehow make this reaction self-sustaining, so as to get continual energy out of the uranium? In the experiment as carried out in the laboratory, slow neutrons must be shot into the uranium, and most of these neutrons will pass through the target, on account of the comparatively small fission cross section. In other words, the laboratory experiment is not a possible source of energy, for most of the energy put into it is used in producing neutrons which pass through the target and are lost. Somehow we must produce the neutrons directly from the reaction itself, and conserve them, so that most of those produced are used in producing further fission reactions.

Several neutrons are produced in the process of a single fission. The reason is clear. From Fig. 11-6, a heavy element like uranium has more neutrons in proportion to protons than a lighter element in the middle of the periodic table. Thus, if the uranium atom splits into two approximately equal fragments, each of these will have a number of neutrons more than it should. Some of these neutrons, one would suppose, will be liberated at once as fragments in the fission process. The resulting isotopes will still have somewhat too many neutrons, and hence will be radioactive beta emitters, converting neutrons into protons. Experiment shows that two or three neutrons are produced immediately in such a case, then one or more after lapse of an appreciable time, before the nuclei settle down to ordinary beta emission, and finally result in stable isotopes.

We may hope, then, that these emitted neutrons somehow can be used to produce further fission processes, producing what the chemists call a chain reaction, but there are formidable difficulties in the way of doing it, and it is these difficulties that had to be overcome in order to produce a successful nuclear reactor. Let us follow the process by which Fermi and his collaborators, in the early 1940's, overcame these difficulties. We must remember that they were working under the stimulus of the military emergency, and their aim was to produce a bomb. A bomb is simply an uncontrolled and violent nuclear reaction, contrasted with the slow and manageable process taking place in a nuclear reactor.

Calculation showed that if a mass of pure fissionable material —U^{235} or Pu^{239}—could be assembled, of sufficient size, called the critical mass, it would automatically set up a self-sustaining reaction. The mass of material has to be big enough so that the neutrons produced in fission in one part of it will produce fission in other atoms, before they have time to escape from the mass. This process can be helped along by surrounding the mass by some material which is effective in reflecting the neutrons back again. Enough was known in the early 1940's, from calculations based on the known fission cross sections of U^{235} and Pu^{239}, which had been determined in laboratory experiments, so that it was clear that this self-sustaining process could occur with a reasonable-sized mass of fissionable material.

The theoretical discussion indicated that if the mass is too small, no self-sustaining reaction is possible, for neutrons escape faster than they are produced.   If it is just the right size, the reaction can be just self-sustaining.   If the critical mass is exceeded, then the rate of reaction builds up at an exponential rate to catastrophic size.   Each nuclear fission results in enough neutrons to produce more than one subsequent fission, and it is clear that this will lead to a multiplication of the number of fissions after a given time interval, which is the characteristic of an exponential rise.   These fissions will all liberate a great deal of energy, which will heat the mass to the point of vaporizing, producing the explosion.   Calculation showed that this exponential rise was so fast that the explosion could be extremely violent, and could result in liberating a very appreciable fraction of all the energy available for fission.

From this picture, it was clear how to produce an atomic bomb.   A mass of fissionable material, greater than the critical mass, had to be assembled.   Once this was done, the explosion would occur practically instantaneously.   The explosion would continue to generate energy, until the material had blown itself apart, when neutrons would be lost, and the nuclear processes would cease, though of course the great energy already released would produce the damaging effect of the blast. Since this all happened extremely fast, it was clear that the critical mass had to be assembled exceedingly rapidly, as, for instance, by shooting various subcritical masses of fissionable material at each other by an ordinary explosive.   Here was a picture of a bomb, which has proved by subsequent experience to be justified.   The workers in the field, then, had a first task: to produce enough pure U^{235} or Pu^{239} to assemble a critical mass.   It was this effort which occupied them for most of the war, though of course the engineering problem of the construction of the bomb also had to be solved.

Two approaches to the problem were decided upon: first, to separate U^{235} from the commoner isotope U^{238} by conventional methods; secondly, to produce Pu^{239} from U^{238} by the reactions which we have already described.   It is possible to separate isotopes by several well-known methods, which had been used previously on a small scale, and these methods were developed into large-scale engineering operations, and used to separate the uranium isotopes.   One of these methods is called gaseous diffusion.   If a gas diffuses through a porous membrane, the rate of diffusion depends on the velocity of the molecules.   By equipartition, the mean kinetic energy of the molecules is proportional to kT.   Hence a heavy molecule will have a smaller velocity, a lighter molecule a greater velocity, at a given temperature, since both have the same kinetic energy $\frac{1}{2}mv^2$.   If we have a mixture of gases of different masses but identical chemical properties, then the lighter gas will diffuse faster, and this differential diffusion can be used as a method of separation. It is very tedious, for only a small amount of separation is obtained, and the process must be repeated many times to get anything approaching complete separation. Nevertheless, gaseous diffusion was operated on a large scale to separate the uranium isotopes, using a suitable gaseous compound, and in this way large amounts of U^{235} have been obtained.

Another method of separation was based on the principle of the mass spectrograph. It is clear that if atoms are ionized, and passed through the sort of electric and magnetic fields used in a mass spectrograph, ions of different mass will come to a focus at different places. If apertures are set up, at the location where ions of one particular mass are focused, only those ions will pass through the aperture and be collected. Such methods had been used on a minute scale before the war, and here again a large engineering development led to large-scale methods of isotope separation based on this principle.

It was possible during the war, then, to separate enough U^{235} to be used for making atomic bombs, and the general ideas behind the construction of the bomb were verified. One understands that there is now sufficient U^{235} available so that under some circumstances it can be used for making nuclear reactors. The characteristic of such a reactor is that it has a controlled reaction going on in it. Clearly, then, it must consist of an almost precisely critical assembly of fissionable material, with some sort of control mechanism. Since the nuclear reaction concerned is inherently unstable, this control mechanism is absolutely necessary for safety, as well as for practical handling of the reaction. The method usually used makes use of so-called control rods, made of cadmium. This material has a characteristic of having a very large capture cross section for neutrons, without any subsequent radioactivity. Hence a rod of cadmium can be inserted in the reactor, absorbing neutrons and hence cutting down the reactivity, and yet the rod does not become radioactive, and hence can be handled for mechanical servicing. By pushing in such a rod, the operation of the reactor can be made to die down; by pulling it out, to build up. By means of carefully designed servomechanisms, it is possible to arrange such a control system so as to maintain the operation of the reactor at any desired power level.

One feature in the fission reaction makes this control feasible. We have mentioned that two or three neutrons per fission are emitted instantaneously, but one or more come off slightly later, as a result of a type of radioactive transformation with neutron emission. As a result of these delayed neutrons, so-called, it turns out that the operation of the reactor does not follow the motion of the control rods instantaneously, but only after a slight time lag. This means that a control system, operating with the sort of speed practical in a mechanical system, can keep the reactor in a very steady state. If it were not for the delayed neutrons, the reaction would be so rapid that the reactor would be likely to run away and explode, whenever the control rods were withdrawn even a slight amount beyond the critical position.

The reactor, in its operation, of course produces a great deal of energy. This is liberated at first in the kinetic energy of the fission fragments, of which there are two, normally one somewhat bigger than half of a uranium atom, one somewhat smaller, and sharing most of the approximately 200 Mev produced in the reaction between them; and in the kinetic energy of the neutrons, which come off with energies of the order of magnitude of 1 Mev. These fast particles collide with other atoms, exchanging part of their energy with them. In a short time, if there were no cooling mechanism, all the atoms of the fissionable material would have a very high energy, or would be extremely hot. Cooling is necessary, and this can be done by various cooling materials. For instance, in a U^{235} reactor, such as we have been describing, water can be used for the cooling. This water must then be circulated to the outside, and can eventually be used to run a steam engine, and so to make the reactor into a producer of energy. The cooling water is not directly used in the steam engine, for it is slightly radioactive. Consequently a heat exchanger must be used, in which the radioactive water from the reactor is circulated, in a closed system, adjacent to a thin wall through which it can interchange its heat with ordinary water, which is then used to run the steam engine. The type of reactor which we have described here is a type which is discussed as a possible source of nuclear energy. It could be run either with U^{235} or with the other fissionable materials, Pu^{239} or U^{233}.

We have been rather getting ahead of our story, however. It was only toward the end of the war that separated U^{235} became available, and reactors had been constructed several years before that. The purpose of making a reactor during the war was twofold. First, it was a research tool: to investigate critical assemblies of fissionable materials, so as to check the calculations which had indicated that critical assemblies should exist, and hence to check the calculations leading to the design of the atomic bomb. Secondly, it was possible that it could be used to produce Pu^{239}, by the nuclear process which we have already described, starting with U^{239}. This process of producing one type of fissionable material, Pu^{239}, from a nonfissionable material, U^{238}, has been called breeding, and the wartime reactors were built as breeders. The reason why it was desired to produce Pu^{239} was the thought that, since it differed chemically from uranium, it could be separated from uranium by an ordinary chemical reaction, rather than by the difficult isotope-separation processes which had to be used to separate U^{235} from U^{238}. Fermi and his associates in Chicago, then, tried to design a pioneer reactor which would operate with natural uranium, a mixture of mostly U^{238} with a little U^{235}, since that was all that was available at the time, and which would produce Pu^{239}.

Such a reactor involves much more difficult problems than we have intimated in connection with the simple U^{235} reactor which we have been discussing. In Fig. 11-13 we showed the cross section of the reaction $_{92}U^{238}(n,\gamma)_{92}U^{239}$, which is the fundamental process in the production of plutonium, as a function of the energy of the incident neutron. This cross section has an extremely high peak at an energy of a few electron-volts. To cause breeding, then, we wish to have neutrons of around this energy. This means that the neutrons which are originally produced with energies of the order of magnitude of 1 Mev must be slowed down greatly. But we must avoid having all the neutrons captured by the U^{238} atoms, to produce the breeding reaction, for then there would be no neutrons left to continue the fission of U^{235}. The fission cross section of U^{235} is approximately proportional to $1/v$, so that thermal neutrons will be most effective in producing fission. It is then desirable to slow down the neutrons, to have a certain number captured by U^{238} atoms for breeding as their velocities decrease, and to have the rest slowed down to thermal velocities and there produce the additional fissions which maintain the reaction.

This slowing-down operation was accomplished by what is called a moderator. This operates by means of the elastic collisions of neutrons with nuclei. We have described a number of types of reaction which a neutron can have when it collides with a nucleus, but we have not emphasized the simplest possible case, namely, that it be elastically scattered, without making any change in the nucleus whatever. In this case, there is no Q liberated in the reaction, and we can calculate the effects of the collision by the sort of application of classical mechanics used in Sec. 11-6, assuming conservation of energy, as well as momentum. It is then easy to show that the atom struck will recoil, with resulting loss of energy by the neutron, and that the loss of the neutron's energy is greater, the lighter the atom which it strikes. If we can let the neutrons traverse a material composed of light nuclei, which can have no nuclear reactions leading to loss of the neutrons, then the neutrons will gradually lose energy, without being lost, and this is just what we wish to accomplish. Such a material is called a moderator.

When one looks through the list of light atoms, to find which ones are suitable as moderators, a few good possibilities appear. Hydrogen is not a very good one; it slows down the neutrons more than any other, on account of its low atomic weight, but it captures enough neutrons on account of the reaction $_1H^1(n,\gamma)_1H^2$ to be rather serious, in a process where we are very anxious not to lose any neutrons, since barely enough are produced to serve for breeding and maintenance of fission. Deuterium, however, is good; it has no reactions leading to neutron capture. The only other light atom which seems practical to use is carbon. It is for this reason that carbon, in the form of graphite, and deuterium, in the form of heavy water (the oxygen in the water does not capture any neutrons), have proved to be the most useful materials for moderators. In the original Chicago reactor, graphite was used as a moderator, since it was easier to obtain than the scarce heavy water.

We can now understand the general construction of a normal uranium-graphite moderated reactor, such as the first one constructed at Chicago. The nuclear reaction sustaining its operation is the fission of U^{235}, which fortunately is present in natural uranium to a sufficiently high extent to make the operation possible. Every time a neutron enters a U^{235} atom, breaking it into fragments, some two or three neutrons are produced, as well as delayed neutrons and fission fragments. These neutrons are slowed down by the moderator, and when they reach the peak energy for radiative capture, some of them are captured by the U^{238} atoms, leading to the reactions resulting in Pu^{239}. The remaining neutrons continue to slow down to thermal velocities, when they will be captured by U^{235} atoms, which at those velocities have a greater cross section for fission than the U^{238} atoms do for radiative capture. The operation will be self-sustaining if, for every initial fission operation, just one neutron is left to result in fission by another U^{235} atom. This obviously requires a very careful balance of neutrons, but such a balance was achieved, and the reactor proved to operate.

Further reactors have been built of many types, and for many purposes. The great reactors at Hanford, Washington, built during the war to produce Pu^{239} in usable amounts, were of the graphite-normal uranium type just described. Other reactors have been built with heavy water as a moderator. The design and construction of reactors has now become a large-scale engineering operation, whose principles are well understood. It is, however, an operation with many difficulties, which we may mention.

One of the difficulties of reactor technology is the very limited choice of materials available, on account of the need of conserving neutrons. Most elements have cross sections for nuclear reactions which are great enough so that if they were introduced into the reactor, too many neutrons would be absorbed, and the reaction would not be self-sustaining. This limitation applies not only to structural elements, but to materials used for cooling, and for other purposes. We have mentioned that ordinary hydrogen absorbs neutrons to some extent; this makes water somewhat undesirable for cooling, though it is used in some reactors, notably the Hanford reactors. Air is used in some reactors; again a slight radioactivity results, but the loss of neutrons is not great enough in either case to be serious.

Another difficulty is the gradual appearance of fission fragments within the fissionable material of the reactor, as more and more of the active material undergoes fission. These fragments are violently radioactive, which makes the interior of the reactor so dangerous that all operations in it must be carried out by remote control. Furthermore, some of these fragments can consist of elements with large cross sections for neutrons, so that as time goes on, they capture more and more neutrons, and the reactor operates more and more poorly. This leads to the necessity of removing the fissionable material before it has been all used up, and of chemically separating the radioactive materials from the fissionable material. These chemical operations are exceedingly difficult ones, on account of the violently radioactive materials which must be handled. Facilities have had to be developed for carrying out complete chemical and mechanical operations on these materials by remote control.

Still another difficulty is that many substances gradually change their properties under the action of the fission reactions going on in the reactor. The fission fragments cause fast recoil particles, and these in turn cause fast secondary recoils, and so on, with the result that many particles with many million electron-volts of energy go ploughing through the material. These displace many atoms from their normal positions in the crystal lattices of solids, and can result in far-reaching and often deleterious effects in chemical and physical properties of the materials. Only those materials can be used in reactor construction which are relatively immune to such damage from radiation.

This illustrates a few of the many features which make the engineering of nuclear energy very difficult. Nevertheless, the difficulties have been overcome, and the indications are that many practical results will come from applications of nuclear fission. Aside from the military applications, the first possibility of course is the development of energy. Here, on account of the scarcity and expense of U^{235} and Pu^{239}, it is likely that ordinary reactors will have to operate with normal uranium, and will have to combine the development of power with the breeding of Pu^{239}, to make them economical. Such power reactors have been developed, and are coming into practical use. For specialized power uses, like submarine propulsion, where economics is not important, presumably reactors using U^{235} or Pu^{239} would be used, without the attempt to breed at the same time.

There are several other important practical uses of reactors aside from the ones we have just mentioned. One is the production of radioactive isotopes. The interior of the reactor is in a region of high neutron flux, and by exposing a sample of a nonradioactive material inside the reactor, it can be made to undergo any of the reactions produced by neutrons, thus resulting in radioactive substances. Many artificially radioactive substances can be made in this way, which cannot be made by bombardment by charged particles. The radioactive substances are useful in a number of ways. Some of them can be used in therapy, as radium has been used for many years. Others can be used as radioactive tracers, in a great variety of cases. This application is so important that we should describe it in more detail.

In many physical, chemical, and biological processes, for example in studying diffusion, it is desirable to know how rapidly atoms move from one place to another. If we use a mixture of a small amount of radioactive material, along with nonradioactive atoms of the same element, we can follow the motion of the radioactive atoms by use of counters or other methods to detect them by their radioactive decay. The half-lives are very characteristic of the elements, so that by measuring these half-lives one can be sure of the element one is dealing with. These radioactive methods of detection, which work with individual atoms, are so much more sensitive than chemical methods that they make many experiments possible which could never have been tried before. Chemists and biologists feel that the use of radioactive tracers is one of the most important experimental advances in their fields since the invention of the microscope.

Still another use of the reactor is in the production of neutron beams. By making a small aperture in the shield which normally surrounds a reactor and prevents the escape of neutrons and other harmful radiation, one can allow a neutron beam to escape, and can use this for physical experiments, such as neutron diffraction. This forms the strongest and most usable neutron beam which we have; and on account of such uses, the nuclear reactor is a piece of experimental equipment for the physicist comparable in its importance with the particle accelerators.

In this section we have sketched some of the main features of the operation and uses of nuclear reactors. This is a vast subject, however, which is rapidly leading into a new branch of engineering, and away from pure physics. Consequently we shall now return to problems of more theoretical importance, dealing with our closer understanding of nuclear structure. We have been devoting a number of sections to the problems of nuclear energy levels. These represent far from the total information which we have from experiment about nuclear structure, however. For one thing, we have nuclear cross sections, which we have mentioned briefly, and information about the probabilities of nuclear transformations, such as gamma-ray transitions. From these probabilities, it has been possible to set up selection rules for nuclear transitions, similar to atomic selection rules. Furthermore, a great deal of information has been piling up, particularly since the war, on nuclear angular momenta and magnetic moments. This information is beginning to show that there is a far-reaching similarity between nuclear and atomic structure, and we now go on to consider some of these problems.

11-9. Nuclear Angular Momenta and Magnetic Moments. There are a number of ways in which the angular momenta and magnetic moments of nuclei can be measured, and the results are as useful in interpreting nuclear structure as are the corresponding quantities in atomic theory. They give us a clue to the quantum numbers of the particles in the nucleus, their coupling, and so on. As such, they furnish invaluable information, in addition to that given by the nuclear energy levels.

The spins, and magnetic moments, of nuclei can be determined in several ways. In the first place, there is an effect in atomic spectra called hyperfine structure, which has been known for a long time. It is a very fine splitting of spectrum lines, or energy levels, on a scale much smaller than the ordinary fine structure of lines, and not explainable by any of the theories we have discussed so far. It was suggested by Pauli that the origin of hyperfine splitting lay in a magnetic moment and angular momentum of the nucleus. He assumed that the nucleus had an angular momentum $I\hbar$, which combined vectorially with the angular momentum $J\hbar$ of the electronic system of the atom to form a resultant. The nucleus was also supposed to have a magnetic moment, and the interaction of this with the magnetic field of the electrons resulted in a splitting of the energy levels. By counting the number of hyperfine components, one could immediately find the nuclear angular momentum I, and by measuring the splitting one could estimate the magnetic moment.

An independent way of measuring the nuclear angular momentum and magnetic moment was provided by the atomic beam method of Rabi. To introduce it, we should first mention a famous experiment of the 1920's, which we have not so far discussed: the Stern-Gerlach experiment. These workers wished to demonstrate experimentally the space quantization of atoms. To do this, they took a beam of neutral atoms, for instance, sodium, emitted from a furnace, and passed them through a magnetic field transverse to the beam, so that they would be space quantized. Then, they passed the atoms through an inhomogeneous magnetic field, which would, for instance, attract a north pole of an atom whose north pole pointed up more strongly than it would repel the south pole, and hence would pull the atom upward, while if the south pole pointed up, it would push the atom downward. The atoms with different orientations were then deflected differently in the system of magnets, and they could be observed when they emerged, giving very graphic indications of the space quantization. The results of the Stern-Gerlach experiment verified results obtained in other ways, showing that the general ideas of spectroscopy were correct.

Rabi, in the 1930's, thought of an ingenious method of making this experiment more versatile. He noticed that, when the atoms with their space quantization were in a magnetic field, the atoms with different magnetic quantum number had different energies, so that by absorbing radiation whose $h\nu$ corresponded to the energy difference, one should be able to change the space quantization of a particular atom. To test this, using apparatus illustrated in Fig. 11-14, he took a beam which would be deflected in a particular way in the inhomogeneous magnetic field, passed it through a radio-frequency field whose frequency was adjusted to agree with the expected $h\nu$ (for calculation showed that this frequency should lie in the radio frequencies), and found in fact that the beam no longer was deflected the same way, indicating that transitions had occurred from the original space quantization to another one. We shall not go further into the various ingenious experimental arrangements which he used. But it is clear that he was able to measure the energy levels of an atom in an external magnetic field very accurately, and hence deduce information about its magnetic moment and angular momentum.

By applying this method to atoms or molecules which had no electronic angular momentum, Rabi was able to deduce information about the nuclear spin and angular momentum, and thus to verify the results of hyperfine structure. By a combination of these two methods, we now possess very complete information about the angular momentum and magnetic moment of a great many atoms and nuclear particles. It is then possible to start generalizing about the structure of the nucleus, by asking how its angular momentum is made up from those of the particles which constitute it.

The first piece of information which comes from this discussion is that, assuming the nucleus to be built of protons and neutrons, each of

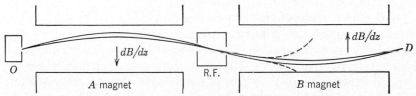

FIG. 11-14. Schematic diagram of Rabi's molecular beam apparatus. Beam of slow atoms or molecules emerges from the opening in oven O. They pass through magnet A, in which there is a magnetic field gradient pointing down, and through magnet B, in which the gradient points up. These gradients exert equal and opposite forces on the magnetic moments of the particles, accelerating them in the paths shown, provided the space quantization is not interfered with. Thus the beam of particles can be detected at the point D. However, the beam passes through a region marked R.F., where a radio-frequency field acts on it, which can change the magnetic quantum number, or the magnetic moment. If this change has occurred, the deflection in magnet B will be different, so that the beam may be deflected along such a path as is shown by dotted lines, and it will no longer focus at D and be detected. Hence, resonance between the radio-frequency field and the atomic transition can be detected as a decrease in the intensity of the beam at D.

these fundamental particles has an angular momentum of $\frac{1}{2}\hbar$. By study of the angular momenta of nuclei, one can set up vector models showing how these angular momenta are combined, much as in atoms, and can get a great deal of information about nuclear structure. For instance, from the study of the lightest elements, one finds that the deuteron, $_1H^2$, which is formed from a neutron and a proton, has an angular momentum of $\hbar$, so that the two nucleons have their spins parallel in this case. The two nuclei $_1H^3$, the triton, and $_2He^3$, have angular momenta of $\frac{1}{2}\hbar$, as if the third nucleon had its spin opposite to that of the two already present in the deuteron. Finally the alpha particle, $_2He^4$, has no angular momentum, as if the two neutrons had opposite spins, and the two protons had opposite spins. Furthermore, as we know, the binding energy of the alpha particle is much greater than in the other cases.

Even from these very simple cases, we conclude that something like the Pauli principle must hold in nuclei, the alpha particle forming a closed shell with two neutrons with the two possible spins, and two protons with the two possible spins.   Furthermore, in the deuteron, we conclude that the ground state, being that in which the spins of proton and neutron are parallel, perhaps arises from the same sort of multiplet formation with nonequivalent particles which we have found with atoms, and that very likely there is a higher state, corresponding to a singlet, with the spins opposite, whereas the ground state corresponds to a triplet, and obeys Hund's rule that triplets lie lower than singlets.   Such information can easily be read out of the empirical observations on nuclear angular momenta.

11-10. The Nature of Nuclear Forces and Nuclear Structure.   The fundamental problem of nuclear physics is the nature of the forces binding the nucleus together.   It is clear that these forces, unlike all those met in the outer part of the atom, cannot be electrostatic; for the preponderant electrostatic forces in a positively charged structure like a nucleus are repulsive, and tend to break it apart.   There must be other sources, of a totally different sort, holding the particles together. One of the most fundamental reasons why nuclear physics involves riddles so much more difficult to solve than the outer part of the atom is that we are here meeting new forces, of a previously unknown type, while with the outer part of the atom we met Coulomb forces, whose behavior had already been studied for a long time.

Some of the properties of these forces can be deduced from very simple and general properties of nuclei.   For one thing, the density of nuclear matter seems to be roughly constant for all atoms.   This can be determined from scattering experiments.   When fast neutrons are scattered elastically by nuclei, their behavior is much as if they were being scattered by rigid spheres, and the scattering cross sections determined from the experiments, unlike the cross sections for other nuclear processes, seem to give a good indication of actual nuclear dimensions.   Similar information is found from scattering of other types of particles.   For one thing, with light nuclei, alpha particles striking the nucleus are scattered as if they were acted on just by the Coulomb repulsion, so long as they do not get closer than a certain distance.   At shorter distances, there is a change in the law of force, indicating that the alpha particles are actually beginning to penetrate into the nucleus.   From evidence like this, and of other sorts as well, it is well established that there is something approximating a sharp radius for a nucleus, and that it is given approximately by the formula

$$\text{Radius} = 1.37 \times 10^{-13} A^{\frac{1}{3}} \quad \text{cm} \tag{11-17}$$

where A is the atomic weight.   Since the volume of the nucleus is proportional to the cube of the radius, this tells us that the volume is proportional to the atomic weight, or to the number of nucleons in the nucleus. That is, the volume per nucleon is the same in all nuclei, or the density is constant. Another piece of evidence is that the binding energy per nucleon is approximately constant. That is, when a nucleon sticks to a nucleus to form a nucleus whose atomic weight is one unit greater, it is bound by just about a constant amount of energy, irrespective of what nucleus it is being bound to. This fact, plus the constancy of the nuclear density, suggests that the attractive forces holding the nucleus together are short-range forces; that is, that they act between adjacent nucleons rather than between nucleons at a distance. For if the nuclear forces were long-range forces, like inverse-square forces, for example, a nucleon approaching a heavy nucleus would be attracted by all the nucleons in it, and hence would be attracted much more than by a light nucleus. On the other hand, if the nuclear forces were short-range, something like the forces holding the atoms of a metal together, a nucleon approaching the surface of the nucleus would be attracted only by those nucleons near the surface, and these surface attractions would be about the same in any case.

There are, in fact, many ways in which a nucleus appears to resemble a small fragment of solid or liquid. A liquid or solid also has a constant density, independent of the number of particles, and has a constant binding energy per molecule, the heat of vaporization. The molecules of the liquid or solid are held together by short-range forces, as are the nuclear particles; and at shorter distances the molecules repel each other, resulting in their impenetrable nature, as the nucleons must somehow do, to maintain the constant density of the nuclei.

It is consistent with this picture to suppose that the potential energy of a nucleon, as it approaches a nucleus, must have the general form represented in Fig. 11-15. Here, in Fig. 11-15(a), we show a hypothetical potential energy curve for a neutron approaching the nucleus, and in Fig. 11-15(b) a corresponding curve for a proton. In the case of the neutron, we indicate that the potential energy decreases as the neutron approaches the boundary of the nucleus, so that the potential energy of the neutron is lower inside the nucleus than out, representing the binding energy. Once the neutron is inside the nucleus, it can presumably wander from one part of the nucleus to another with no great change of energy, as an atom in a liquid can wander through the liquid without change of energy, but has an energy which increases by the heat of vaporization when it is removed from the liquid.

If a picture like Fig. 11-15 has any meaning, it indicates that in some sort of way we can apply a self-consistent-field sort of picture to the nucleus, replacing the real interaction problem of all the nucleons by the interaction of a single nucleon with the averaged fields of the others. It is in such a sense that Fig. 11-15 is to be interpreted. In this case, we must expect that the single nucleon inside the nucleus will have a set of energy levels, like those of a single particle in a potential well such as is shown in Fig. 11-15(a). The solutions of Schrödinger's equation for such a potential well are easy to work out, and there are good indications that the lower excited states of a nucleus correspond to just such energy levels of a single nucleon. There will be a ground state, as indicated in Fig. 11-15(a), and the binding energy of the neutron into the nucleus is the energy given up when the neutron falls into this ground state. Several excited states are also shown, and

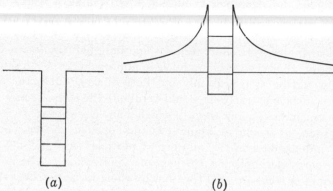

(a)   (b)

Fig. 11-15. (a). Square-well potential for neutron in a nucleus, showing energy levels within nucleus. (b). Similar curve for proton, showing Coulomb repulsion as proton approaches nucleus, and barrier at edge of potential well.

these correspond to the type of excited state discussed in Sec. 11-5, transitions between such excited states occurring with gamma emission. We may further expect that such a one-particle picture as this will be only partially correct, and that we shall have to amplify it by considering multiplet structure. The sketch of nuclear angular momenta in the preceding section indicates that this is the case. Shortly we shall come to further evidence indicating that such a multiplet theory really has validity in nuclear structure.

Before doing so, however, we wish to consider the case of the proton, which is quite different from the neutron. Here there is a Coulomb repulsion as the proton approaches the nucleus, as we have indicated in Fig. 11-15(b). As the proton enters the nucleus, however, there will be the short-range attraction setting in again, so that again we have a sort of square well representing the binding energy, just as for the case of the neutron. We can see, however, why protons and positive particles are not effective in disintegrating heavy nuclei. They must be shot in with a very high energy, high enough to surmount the potential barrier in Fig. 11-15(b), in order ever to get into the nucleus, while the neutron has no such barrier.   One can easily calculate the height of this barrier, from a knowledge of the Coulomb repulsion, and of the size of the nucleus.   The value of the Coulomb repulsive potential, at distance r from the nucleus of charge Z units, where Z is the atomic number, is $Ze/4\pi\epsilon_0 r$, in mks units.   If we set r equal to the nuclear radius, as given in Eq. (11-17), we find the barrier height to be given by

$$
\begin{aligned}
\text{Barrier height} &= \frac{Ze}{4\pi\epsilon_0 R} \\
&= \frac{1.602 \times 10^{-19}}{4\pi \times 8.85 \times 10^{-12} \times 1.37 \times 10^{-15}} Z A^{-\frac{1}{3}} \\
&= 1.06 Z A^{-\frac{1}{3}} \quad \text{Mev}
\end{aligned}
\tag{11-18}
$$

where in the formula for R we have expressed it in meters, so as to use the mks units.

In Fig. 11-15(b), we show not only proton energy levels whose energy is lower than the energy of the proton at infinite distance, but also levels which lie higher, so that the proton could jump out of the nucleus and go to infinity with a finite energy, but is restrained from doing so by the potential barrier.   In considering this case, an interesting phenomenon of quantum mechanics enters in, called the tunnel effect, which we did not discuss in Chap. 9.   It turns out according to quantum mechanics that in such a problem, if the particle is confined within the well, there is a finite probability that it will leak out through the barrier, as if there were a tunnel through it, and escape.   This possibility arises from the nature of the Schrödinger wave function. In classical mechanics, there would be no possibility at all of finding the particle within the barrier, where its energy is less than the potential energy, so that its kinetic energy would have to be negative, an impossible condition.   In wave mechanics, however, this merely means that the wave function is small, and there is a finite value of the wave function outside the barrier, resulting in a finite chance of the particle's escaping.   This chance decreases very rapidly, however, as the barrier becomes either higher or broader.

As a result of the tunnel effect, the energy levels above the energy at infinite separation do not really represent stationary states, in which the proton can exist permanently.   If the probability of escape is small, however, they may be considered as stationary states for all practical purposes.   Such levels were considered, in their relation to alpha-particle emission by the radioactive elements, by Condon and

Gurney, in the very early days of wave mechanics. They assumed that one could draw a potential curve like Fig. 11-15(b) for a complete alpha particle as it approached the nucleus. They assumed furthermore that the alpha particle in a radioactive atom existed in a level such as we are considering, so that it had a finite possibility of escaping through the barrier by the tunnel effect. Calculations based on this model give probabilities of escape that agree with experimentally observed values. In particular, they can explain the very wide range of half-lives observed with alpha emitters; for the probability of escape, and hence the half-life, varies exceedingly rapidly with the height and width of the barrier. From such calculations, the barrier heights and widths can be estimated for the naturally radioactive elements, and thus gives information on nuclear radii, which supplements that obtained by scattering experiments, and is consistent with it.

The tunnel effect is significant, not only in radioactive disintegration, but in nuclear reactions in which a proton or other positively charged particle strikes a nucleus and must enter it to produce the reaction. In such a case, the final energy level of the proton in its ground state within the nucleus, as shown in Fig. 11-15(b), may be lower than that outside, but there is the high potential barrier between. This situation is analogous to the situation generally found in chemical reactions, where a similar barrier must be surmounted before a reaction can occur. In the chemical case, the energy required to surmount the barrier is called the activation energy, and this term is generally taken over into the nuclear problem. We say, then, that there is a high activation energy for reactions with protons or charged particles, though not generally for neutron reactions. In such cases, there are two possibilities for the proton to get into the nucleus: if it has enough energy, it can pass over the top of the barrier; or it can tunnel through. The question as to which mechanism is more important is one that depends on the distribution of energy of the particles: if there are many with high energy, they will go over the barrier, while if there are none of high energy, but many of low energy, the preponderant mechanism will be that of tunneling through.

A well-known example of a reaction with a high activation energy is the reaction $_6C^{12}(p,\gamma)_7N^{13}$ which is the first step in Bethe's carbon cycle. For $_6C^{12}$ we set $Z = 6$, $A = 12$, in Eq. (11-18), and find a barrier of about 2.8 Mev. As a result of this high barrier, the reaction goes very slowly, even at the temperature of about 20 million degrees which one assumes at the center of the sun, where the protons have an average energy of only a few thousand electron-volts. As a result of the Maxwellian distribution of velocities, there will be a few protons, even at this temperature, which have enough energy to surmount the barrier; but most of them must get into the nuclei by the tunnel effect. Since both of these processes are very unlikely, we have a slow reaction; if it were not for this, the sun would burn much hotter than it does. Another example of such a situation is found in the reactions involved in the hydrogen or fusion bomb. They also have a high activation energy, and it is well known that one must start such a reaction with an atomic bomb, raising the temperature to a value such as is found in the interior of the sun. At a lower temperature, the reaction goes too slowly to be of significance.

Let us now return to our study of the nature of nuclear energies. We remember that the hypothetical potential energy curves of Fig. 11-15 are supposed to arise from the averaged interaction energies between pairs of nucleons. Let us next inquire what sort of evidence exists about these interaction energies. First, we have already stated the arguments indicating that the forces have short ranges. Next, there is a great deal of evidence that the attractive forces between two protons and between two neutrons are at least approximately equal. The protons, of course, have in addition their electrostatic repulsions, which decrease the net effect of the attractions.

The most straightforward evidence for this belief comes from the mirror nuclei, such as $_6C^{11}$ and $_5B^{11}$, whose energy levels were shown in Fig. 11-10. Experimentally, it is found in such cases that the energies of the two mirror nuclei are remarkably similar, as if one were having to solve essentially the same problem in quantum mechanics in each case. The one difference between them is that the nucleus with the higher atomic number, in this case $_6C^{11}$, has all its energy levels pushed upward with respect to the other. This is corrected for in Fig. 11-10, the ground states being made to agree by moving the levels of $_6C^{11}$ down by an appropriate amount. It is thought that this added height of the energies of the atom with higher atomic number comes from the electrostatic repulsion of the extra proton. This contributes a positive electrostatic term to the energy, present in all the stationary states. One can calculate this positive energy term, as one would deduce from Fig. 11-15; all the proton levels are pushed up with respect to the neutron levels, by the amount of the Coulomb repulsion. When one makes such a correction to the energy levels of $_6C^{11}$, it brings its levels substantially into coincidence with those of $_5B^{11}$. Such calculations, in this and similar cases, convince us of the correctness of the Coulomb energy term, and of the fact that except for this, the neutron-neutron and proton-proton attractive forces are substantially identical.

The next piece of evidence which one has regarding the interaction forces between nucleons concerns the neutron-proton forces. Let us consider a set of different elements with the same atomic weight, but different atomic numbers. The two mirror nuclei $_6C^{11}$ and $_5B^{11}$ are two such, but for this argument it is more interesting to take for instance the three nuclei $_5B^{12}$, $_6C^{12}$, and $_7N^{12}$. In Fig. 11-16 we show the energies of the ground states of these three nuclei. These energies are corrected for the Coulomb effect which we have just mentioned, and for the difference in mass between neutron and proton. We see that, when we make this correction, the two mirror nuclei $_5B^{12}$ and $_7N^{12}$ have almost exactly the same energy, but the nucleus $_6C^{12}$ has a decidedly lower energy. In fact, it was the beta disintegration of $_5B^{12}$ into $_6C^{12}$, in which the beta particle comes off with 13.43 Mev of energy, which we mentioned in Sec. 11-5 as indicating a specially tight binding of $_6C^{12}$. The feature which we observe in this triad of elements is characteristic of the whole periodic table: elements tend to be most stable when they have equal, or approximately equal, numbers of protons and neutrons, and departure from this equality in either direction increases the energy.

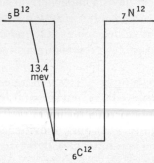

FIG. 11-16. Energies of ground states of $_5B^{12}$, $_6C^{12}$, and $_7N^{12}$, corrected for Coulomb repulsion of protons, and mass difference of proton and neutron. The transition indicated as corresponding to 13.4 Mev is the beta transition of $_5B^{12}$ to $_6C^{12}$ described in the text.

The interpretation of this observed fact is that the neutron-proton force must be somewhat stronger than the neutron-neutron or proton-proton forces. Among a set of atoms with given atomic weight, the particular atom with equal numbers of neutrons and protons will have the maximum number of neutron-proton pairs, so that if the neutron-proton binding is greater than the neutron-neutron or proton-proton binding, it will have the lowest energy, and be the most stable. Thus, in Table 11-1 we give the number of pairs of each type in each of the

TABLE 11-1. NUMBER OF n-n, n-p, AND p-p PAIRS IN ATOMS WITH TWELVE NUCLEONS

Atom	n-n	n-p	p-p
$_5B^{12}$	21	35	10
$_6C^{12}$	15	36	15
$_7N^{12}$	10	35	21

three atoms we have been discussing, and we see that there is one more neutron-proton pair in $_6C^{12}$ than in the other two atoms. The tighter binding of $_6C^{12}$ is ascribed mostly to the extra strength of the n-p binding.

The same additional strength of the n-p binding explains the general tendency, throughout the periodic table, for atoms to have equal numbers of neutrons and protons. We can go further than this, however, and understand the additional fact, clear from Fig. 11-6, that among the heavier atoms the stable atoms have somewhat more neutrons than protons. This ties in with the Coulomb repulsion of the protons. An atom with more protons, on account of the Coulomb effect, will have a higher energy than one with more neutrons. Thus, if we plot the energy of a set of atoms, all of the same atomic weight, but different atomic numbers, as a function of the atomic number, there will first be a contribution coming from the purely nuclear forces, which will give a minimum energy for the case where there are equal numbers of neutrons and protons, as we saw in Fig. 11-16. If we add to this the Coulomb term, however, this raises the energy of the atoms of higher atomic number, and lowers that of the atoms of lower atomic number. This shifts the minimum of the curve, which corresponds to the most stable nuclei, toward the smaller atomic numbers, for which the number of neutrons is greater than the number of protons.

A calculation of this type is capable of explaining quantitatively most of the features of the binding energies of the nuclei, and the chart of nuclei shown in Fig. 11-6. We need to add only one feature to make the agreement almost perfect. This is the phenomenon of surface tension. A nucleon on the surface of the atom will be bound by one-sided forces to the nucleons in the interior, and this is exactly equivalent to the phenomenon of surface tension found in drops of liquids. Surface tension results in a binding energy, proportional to the surface area. In studying nuclear binding energy, it has been found possible to assume that the total binding energy of the nuclei is a sum of three parts: the part proportional to the atomic weight, or to the volume of the nucleus, coming from the neutron-neutron, neutron-proton, and proton-proton attractions; the surface tension effect, proportional to the surface; and the Coulomb repulsion. When these are properly taken into account, the binding-energy curve is almost completely explained, except for the small amounts of excess binding found in such particularly stable nuclei as the alpha particle.

We have now seen how many of the properties of nuclei follow from a number of simple hypotheses concerning the forces between nucleons: these forces (except for the Coulomb repulsion between protons) are of short range, and represent attractions between pairs of nucleons, approximately equal for neutron-neutron and proton-proton pairs, but somewhat greater for neutron-proton pairs. Also, from the preceding section, we saw that there seemed to be something like multiplet structure in the nucleus. This seemed to indicate that nucleons in the nucleus had something like a Pauli exclusion principle, so that not more than two nucleons, one of each spin, could be in a given stationary state at the same time. Furthermore, there seemed to be something like a singlet-triplet interaction, so that the lowest state of the deuteron corresponded to a triplet state, with the two spins parallel. The alpha particle would correspond to a closed shell, of two neutrons and two protons, one of each spin, in the lowest energy levels, and hence corresponding to the tight binding observed with the deuteron.

As one can imagine, there has been a great deal of effort in the last few years to make these considerations more quantitative, and to try to find, if possible, the precise laws of force between the various nucleons. At the outset, we should state that this problem has not been satisfactorily solved: the exact laws of force have not been found. But there are fairly satisfactory, though quite complicated, approximate forms of laws of force which work fairly well.

It has been found, in the first place, that we cannot simply assume definite laws of force for the neutron-neutron, neutron-proton, and proton-proton interactions, and come out with a correct answer. The reason for this statement is that attempts have been made to set up models of all the various light nuclei: $_1H^2$, $_1H^3$, $_2He^3$, and $_2He^4$, using the same law of force, and it proves to be impossible. The law of force determined from one nucleus does not work with another. Thus the workers in the field have been led to think that the law of force must be more complicated than simply an attraction which is a function of the distance between the nucleons. In particular, they have had to assume that it depends also on the spins of the two nucleons. Such an assumption is natural from the atomic problem, and amounts to an attempt to introduce the exchange effects which explain the singlet-triplet separations in atomic multiplets, into nuclear theory. We have already seen, from the example of the deuteron, that something of this sort is to be expected. These efforts have led to something approaching a quantitative explanation of the energy levels of the light nuclei, but they have been far from completely successful. It is clear that we have not yet found the correct answer to nuclear forces; and unfortunately the efforts to find it run into more and more complicated mathematical theories, which so far have not really succeeded.

Study of the heavier atoms has, in some ways, been more fruitful in suggesting the nature of nuclear forces in the last few years than has the study of light atoms. One very definite piece of information comes merely from the study of the abundance of the elements in nature. It is found that by far the most abundant elements have even numbers of neutrons, and even numbers of protons. Less abundant are those with an even number of protons and an odd number of neutrons, or vice versa. Elements with odd numbers of both neutrons and protons are very scarce. This certainly seems to verify the existence of the Pauli exclusion principle, which we have just been discussing. It certainly seems that nucleons tend to wish to form pairs, with opposite spins, the nuclei with these paired nucleons being more stable than those with unpaired nucleons, and hence being more likely to be non-radioactive and observed in nature.

Going beyond this very simple sort of evidence, there have fortunately appeared more and more indications in the last few years that a self-consistent-field type of theory forms a fairly good approximation for nuclear structure. Perhaps the most striking such evidence comes from the existence of a regularity in nuclear structure, resembling the periodic system of the elements in the extranuclear structure of the atom. We have pointed out that careful study of nuclear energy levels has shown not only that even numbers of neutrons or protons lead to more stable nuclei than odd numbers but furthermore that nuclei containing certain definite numbers of neutrons or protons or both are specially stable, like the inert-gas structures of atoms; and since the atomic structure is explained from a central-field model, this obviously suggests a similar situation for nuclei. These definite numbers of neutrons or protons, which have been called "magic numbers," are 2, 8, 20, 50, 82, and 126. It is not only the energy levels which indicate particularly tight binding of nuclei with a magic number of protons or neutrons, or particularly of both. The angular momentum also shows properties similar to those observed in closed shells of atoms, being zero for a closed shell, and having values, in case there are a certain small number of nucleons (neutrons or protons) outside closed shells, which are determined from these excess particles alone. It certainly seems plausible that we are dealing with a central-field problem, and something very much like the periodic system of the elements. Naturally physicists have tried to interpret the exact values of the magic numbers, so as to find why these numbers in particular have the significance they do.

A great deal of progress toward explaining these numbers was made in 1949, by Feenberg, Nordheim, and Maria Mayer, in independent but correlated work. Clearly the numbers are quite different from those found in closed shells of atoms, except for the first one, 2, which is the same number found in the helium atom, and certainly seems in some sense to represent a closed shell of 1s particles. The number 8 suggests that the six 2p particles are added to the two 1s's. What these writers have done is to go over all the experimental evidence, and to show that by combining two hypotheses one can explain essentially all the observations. In the first place, one must assume that the central field concerned is nothing like that met in an atom, but consists of a square well like that shown in Fig. 11-15. That is, the potential is constant throughout the interior of a sphere, but there are very high barriers at the surface of the sphere. The solutions of this problem are well known, and the levels come in quite a different order from the order of electronic levels in an atomic problem. The 1s comes lowest, but the next is the 2p, explaining the magic number 8; next one has 3d, then 2s, and so on. The 3d, with its ten levels, and the 2s with its two, add twelve units to the magic number 8, giving 20, the next such number. This looks very encouraging, and seems to supply the first part of the explanation of these numbers.

This simple scheme does not carry through the whole way, however, and Mrs. Mayer has found it necessary to supplement it with another hypothesis: that there is very strong spin-orbit interaction between the spin and orbit of a particle. We have seen in our discussion of atomic spectra that in the ordinary L-S coupling, the orbital angular momenta of the various electrons are coupled together to give L, the spin angular momenta are coupled to give S, and finally these two vectors are coupled to give J. This is a suitable description of the facts, provided the couplings between the l's and between the s's are large compared with the spin-orbit interactions. In some atoms, however, particularly heavy atoms such as the rare earths, we have seen that the order of magnitude of the various interactions is different. The spin-orbit interaction, the coupling between a given l and its spin, is larger than the coupling of the l's together, or of the spins together, and in this case each l and spin couple to give a vector j, and the j's couple together to give J, leading to the type of coupling called j-j coupling.

One now has to assume that in the nuclear problem one has this case of j-j coupling. Furthermore, one assumes that the lower of the two states is that with the angular momenta parallel, the upper that with the angular momenta antiparallel. Analysis of the order of the levels then shows that closed shells come just at the numbers which are observed experimentally to be the magic numbers. Simple theories based on these ideas explain practically every nuclear angular momentum.   It seems unquestioned that this type of theory is on the right track, and expresses some real approximation to the nuclear structure.

We have just seen some of the evidence for believing that a one-nucleon self-consistent-field model of the nucleus, supplemented by something like multiplet structure, can be carried rather far, and certainly forms some sort of approximation to the true structure of the nucleus.   We have also seen, however, that the nucleus has a good deal of resemblance to a small fragment of solid, or more accurately of liquid, held together by surface tension and by nuclear binding forces which are not completely different from the forces found in liquids. These facts led Bohr and Wheeler, a number of years ago, to ask how far one could get with the understanding of the nucleus, just by using this analogy to a liquid drop.   One fact in which the nucleus resembles a liquid drop is the existence of the compound nucleus.   When a particle is shot into a nucleus, we have stated that a compound nucleus is formed, consisting of the original nucleus and the particle shot in.   It persists for a very short time (thought to be of the order of magnitude of 10^{-14} sec), after which another particle is shot out.   This process is similar to what we should have if a small liquid drop were bombarded by a fast molecule which stuck to it, increased its energy and temperature, and finally led to the evaporation of one of the molecules of the drop.

Fig. 11-17. Dumbbell shape of vibrating liquid drop, according to Bohr and Wheeler.

Another phenomenon which seems to fit in with the liquid-drop model is nuclear fission.   Bohr and Wheeler assumed that a very heavy nucleus, such as is able to undergo fission, is almost unstable under any circumstances.   A liquid drop is capable of vibrating into dumbbell shapes such as are shown in Fig. 11-17, and it can even break apart.   Bohr and Wheeler investigated such vibrations, and found good reasons for thinking that an impinging neutron is able to induce such vibrations in a fissionable nucleus, which sometimes become so intense that the nucleus breaks apart into two particles of approximately equal mass, as in fission.   Bohr and Wheeler could even show that some of the finer details of fission are shown in the breaking apart of the liquid drop: with liquid drops, one of the two fragments is generally larger than the other, as in fission, and furthermore, several minute droplets are generally formed, in addition to the two main fragments, reminding us of the excess neutrons which are given off in fission.   These simple considerations surely are not exactly applicable to nuclear problems, but it is surprising how far this simple mechanical model can go in describing some of the properties of nuclei.

We have tried in this section to give a picture of the type of argument which is being used in trying to unravel the nature of the forces between the particles in the nucleus, by working backward from known properties of the nuclei. Much progress has been made; but much more progress remains to be made. This is not surprising. The problem is clearly similar to the one which was faced in working out atomic spectra, but in one way much more difficult: we do not know the nature of the forces between the particles. Furthermore, though there has been much work in the measurement of nuclear energy levels, much more remains to be done, and if the atomic problem is any sound guide, further progress in the theory is likely to be made as more regularities, such things as multiplets, appear in the observed spectra. One can be optimistic about the future of the theory of nuclear energy levels, and yet realize that a great deal of work is still needed before it can be complete.

11-11. Cosmic Rays, Mesons, and Nuclear Forces. There is an entirely different sort of approach to these problems: through an attempt to guess at the real law of force between particles, by purely theoretical arguments. There are many hints, in current theories of the electron, and of the electromagnetic field, as to the type of theory one might expect to hold for nuclear structure. Some of these theories lead one to postulate heavy particles with new types of properties, particles which have now been discovered in cosmic rays, and have been named mesons. These theories, in other words, tie together two rather disconnected fields of research: nuclear energy levels and cosmic rays. Before we go into the nature of these theories, we had better say something of the history of research on cosmic rays, and the nature of these rays.

In the early days of research on radioactivity, it was discovered that a Geiger counter, detecting ionizing particles passing through it, had a continuous background of counts, even when no radioactive material was present. Some of these counts came from minute amounts of radioactive elements present as impurities in all ordinary substances, rocks, and so on. But there seemed to be more than could be accounted for in this way. It occurred to Hess and others to investigate the variation of this background with altitude: if these counts came from the rocks, we should expect the number of counts per second to decrease as one went up above the earth, as in a balloon. This did not seem to be the case: the intensity was greater at high altitude. In the 1920's, Millikan and his collaborators followed this line of research further, sending balloons to great height, and finding that the intensities continued to increase with height. It certainly looked as if radiation were coming in from outer space.   Furthermore, it looked as if this radiation were very penetrating.   Counters were taken down in deep mines, and the radiation decreased only slowly with depth, as if it penetrated great thicknesses of matter.

This radiation was named cosmic radiation, and its properties have been studied in great detail since then, by use of cloud chambers and counters, often in very ingenious combinations.   One important type of research has been to experiment at different points of the earth's surface.   For it appears that there is a very large change in intensity, depending on whether we are near the poles or near the equator. Furthermore, this effect seems to depend on the magnetic poles and equator, rather than on the geographic poles.   It seems, in other words, as if the incoming rays were charged particles, affected by the earth's magnetic field.   Careful analysis of the paths of such charged particles in the earth's field has shown that the effects can be explained if the primary rays are almost entirely positively charged particles, presumably protons, of very high energy.   These energies are usually of the order of magnitude of a few billion electron-volts; from the magnetic effects, one can draw some conclusions as to the energy distribution, and one finds that the number per unit energy range decreases fairly rapidly as one goes above a few billion volts.   On the other hand, there is evidence that occasional particles come in with energies as high as 10^{16} ev.   This evidence comes from spectacular events in which a whole enormous area, many hundreds of yards in diameter, simultaneously becomes instantaneously filled with ionization.   Such events are supposed to originate from one primary particle, which has produced many other ionizing particles in its trip down through the atmosphere, and the energy is estimated from the amount which would have been required to produce all this ionization.

These occasional very spectacular showers are different in magnitude, but not in general form, from what happens when an ordinary cosmic-ray particle hits the atmosphere.   The primary particle does not penetrate far into the atmosphere; it almost immediately has collisions, producing secondary particles; they collide and produce tertiaries, and so on; and what we see at ordinary heights is a great mixture of all sorts of fast particles, resulting from all these collisions.   In cosmic rays, in other words, we have ready-made a chance to observe the results of all sorts of nuclear collisions, disintegrations, and other processes.   A typical cosmic-ray cloud-chamber photograph, such as is shown in Fig. 11-18, looks like a maze of tracks; but the cosmic-ray experts have become used to such pictures, and can easily sort out all the familiar processes, and fix their attention on unfamiliar or unknown

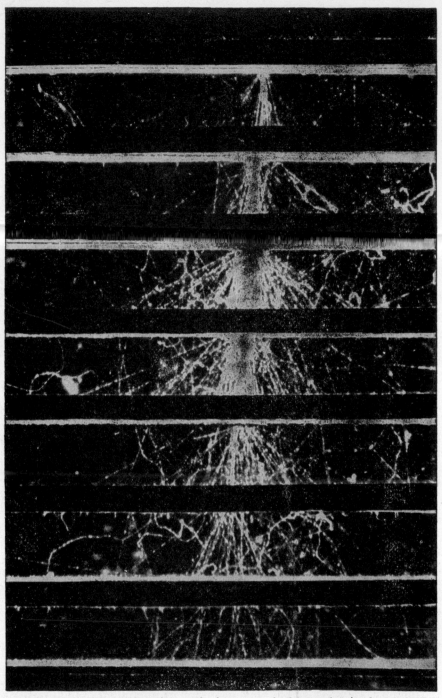

FIG. 11-18. Cloud-chamber picture of a large cascade shower, showing how a single incident particle of high energy can lead to many secondary, tertiary, etc., particles. [*From C. Y. Chao, reproduced from B. Rossi, "High-energy Particles" (copyright 1952, Prentice-Hall, Inc.), by permission of the publisher.*]

types of collisions or particles.   It is by study of such pictures that most of our knowledge of cosmic rays has come.   It is even possible, by ingenious methods, to arrange counters in such a way that a photograph will only be taken if an event of some particular prearranged type has occurred in the cloud chamber; thus we do not waste photographs on uninteresting events.

Most of the things going on in any such picture are of well-known types.   For one thing, there will be many nuclear disintegrations.   A disintegration produced by a very fast particle will produce something called a star on the photograph: a set of tracks, all originating from the exploding atom, showing the paths of the various fragments of the atom.   Sometimes we see the track of the particle producing the disintegration; then we know that this particle was charged (for it is only charged particles which produce the trail of ions necessary to photograph the track in the cloud chamber).   In other cases, the incoming particle is not seen.   Then we know it is uncharged: it may have been a neutron, or else a photon, producing the disintegration by electromagnetic radiation.

Other events can be the conversion of photons into pairs of positive and negative electrons, or the converse effect.   We saw in Sec. 11-2 that a photon can produce such a pair of particles, provided its energy is greater than about a million electron-volts.   It was in such a way that Anderson first discovered the positron.   Processes like this, far from being rare, are extremely common, in the proper energy range. Then again, a positron, striking an atom, can annihilate itself, combining with one of the outer electrons of the atom to produce two photons of about a half million electron-volts each, the annihilation radiation.   Still another type of particle is a Compton recoil electron. We have seen, in discussing X rays, that a photon scattered by an electron loses a little energy, which appears as recoil energy of the electron.   With the high-energy photons found in cosmic rays, this recoil energy becomes extremely important, and recoil particles are found very commonly in cloud-chamber photographs.

These are a few of the well-understood phenomena going on in cloud chambers, and for some time it was supposed that they accounted for everything found in cosmic rays.   Further examination, however, showed that there were some tracks which gave evidence of particles much more penetrating than those usually observed, and of a quite different sort.   During the years following 1934, evidence became overwhelming that particles with the charge of the electron, but with masses of the order of magnitude of 200 electron masses, were contained in the cosmic rays; Anderson and Neddermeyer, Street and Stephenson, and others, contributed to this discovery. The particles were named mesons, and their properties have since been investigated a great deal.

Their discovery was very exciting to physicists, for in a way they had already been predicted theoretically. We have already stated that cosmic-ray particles seem to have a good deal to do with nuclear forces. The reason for this statement was a remarkable theoretical paper in 1935, by the Japanese physicist Yukawa. He started with the electromagnetic theory, and tried by analogy to set up some sort of theory of nuclear forces. He noted that the electromagnetic theory is based on Maxwell's equations, and on Poisson's equation derived from them. When we take this theory into the quantum mechanics, we find that we must postulate the existence of photons, particles carrying the energy of the radiation. These photons in many ways are similar to relativistic particles, but with zero rest mass. We remember that a particle of finite rest mass, accelerated to the velocity of light, would attain infinite mass, and infinite energy, according to the theory of relativity. A photon, on the contrary, has finite energy, though it is traveling with the velocity of light; it therefore has an analogy to a particle of zero rest mass, accelerated to the velocity of light.

The electromagnetic theory leads to Coulomb's law, a force going inversely as the square of the distance, or to a potential going inversely as the distance. On the other hand, we have seen that the nuclear forces have a much shorter range of action. Yukawa suggested as a possible law that the energy of interaction of two nuclear particles might have the form

$$\frac{e^{-r/a}}{r} \tag{11-19}$$

where a is a distance of nuclear order of magnitude (use of this potential shows that to explain nuclear energy levels with it, one must set a equal to something of the order of 10^{-13} cm). He then tried to set up a theory which would lead to such a law of force, as the electromagnetic theory leads to Coulomb's law.

He found that Poisson's equation can be easily modified to give a law of force of the type of Eq. (11-19). If this is done, however, and we then try to set up a quantum-mechanical analogue of the theory, similar to quantum electrodynamics, we find that again the energy in the field must be carried by photonlike particles, but now these particles have a finite rest mass. In fact, as far as order of magnitude is concerned, one finds the relation

$$mca = \hbar \tag{11-20}$$

between the rest mass, c the velocity of light (so that mc is a momentum), and a the radius of action of the nuclear force. And when Yukawa put in for a a value of the appropriate order of magnitude, he found a rest mass of the order of magnitude of 200 electron masses.

We can see, then, the reason for the excitement of the physicists when the meson was discovered: it really looked as if Yukawa's rather simple formulation of a theory of the nuclear force might be right, and as if he had really predicted the existence of the meson in advance. Unfortunately, nature has proved too complicated for this hope to be justified. Yukawa's simple law of force of Eq. (11-19) for nuclear particles has not solved all the problems of nuclear binding energy; and more conspicuously, the situation regarding mesons has proved to be vastly more complicated than it appeared at first. For these reasons, this prediction of Yukawa's is one of those tentative guesses at fitting together the puzzle of nuclear theory, a guess which may in the end prove to fit into a more complete theory, but may on the other hand prove to have been merely an accident, not leading to further progress.

The real difficulty, as we have suggested, was that the experimental situation regarding mesons proved to be immensely more complicated than appeared at first: the experimentalists have now found not just one sort of meson but more and more of them, of various kinds. The first indication of this came in 1947, when Powell, in England, and his collaborators discovered a second type, with a different mass, which in fact seems to have more nearly the properties to be expected of Yukawa's particle than the earlier mesons had. Since then, both in cosmic rays and in collisions produced by the high-energy particles from large accelerators, more and more types of heavy particles are being discovered, with many different masses, ranging up toward proton masses, or even beyond; some positively charged, some negative, some neutral; and having many different properties, in the sense that one kind can disintegrate into other sorts. Clearly we have an immense complication in nature, which had hardly been suspected before. And clearly any fundamental theory of the nature of nuclear forces is likely to be based on this multiplicity of types of heavy particles.

This is the confusing situation that we are in in 1955. Some physicists even suspect that there may be an infinite number of types of masses. Their masses, by Einstein's relation, of course are related to energies. Is it possible that there is a sort of Schrödinger equation, predicting a set of discrete energy levels, which in turn are the infinite number of masses we have just suspected? If this were to be the case, we should hardly expect to be able to formulate the general laws of nuclear physics without knowing this equation, and we should hardly be able to guess at its form without at least knowing accurately some of these energy levels (or masses). Whatever may be the future of fundamental theory, the discoveries which are coming so rapidly in cosmic rays must convince us that we are not as close to the answers as we might have been tempted to think a few years ago. The two main lines of research—nuclear energy levels, and cosmic rays—are likely to keep on turning up more and more valuable experimental data. We are likely to have more and more generalizations of a somewhat limited sort. And finally, we hope, some general theory will appear, so broad that all our present branches of physics appear as special cases of it. This is the sort of thing which, in its more limited way, has already happened in the discovery of Schrödinger's equation. We may hope that the progress toward this greater generalization will not be too discouragingly slow.

PROBLEMS

11-1. A cyclotron operates with magnetic field of 15,000 gauss, and the maximum radius of the orbit is 25 in. Find the energy to which deuterons will be accelerated by this cyclotron. What frequency must the radio-frequency generator provide for the dees?

11-2. What is the transverse mass of a proton going with a velocity v, in atomic mass units, in the case where relativity must be used? What is its equivalent energy, in million electron-volts? If the proton is moving with an energy of 3,000 Mev (3 bev), what is its transverse mass?

11-3. Prove that the energy of a relativistic particle of mass m_0, traveling in a circular orbit of radius ρ in a magnetic field B, is given by

$$\text{Energy} = m_0 c^2 \left\{ \left[1 + (B\rho)^2 \left(\frac{e}{m_0 c} \right)^2 \right]^{\frac{1}{2}} - 1 \right\}$$

Show that for small values of energy, this approaches the value of Eqs. (11-8) and (11-9), by expanding the square root in powers of $(B\rho)^2(e/m_0c)^2$, regarded as a small quantity. Derive a formula for the value of $B\rho$ in terms of the energy.

11-4. A proton synchrotron produces protons of an energy of 3 bev and uses a maximum magnetic field of 12,000 gauss. What is the radius of the orbit? Note that we must use relativistic mechanics. What frequency of radio-frequency field will be required when the protons have maximum energy? If the protons are injected at an energy of 4 Mev, what must be the magnetic field and radio frequency when they are injected?

11-5. A synchrocyclotron is designed to produce deuterons of 300-Mev energy. It operates with a magnetic field of 15,000 gauss. Find the cyclotron frequency at the time of injection of the deuterons, and at the time when they reach their maximum energy. What is the maximum radius of the orbit?

11-6. How much energy is liberated when a deuteron bombards a nucleus of $_3\text{Li}^6$, according to the reaction $_3\text{Li}^6(d,\alpha)_2\text{He}^4$? Does this check the statement of Dampier quoted in Sec. 11-1?

11-7. In Fig. 11-8, the peak marked $B^{12}(1)$ comes for $B\rho = 365$ kilogauss-cm. Assuming that this corresponds to the protons ejected when the B^{12} nucleus is created in its first excited state in the reaction $_5B^{11}(d,p)_5B^{12}$, and using the numerical values given in Sec. 11-5, calculate the energy of the first excited level above the ground state of $_5B^{12}$.

11-8. In a collision of an 8.06-Mev deuteron with a B^{11} nucleus, as in Sec. 11-5, the proton ejected in the reaction $_5B^{11}(d,p)_5B^{12}$ is shot out straight ahead, rather than at 90° to the incident beam as in the case described in the text. Find the energy of the ejected proton in this case, using the Q for the reaction given in the text, and assuming that the $_5B^{12}$ nucleus is left in its ground state.

11-9. A neutron strikes an atom head on, and collides elastically with it. Find the ratio of the kinetic energy of the neutron after collision to its kinetic energy before collision, and show that the neutron is slowed down more, the lighter the atom it strikes.

11-10. U^{238} has a cross section of several thousand barns at the peak of the cross-section curve for radiative capture of neutrons, given in Fig. 11-13. For the purpose of this problem, assume the peak cross section to be 1,000 barns. The density of uranium is 18.68. Find the mean free path of neutrons of just the energy corresponding to the peak of the cross-section curve, in U^{238}. What would be the mean free path in a material with the same number of atoms per unit volume, but with a cross section of 1 barn?

11-11. Neutrons emerge from a reactor with an energy corresponding to the equipartition value for thermal equilibrium at 400°K. Find their velocity and de Broglie wavelength.

11-12. A reactor is developing nuclear energy at a rate of 30,000 kw. How many atoms of U^{235} undergo fission per second? How many kilograms of U^{235} would be used up in 1,000 hr of operation? Assume an average energy of 200 Mev released per fission.

11-13. A reactor has a flux of thermal neutrons of 10^{13} neutrons/sq cm-sec. A substance is exposed to the flux for 1,000 hr. The neutrons induce a nuclear transformation, the cross section being 1 barn. What fraction of the atoms will have undergone the transformation, in the exposure of 1,000 hr?

11-14. A proton of energy 5 bev, roughly the energy of a primary cosmic-ray proton striking the earth, moves in a magnetic field of 0.01 gauss, the order of magnitude of the field which one might expect to find at some distance from the earth. Find the radius of its path, if the magnetic field were uniform, and show that this is comparable with the diameter of the earth. This, of course, does not represent very accurately the situation of the cosmic-ray particle in the earth's field, but at least it illustrates the orders of magnitude encountered.

APPENDIX 1

IMPORTANT PHYSICAL CONSTANTS

Velocity of light	$c = 2.9973 \times 10^8$ m/sec
	$= 2.9973 \times 10^{10}$ cm/sec
Constants in mks units	$\epsilon_0 = 8.8542 \times 10^{-12}$ farad/m
	$\mu_0 = 4\pi \times 10^{-7}$ henry/m
Planck's constant	$h = 6.625 \times 10^{-34}$ joule-sec
	$= 6.625 \times 10^{-27}$ erg-sec
Avogadro's constant	$N_0 = 6.0247 \times 10^{23}$ per g-mole
Boltzmann's constant	$k = 1.3804 \times 10^{-23}$ joule/deg
	$= 1.3804 \times 10^{-16}$ erg/deg
Gas constant	$R = 8.3166$ joule/mole per deg
	$= 8.3166 \times 10^7$ erg/mole per deg
	$= 1.9870$ cal/mole per deg
Normal atmosphere	1 atm $= 1.013 \times 10^6$ dynes/sq cm
Ice point	Temp. $= 273.2°$ abs
Volume of 1 mole of perfect gas, ntp	Volume $= 22.421$ liter
Electronic charge	$e = 1.6021 \times 10^{-19}$ coulomb
	$= 4.8029 \times 10^{-10}$ esu
Electronic rest mass	$m = 9.1085 \times 10^{-31}$ kg
	$= 9.1085 \times 10^{-28}$ g
Proton rest mass	$m_P = 1.6724 \times 10^{-27}$ kg
	$= 1.6724 \times 10^{-24}$ g
Ratio of proton mass to electron mass	$m_P/m = 1836.1$
Charge-to-mass ratio of the electron	$e/m = 1.7589 \times 10^{11}$ coulomb/kg
	$= 5.2730 \times 10^{17}$ esu/g
Rydberg number	$R = 109{,}737.3$ cm^{-1}
Rydberg energy in volts	$Rhc/e = 13.605$ ev
Radius of first hydrogen orbit	$a_0 = 0.52916$ angstrom
Electron mass in ev	Electron mass $= 0.51098$ Mev
Atomic mass in ev	Atomic mass unit $= 931.16$ Mev

MASSES OF LIGHT NUCLEI AND ELEMENTARY PARTICLES

Atomic number	Symbol	Mass number	Mass	
	Electron	—	0.00054876	
1	Proton	1	1.00759	
0	Neutron	1	1.00898	
1	H	1	1.00814	Stable
		2	2.01474	Stable
		3	3.01700	
2	He	3	3.01698	Stable
		4	4.00387	Stable
		5	5.01356	
		6	6.02047	
3	Li	6	6.01702	Stable
		7	7.01822	Stable
		8	8.02502	
4	Be	7	7.01915	
		8	8.00785	
		9	9.01504	Stable
		10	10.01671	
5	B	9	9.01619	
		10	10.01611	Stable
		11	11.01279	Stable
		12	12.01816	
6	C	10	10.02061	
		11	11.01492	
		12	12.00380	Stable
		13	13.00747	
		14	14.00768	
7	N	13	13.00986	
		14	14.00752	Stable

Atomic number	Symbol	Mass number	Mass	
		15	15.00486	Stable
		16	16.01074	
		17	17.01404	
8	O	15	15.00777	
		16	16.00000	Stable, standard mass
		17	17.00453	Stable
		18	18.00487	Stable
		19	19.00948	
9	F	17	17.00749	
		18	18.00667	
		19	19.00446	Stable
		20	20.00635	
10	Ne	19	19.00792	
		20	19.99886	Stable
		21	21.00059	Stable
		22	21.99827	Stable
		23	23.00168	

APPENDIX 3

SUGGESTED REFERENCES

History and Biography

Dampier, W. C.: "A History of Science," 4th ed., Cambridge University Press, London, 1949.

Einstein, A., and L. Infeld: "The Evolution of Physics," Simon and Schuster, Inc., New York, 1938.

Eve, A. S.: "Rutherford," The Macmillan Company, New York, 1939.

Fermi, Laura: "Atoms in the Family: My Life with Enrico Fermi," University of Chicago Press, Chicago, 1954.

Frank, P.: "Einstein," Alfred A. Knopf, Inc., New York, 1947.

Magie, W. F.: "A Source Book in Physics," McGraw-Hill Book Company, Inc., New York, 1935.

Millikan, R. A.: "Autobiography," Prentice-Hall, Inc., New York, 1950.

Rayleigh, Lord: "The Life of Sir J. J. Thomson," Cambridge University Press, London, 1942.

General Elementary and Theoretical Physics

Frank, N. H.: "Introduction to Mechanics and Heat," 2d ed., McGraw-Hill Book Company, Inc., New York, 1939.

————: "Introduction to Electricity and Optics," 2d ed., McGraw-Hill Book Company, Inc., New York, 1950.

Sears, F. W.: "Principles of Physics," vols. 1–3, Addison-Wesley Publishing Company, Cambridge, Mass., 1944–1945.

Slater, J. C., and N. H. Frank: "Introduction to Theoretical Physics," McGraw-Hill Book Company, Inc., New York, 1933.

———— and ————: "Mechanics," McGraw-Hill Book Company, Inc., New York, 1947.

———— and ————: "Electromagnetism," McGraw-Hill Book Company, Inc., New York, 1947.

General Texts on Modern and Atomic Physics

Andrade, E. N. daC.: "The Structure of the Atom," Harcourt, Brace and Company, Inc., New York, 1927.

Born, M.: "Atomic Physics," 3d ed., Blackie & Son, Ltd., Glasgow, 1944.

Brown, T. B.: "Foundations of Modern Physics," John Wiley & Sons, Inc., New York, 1948.

Darrow, K. K.: "Introduction to Contemporary Physics," 2d ed., D. Van Nostrand Company, Inc., New York, 1939.

Finkelnburg, W.: "Atomic Physics," McGraw-Hill Book Company, Inc., New York, 1950.

Harnwell, G. P., and J. J. Livingood: "Experimental Atomic Physics," McGraw-Hill Book Company, Inc., New York, 1933.

Hoag, J. B., and S. A. Korff: "Electron and Nuclear Physics," 3d ed., D. Van Nostrand Company, Inc., New York, 1948.

Hull, G. F.: "Elementary Modern Physics," 2d ed., The Macmillan Company, New York, 1949.

Oldenberg, O.: "Introduction to Atomic Physics," 2d ed., McGraw-Hill Book Company, Inc., New York, 1954.

University of Pittsburgh, Physics Staff, "An Outline of Atomic Physics," 2d ed., John Wiley & Sons, Inc., New York, 1937.

Richtmyer, F. K., E. H. Kennard, and T. Lauritsen: "Introduction to Modern Physics," 5th ed., McGraw-Hill Book Company, Inc., New York, 1955.

Ruark, A. E., and H. C. Urey: "Atoms, Molecules, and Quanta," McGraw-Hill Book Company, Inc., New York, 1930.

Semat, H.: "Introduction to Atomic Physics," 3d ed., Rinehart & Company, Inc., New York, 1952.

Tolansky, S.: "Introduction to Atomic Physics," Longmans, Green & Co., Inc., New York, 1949.

Van Name, F. W., Jr.: "Modern Physics," Prentice-Hall, Inc., New York, 1952.

Kinetic Theory and Statistics

Allis, W. P., and M. A. Herlin: "Thermodynamics and Statistical Mechanics," McGraw-Hill Book Company, Inc., New York, 1952.

Gurney, R. W.: "Introduction to Statistical Mechanics," McGraw-Hill Book Company, Inc., New York, 1949.

Kennard, E. H.: "Kinetic Theory of Gases," McGraw-Hill Book Company, Inc., New York, 1938.

Lindsay, R. B.: "Introduction to Physical Statistics," John Wiley & Sons, Inc., New York, 1941.

Loeb, L. B.: "Kinetic Theory of Gases," McGraw-Hill Book Company, Inc., New York, 1927.

Slater, J. C.: "Introduction to Chemical Physics," McGraw-Hill Book Company, Inc., New York, 1939.

Electron Theory and Relativity

Crowther, J. A.: "Ions, Electrons, and Ionizing Radiations," 8th ed., Edward Arnold & Co., London, 1949.

Einstein, A., H. A. Lorentz, and others: "The Principle of Relativity," Methuen & Co., Ltd., London, 1923.

Lorentz, H. A.: "The Theory of Electrons," Stechert-Hafner, Inc., New York, 1909.

Lorentz, H. A.: "Problems of Modern Physics," Ginn & Company, Boston, 1927.

Millikan, R. A.: "Electrons (+ and −), Protons, Photons, Neutrons, and Cosmic Rays," 2d ed., University of Chicago Press, Chicago, 1949.

Thomson, J. J.: "Conduction of Electricity through Gases," Cambridge University Press, London, 1928.

X Rays and Crystal Structure

Barker, G. F.: "Röntgen Rays: Memoirs by Röntgen, Stokes, and J. J. Thomson,"
Harper & Brothers, New York, 1899.

Bragg, W. H., and W. L. Bragg: "X Rays and Crystal Structure," George Bell &
Sons, Ltd., London, 1916.

Bragg, W. L.: "The Crystalline State," vol. 1, General Survey, The Macmillan
Company, New York, 1934.

————: "A History of X-ray Analysis," Longmans, Green & Co., Inc., New York,
1943.

Clark, G. L.: "Applied X-Rays," 4th ed., McGraw-Hill Book Company, Inc.,
New York, 1955.

Compton, A. H., and S. K. Allison: "X Rays in Theory and Experiment," 2d ed.,
D. Van Nostrand Company, Inc., New York, 1935.

Atomic and Molecular Structure and Spectra

Bohr, N.: "The Theory of Spectra and Atomic Constitution," 2d ed., Cambridge
University Press, London, 1924.

Candler, A. C.: "Atomic Spectra," Cambridge University Press, London, 1937.

Herzberg, G.: "Molecular Spectra and Molecular Structure," Prentice-Hall, Inc.,
New York, 1939.

————: "Atomic Spectra and Atomic Structure," 2d ed., Dover Publications,
New York, 1944.

Pauling, L., and S. Goudsmit: "The Structure of Line Spectra," McGraw-Hill
Book Company, Inc., New York, 1930.

Sommerfeld, A.: "Atomic Structure and Spectral Lines," E. P. Dutton & Co., Inc.,
New York, 2d ed., 1922; 3d ed., 1934.

White, H. E.: "Introduction to Atomic Spectra," McGraw-Hill Book Company,
Inc., New York, 1934.

Quantum Mechanics and Application to Atoms, Molecules, and Solids

Condon, E. U., and P. M. Morse: "Quantum Mechanics," McGraw-Hill Book
Company, Inc., New York, 1929.

Dushman, S.: "Elements of Quantum Mechanics," John Wiley & Sons, Inc.,
New York, 1938.

Houston, W. V.: "Principles of Quantum Mechanics," McGraw-Hill Book Company, Inc., New York, 1951.

Hume-Rothery, W.: "Atomic Theory for Students of Metallurgy," 2d ed., Institute
of Metals, London, 1952.

Pauling, L., and E. B. Wilson: "Introduction to Quantum Mechanics," McGraw-
Hill Book Company, Inc., New York, 1935.

Raynor, G. V.: "An Introduction to the Electron Theory of Metals," Institute of
Metals, London, 1949.

Rice, F. O., and E. Teller: "The Structure of Matter," John Wiley & Sons, Inc.,
New York, 1949.

Rojansky, V.: "Introductory Quantum Mechanics," Prentice-Hall, Inc., New York,
1938.

Schiff, L. I.: "Quantum Mechanics," 2d ed., McGraw-Hill Book Company, Inc.,
New York, 1955.

Seitz, F.: "Modern Theory of Solids," McGraw-Hill Book Company, Inc., New
York, 1940.

Shockley, W.: "Electrons and Holes in Semiconductors," D. Van Nostrand Company, Inc., New York, 1950.

Slater, J. C.: "Quantum Theory of Matter," McGraw-Hill Book Company, Inc., New York, 1951.

Thomson, G. P.: "The Wave Mechanics of Free Electrons," McGraw-Hill Book Company, Inc., New York, 1930.

Nuclear Physics and High-energy Particles

Aston, F. W.: "Isotopes," Longmans, Green & Co., Inc., New York, 1933.

Bitter, F.: "Nuclear Physics," Addison-Wesley Publishing Company, Cambridge, Mass., 1950.

Cork, J. M.: "Radioactivity and Nuclear Physics, 2d ed., D. Van Nostrand Company, Inc., New York, 1950.

Evans, R. D.: "Introduction to the Atomic Nucleus," McGraw-Hill Book Company, Inc., New York, 1955.

Lapp, R. E., and H. L. Andrews: "Nuclear Radiation Physics," Prentice-Hall, Inc., New York, 1948.

Leprince-Ringuet, L.: "Cosmic Rays," Prentice-Hall, Inc., New York, 1950.

Millikan, R. A.: "Electrons (+ and −), Protons, Photons, Neutrons, and Cosmic Rays," 2d ed., University of Chicago Press, Chicago, 1949.

Pollard, E., and W. L. Davidson Jr.: "Applied Nuclear Physics," John Wiley & Sons, Inc., New York, 1942.

Rossi, B.: "High Energy Particles," Prentice-Hall, Inc., New York, 1952.

Segre, E. (ed.): "Experimental Nuclear Physics," vols. 1, 2 (3 to appear), John Wiley & Sons, Inc., New York, 1953.

Smyth, H. D.: "Atomic Energy for Military Purposes," Princeton University Press, Princeton, N.J., 1945.

APPENDIX 4

ANSWERS TO PROBLEMS

Chap. 1

1-1. Weight of 1 liter H_2, 0.090 g; Cl_2, 3.16 g; O_2, 1.43 g.

1-2. Expected C of H_2, 0.75 cal/g; N_2, 0.178 cal/g.

1-3. Dulong-Petit specific heat of Pb, 0.0289 cal/g; of C, 0.50 cal/g.

1-4. At 1 km, density = 0.90 times that at surface; at 10 km, 0.33.

1-6. 2.81 A = 2.81×10^{-8} cm.   **1-7.** 3.20×10^{-20} cc.

1-9. 1.91×1^50 cm/sec.   **1-10.** 1.34.

Chap. 2

2-1. 2.5 cm.   **2-2.** 0.47 cm.

2-4. Electron, 0.511 Mev; proton, 938 Mev.

2-5. 1 kev, 1.87×10^9 cm/sec; 100 kev, 1.64×10^{10} cm/sec; 1 Mev, 2.83×10^{10} cm/sec.

2-7. 45.5 cm.   **2-8.** 2.80×10^{10} cycles/sec.

2-9. Frequency = 2.53×10^{15} cycle/sec, wavelength = 1,180 A = $1,180 \times 10^{-8}$ cm.

2-10. n^2 = dielectric constant = $1 + 12.6/[1 - (1,180 A/\lambda)^2]$.

Chap. 3

3-5. Debye value = 0.088 cal/g.

3-6. At 15°K, 0.00075 cal/g; at 1°K, 2.2×10^{-7}.

3-8. 2.93 gauss.

3-9. 5.1×10^{15} photoelectrons/sq cm-sec.

3-10. 0.0235 ev.

Chap. 4

4-6. 3.7×10^4 disintegrations/sec from 1 μg of Ra^{226}.

4-7. 0.54.

4-9. 4.4×10^{-10} g of Ra^{228} per gram of Th^{233}.

4-10. 1.4×10^{-11} g of Th^{234} per gram of U^{238}.

Chap. 5

5-1. 6,561 A; 1,215 A; 911 A.

Chap. 6

6-5. 2.814 A; 1.407 A; 0.938 A; etc.

314

6-6. Some of the angles between incident and diffracted beams and corresponding wavelengths are 27.8°, 0.33 A; 36.8°, 0.57 A, 0.28 A; 52.8°, 1.13 A,
0.57 A; 67.6°, 0.87 A, 0.43 A; 90.0°, 2.81 A, 1.41 A, 0.94 A, 0.70 A; 112.4°,
1.30 A, 0.65 A; 127.2°, 2.24 A, 1.12 A, 0.75 A; 143.2°, 1.70 A, 0.85 A, 0.57 A;
152.2°, 1.32 A, 0.66 A.

6-7. 32°, 46°, 67°, 76°, 102°, 111°, 121°.

Chap. 7

7-2. 5.12 ev.

7-6. Observed ionization potential of Mg^+, 15.03 ev; of Al^{++}, 28.44 ev.

Chap. 8

8-3. g's for $^3P_2$, $^3P_1$, $^3P_0$, $^3D_3$, $^3D_2$, $^3D_1$ are $\frac{3}{2}$, $\frac{3}{2}$, $\%$, $\frac{4}{3}$, $\frac{7}{6}$, $\frac{1}{2}$.

Chap. 9

9-1. For 1 ev, 12.2 A; 100 ev, 1.22 A; 10,000 ev, 0.122 A.

9-2. 1.45 A.

9-8. Angle $= 1.2 \times 10^{-4}$ radian; distance $= 0.8$ cm.

Chap. 10

10-2. 5.3 ev.   **10-3.** 1.0×10^{13} cycles/sec.

10-5. 4.7×10^{12} cycles/sec; 1.8×10^{-38} g-cm^2.

10-6. Vibrational level spacing $= 0.020$ ev; rotational energy $= 1.9 \times 10^{-5}k^2$ ev;
expect about 37 vibrational levels.

10-7. 8.0×10^{-9}.   **10-9.** 6.9 ev.

10-10. 10^{-57}; ratio of conductivities $= 10^{-47}$.

Chap. 11

11-1. 21.5 Mev, 11.4×10^6 cycles/sec.   **11-2.** $4.2m_0$.

11-4. Radius $= 10.6$ m; at maximum energy, frequency $= 4.4 \times 10^6$ cycles/sec;
at injection, 270 gauss, 0.42×10^6 cycles/sec.

11-5. 11.4×10^6 cycles/sec at beginning, 9.8×10^6 cycles/sec at end; 2.95 m.

11-7. 1.08 Mev above ground state.   **11-8.** 9.25 Mev.

11-10. 0.021 cm; 21 cm.   **11-11.** 3.2×10^5 cm/sec; 1.26 A.

11-12. 0.94×10^{18} fissions/sec; 1.34 kg.   **11-13.** 3.6×10^{-5}.

11-14. 19,600 km.

INDEX